A DIME IN THE DUST

CRYSTAL HOOPER

MINERVA PRESS
MONTREUX LONDON WASHINGTON

A DIME IN THE DUST
Copyright © Crystal Hooper 1995

ISBN 1 85863 274 9

First Published 1995 by
MINERVA PRESS
10 Cromwell Place
London SW7 2JN

Printed in Great Britain by
B.W.D. Printers Ltd., Northolt, Middlesex

A DIME IN THE DUST

❖

This book is dedicated to my daughter Lorraine and my grandchildren; to Ken whom I love dearly, who has been a pillar of strength to me for most of my life, my "Special Friend" who was always there to pick up the pieces when I fell and who gave me so many chances in life.

"Special thanks" to the editing staff of Minerva Press.

❖

PROLOGUE

Dear Lorraine,

Where do I start? What do I say? The hurt and fear wash through me over and over and the words and emotions boil around so that I don't even know what I'm thinking or feeling anymore. I haven't got much time to try and straighten it out. Gary will be here any moment. I'm scared to believe it's true. What happens if we get to the airport and you're not there? I could never bear that pain. I think I'll go mad. To have searched, and longed and hoped and cried out in such agony and such anguish for so long and then to have you snatched away before I can hold you - oh God no, I couldn't stand it.

I must get hold of myself. My emotions are running crazy, my eyes are so flooded I can't see the screen properly - the words are all smudging into each other. I must look such a fool. Soon my lenses will be afloat too, I must calm down.

Hearing your voice on the phone, listening to you sob... I think it was only because Keith was there that I didn't have an emotional collapse. I don't know what I would have done without Keith, supporting me morally, standing by me, he has been a pillar of strength just about my whole life, I seldom cry in front of him. You know every time the tears start to surge up I hear the harsh, abrupt voices from years ago. "Stop that! Take hold of yourself girl. Why on earth do you think tears are going to help?" And I remember the hurt, the awful hurt. Tears are a sign of weak character, you know. That's what they said. I suppose I believed them, because I choked down the anguish and pain. I learnt never to cry in front of others. I would crawl deep down into myself and alone in that total loneliness let the tears pour where no one could see or hear.

Somehow, since I have spoken to you, something has broken. I can't stop the tears anymore, I don't even want to. Maybe if I don't let go something would burst inside. Maybe if I cry now I won't cry at the airport.

You called me "Mum" on the phone. No one has ever called me that in my whole life. My foster son knows I'm his friend, not his mother. I have gone through my whole life knowing I have a daughter and not knowing where she is. Now I've spoken to you and you called me Mum and I find I can't handle it - isn't it silly? For forty-one years I have looked for you, longed for you. I've lost count of the times that with wild hope beating in my chest I followed up a trace. My heart in my mouth I would phone, or knock at the umpteenth door. Keith's father helped me on each of these wild goose chases. Then the crushing disappointment when hope just shattered. I have always known, without any doubt, that I would recognise you immediately from a photo, from a glimpse in the street. Forty-one years cannot blot out the knowing from my heart, the loving and the longing. Even now, I know that the moment I see you I will know it is you, my daughter!

Gary will be here just now. Maybe I should dress up a bit. But then I think that would be hypocritical. I want you to know me as I am, me, not a toffed-up version of me trying to impress you. So that's how you are going to see me, ski pants and sloppy joes. Funny, Hugh said you even dress like me.

Is it possible that you can be anything like me after forty-one years? Another life - another world, how can we possibly be like one another or have anything similar? Yet deep inside me I know we are alike in so many ways, because you are my daughter and because of the love that has bound me to you over years of longing and pain, and miles of hope and searching. I have missed you so much these forty-one years. Every night I have longed that just once I could hold you tight and hug you before I lay my head down. Now it's becoming reality and I feel like an earthquake has shaken me apart. I can't understand why I keep crying like this. I don't even know what I'm feeling anymore, just that it's overwhelming me in waves and surges of mad joy, delirious happiness, fear, and anxiety and panic and feelings I don't recognise and don't understand. Maybe it's the pain, hurt and rejection of forty-one years being washed away. Maybe it's the freedom of the truth. I've never lied to anyone about my past. But I have also never told anyone the truth about it. I've answered questions with questions.

My past was mine. It was sacred. I didn't want it defiled and contaminated with prying eyes and probing fingers. I know how people judge and condemn. So over the years I have become a very private person. Don't think it's vain, but I know I carry my years well, and few would ever guess that I'll be sixty-two, one of these days. Only Keith knows that. Keith knows everything about me. And he has never spoken a word of accusation or judgement. It has been his compassion and trust that have helped me to pull through. I suppose that more than anything else, even his high position, has made me determined that he would never have cause to be ashamed of me.

I don't think you will either. You'll see that since I gave birth to you I have become a strong-willed, self-disciplined woman. I knew it would be the only way to fight the world and its condemnation. Knowing you were there somewhere, that you were my daughter helped to keep me going. I have always wanted you to feel proud of me. Even though you didn't know me. I can hardly believe that I would soon be able to hold you. The last time you were in my arms you were three months old. You're forty-one now, and I'm no more the frightened nineteen-year old, though sometimes I feel it. Gary will be here soon.

He works for the Adoption Society. He's been adopted, so he knows what it's like - at least from one side. And he has given me so much moral support this week.

I'm jabbering aren't I? This is like a dream. I feel I'm going to wake up in a moment and find I'm imagining things.

I can almost see you in the plane, looking down on me. I feel like running out in the street and shouting at the top of my voice. "My daughter is coming! My daughter is coming!" I want to sing, but I'm crying so much and my voice cracks and goes wavery. You know that song, "I hear music and there's no one there. I smell blossoms and the trees are bare?" That's how I feel! I'm so happy, I want to sing, I want to shout, I want to run around, but I'm crying so much I can't see. I feel I could run all the way to the airport. It's like a dam breaking after all these years of pushing everything down. It's like breaking free after years of being chained and pushed in a corner. I don't want any more secrets, any more darkness.

I'm going to write to you Martoinette, a page a week, a page a day, or whatever it takes, until it is all out in the open and my whole life is before you. It's something I want to do for you. And writing is the only way I know to do it. It's because you are so special, because I love you so much. I have never shared my life with anyone. My "marriage" was never more than a contract, a paper agreement - there was no love, no real sharing. Only once in my life did I ever really love anyone, and you are the fruit of that beauty and that wonder.

Since then I have never been capable of really loving and trusting another man. The car has arrived, Gary is hooting.

Oh dear God, please don't let something happen on the way to the airport.

At last I can end a letter with the words I have longed to write, take care.

Your loving Mum.
22 June 1993

CHAPTER ONE

I came sliding down the banisters, as usual, clutching my favourite doll with one hand and guiding my descent with the other. Expert by now, I landed sure-footed on the carpet at the bottom, where I remember it was getting a little worn. My little brother was already on his way out and I had to run fast to beat him to the cottage at the bottom of the garden - that was my special place where I lived in a beautiful fantasy world with my dolls. He could only come in if he played too, and generally he did and was very good. Sometimes though he was just a spiteful little boy and wouldn't listen when I told him what to do. So I had to get there first to see whether he was going to play or be nasty.

I needn't have worried, because Jimmy had got side-tracked. As I ran towards the cottage, I could see the door was still closed so I stopped and looked round. He was sitting at the top of the stairs that went down to the basement, peering down to see if the old man was busy. Jimmy was still a bit wary of him because of his hunchback. But I wasn't. So I pushed past him and went down the gloomy stairs to the basement where the old man was bent over his work. I loved to sit there and watch him. He had bent, twisted fingers, full of funny bumps and scars. But the toys he produced were exquisite and to my child's eyes, wonderful and perfect. He worked with wood and I remember the smell of shavings and dust that lingered in the air, especially when the late afternoon sun managed to slip a few mellow, rusting rays into the basement.

Jimmy would trail after me and crane his neck around me to see what the old man was doing. He had wispy hair that always had flecks of sawdust and his baggy overalls would catch the smaller shavings in the odd folds and creases that hung round his misshapen body. If we just sat quietly and watched him he didn't even notice we were there. He lost himself in what he was doing, the gnarled fingers working the grainy wood, feeling the shapes inside, smoothing away the rough edges so that the toy slowly came to life, easing itself up from its wooden womb.

It fascinated me, and I loved the rough grating noises and the dusty smells. But Jimmy would get impatient and, forgetting his fear of the hunchback, would start poking around amid the shavings and pieces of wood on the floor. Once he stretched up to pull at something that had attracted his attention and a whole lot of stuff fell down.

The old man yelled and got furious. Brandishing a stick he shouted at us and chased us up the stairs. It was days before I plucked up the courage to sneak down there again, weeks before Jimmy ventured in, and that was only because I kept teasing and scorning him.

Some evenings my older sister would take me down with her. She chatted to him about all kinds of things. He listened and would nod his head or sometimes give her advice and talk to her about the things that happened in her little world. I know he cared for us, because of the beautiful toys that kept ending up in our eager hands. I don't know what he was making the toys for. He must have been wanting to sell them. I wonder now how many of those destined for sale actually did end up with us instead.

The mind is a strange thing. So much of those earlier years has been blotted out. At times a scent, a sound will bring scraps and shreds of memory flitting brilliantly from the darkness. But then the blackness would well up and smother them and I'm left with meaningless pieces that fit nowhere. Why do I keep remembering the huge kitchen with the big old wooden table in the middle and the ever present bread knife on it? Why is there a surge of foreboding and fear whenever that scene flashes through my memory?

I was the second youngest of six, but there were such big gaps between me and the eldest sisters that I can't remember them as part of my childhood. To me they were big already, grown up, distant. Strange though, they were family, they were my sisters and I believe I loved and trusted them just as a natural response. Maybe that is why it was such a devastating hurt later on when they did nothing to help. Worse, when they turned their backs on me.

Dad wasn't around much at all. I know now that it was because he was in the army. These were hard years, bad years. The Second World War was starting and the economic climate was grim, particularly in our little corner of the world. It must have been poverty or desperation that led my mother to decide that the only hope I could have was to give me to another family.

The utter misery of those weeks, or was it months, is something I can't describe. Why had my mummy given me away? Had I been so bad? Didn't she love me anymore? The new family must have loved and cared for me, but so great was the despair that I can remember very little of them. I don't know to this day whether it was suppose to be a permanent arrangement or whether it was just something to tide us all over a particularly bad time.

I just remember one day, sitting on an old fallen tree trunk, weeping and weeping with loneliness and heartbreak. There was a strong smell of Sunlight soap. Then through the blur of tears I saw my mother walking towards me. I screamed and ran towards her, little arms outstretched, terrified she might disappear. To this day, that scene flashes through my mind every time I smell Sunlight soap. She took me home then. I still don't know the whole truth of that episode. It is another of those paragraphs of questions that my sisters will not deign to answer. I'm not worth it, you see. And there is something about my parents, about those early years that they seem ashamed of. Perhaps they think that if they can pretend it didn't exist, then it won't have happened. They don't realise that they are trying to negate life itself.

Wisps and fragments of the first seven years flit through my memory - some sunlit and happy, carefree, playing in the school grounds in front of the huge school, where we swapped our samies, "Have you got Marmite? Please swop me, I've got peanut butter today." I loved playing touches, because I was so much smaller than the others it was easier for me to dodge, so I hardly ever got caught. I used to collapse, out of breath and laughing so much I had to gasp, from outrunning the bigger kids. It was easy for me to make friends and I had lots, older and younger than me. But even then there were my precious things, my secrets, that I shared with no one. So even though there were nearly always other people around me, somehow I was always alone - inside - I was separate, I was different from them.

The first dramatic change came at Christmas. It was 1939 and the Military were giving a party for the kids of Military personnel. I was wildly excited and still in my vest and panties went rushing to my Mum's bedroom. "Mummy, please blow up my balloon!" I had tried in vain with bursting cheeks and frantic puffs and the thing resisted my childish efforts. She looked awful. She couldn't stand properly and trying to walk down the hall she collapsed. Grasping uncomprehendingly at her hand, "Mummy, Mummy get up! Get up!" My cries brought others running and I was shoved roughly aside. When they picked her up, her head fell backwards and as I stared in

14

horror I saw her eyes closed and her hair trailing down on the floor as they carried her away.

Then rough hands pushed me into the bedroom and people were there telling me to hurry up and get dressed or I would be late. "Don't worry, everything will be all right. Now just hurry up, Uncle Phillip will be here just now and then you won't be ready. Come on, you can't keep Father Christmas waiting!"

The excitement and the anticipation as well as the thrill of the "new" dress, a revamped hand-me-down from one of my sisters, drove everything else out of my head. Bubbling with delight I joined my friends who had come to fetch me and off we went to the hall.

Christmas decorations streamed from one corner to the other. The piney smell of the tree mingled with the taste of mince pies and ice-cream. We played musical chairs and I hit the floor with such a hard thump when a bigger girl pushed me off the chair I was going to sit on. I choked back the tears as kind hands picked me up onto my feet and gave me a handful of sweets for consolation.

Then it was time for the presents. The excitement was unbearable! We sat down in front of Santa, hearts beating furiously in anticipation and anxiously watching, each child got up for his gift. I was tense with eagerness, a little afraid they would forget me and desperately hoping that no one would be given that beautiful little sewing machine.

But oh the relief! As Santa picked the machine up they called my name! I got up to run forward and suddenly I saw a huge cross with a blinding light behind it. Nausea, fear and then total blackness.

I opened my eyes and stared up at the ceiling above my bed. There was a heavy, thick silence in the room, but I could hear voices and lots of people moving around in the house. From somewhere inside me welled up the knowing that my mother was dead. I got up. I felt weak and nauseous. Downstairs there was a big man I had never seen before. He was ordering everyone around. Voices were raised and the house was crowded with people. "I am her father, and I am the only one here who has the right to make decisions." He was shouting and his voice was hard and ugly. I crept down the stairs. There was a lady there that looked so much like my mother. I pulled her hand and hugged her round the neck when she bent down towards me. The big man was still talking loudly and angrily. I couldn't understand why there was so much anger when he spoke about my mother, as though he had hated her. Yet he said he was her father.

There were many things about this hard, heartless man, my grandfather, that I couldn't understand. To this day the more I question and wonder about him and his actions the more mysteries and secrets there seem to be.

I clung tightly to the pretty lady. It turned out she was my aunt, and moved by my despair and grief, she took me home with her. There I was to stay for six months, before the hard, ugly man demanded I go to him, my eldest sister and brother came to fetch me. If I had known then what was waiting for me I have no doubt I would have run away. I would have locked myself in. I would have refused to go. But how can a seven-year old know that her world has ended and her hell begun?

CHAPTER TWO

I remember clearly the day my elder sister and brother came to fetch me. I loved my aunt and though the ache of longing for my mother was still there, the months I had spent with Aunt Kay had helped to dull the pain. I knew my mother was dead, but somehow in the back of my head I hung on to the hope that one day I would look up and she would be coming through the door to fetch me home.

I was sitting on the swing with my doll on my lap and idly rocking back and forth, humming while I brushed her hair. A car stopped in front of the garden gate and I saw these people get out and go to the door. I suddenly felt nauseous and knew that they were bringing bad tidings. I could feel my heart beating hard and thick in my chest and getting up I started to walk towards the kitchen door; I knew Aunt Kay was going to open it and call me. I stood on the step as she appeared in the doorway. Her mouth was pulled down and her face was tight and sad.

"Amber, you must come and help me pack your things. Your grandfather wants you to come home."

Home? This was home. What did she mean, home? She must have noticed the reaction, because she started telling me how much fun it would be to be back with my brothers and sisters, about the lovely town my grandfather lived in, how exciting it would be to go to a new school and make lots of friends and see new things. In the rush and flurry of pulling clothes out of drawers and finding precious hidden treasures that had to go with me, the foreboding was forgotten. When I got into the car with my sister and brother I was quite excited, clutching my favourite doll as a kind of anchor to reality.

As we pulled away, I looked out of the back window and waved at Aunt Kay. It would be the last time I would ever see her - and I remember how she held her left hand up to the side of her face as she raised her right hand hesitantly to wave good-bye. I was a bit confused about the thing called "granddad". My mother had never spoken of him. At first I pictured a bigger vision of my Dad, of whom I didn't have a very clear memory in the first place. Maybe "grand" -dad meant that he dressed in very smart clothes. When I questioned my sister and brother about it, they were reticent.

"It's Mum's father. Granddad is just the name you give to the fathers of your own father and mother."

I suppose the excitement of the journey supplanted all other queries, because I don't recall receiving any more information on the matter.

By the time we arrived, I was tired, fretful and not a little apprehensive. My sister and brother were that only in name - so much older than myself, they were little more than strangers to me. I felt very much alone, and intimidated by the strangeness of it all. They had spent the last miles of the journey cautioning me to be on my best behaviour, to speak only when spoken to, not to ask questions and above all never to talk about my mother or father. The foreboding I had felt on the garden swing started to seep back into my stomach.

The sun had just dipped behind the trees when we drove up to the house. He must have heard the car because he came out and stood at the door. I remember the man who had been shouting and ordering everyone around the day my mother died. He stared at me as we walked towards the house. I had my school suitcase with precious treasures in one hand and my doll in the other. He seemed immense. I hung back and tried to hide a bit behind my sister's skirt. His eyes narrowed and he shouted something I didn't understand. She quickly grabbed my hand and pulled me out in front of her.

"See Granddad, she looks a lot like mother doesn't she?" My sister's voice was nervous. I could feel myself shrinking under his glare. His eyes were slits by now and bored into me.

"Yes," he snarled and turning on his heel walked heavily back into the gloom of the darkening house.

I clutched at my sister's hand and stared up at her confused and bewildered. What had I done to inspire such hatred? My brother shook his head as he bent to pick up the luggage.

"You shouldn't have said that sis, you know how he feels about that whole business."

Irritated, my sister shook my hand loose and snapped.

"Oh don't be so stupid. She was his favourite daughter wasn't she?"

He just shook his head again and followed my grandfather into the darkness. I wanted to run. Tears were pricking my eyes and my mouth was dry. But I had to follow her into that house.

My grandfather lived in a small town. Though not at all that far from "the mother city", it was impervious to change, to new breezes of life and thought. Anything foreign, anything different was regarded with distrust and suspicion. It was resisted as some kind of evil corruption that would pollute the purity of their cocoon-like existence. The society was patriarchal, religious and ultra-conservative. The face you turned outward had to conform to very clearly defined conventions and traditions. Straight-laced, highly principled and patriotic, people clung to much of what they believed to be right and wrong that they had long since forgotten the meaning of compassion and mercy. So preoccupied with living right and being respected, they failed to see the hypocrisy of their shallow existence - the dead man's bones in the whitely plastered sepulchres. While they smiled and curtsied to society, their private lives were narrow, harsh and often immoral. As long as they sinned in private, it didn't seem to matter. The important thing was keeping the sins and unrighteousness behind the closed doors of the home where the "good neighbours" couldn't see or hear it.

South Africa of the thirties and forties was not a joyful place. Though to a certain extent the country was isolated from the epoch-making events in Europe, yet ripples from those far shores brought a kind of introversion. a closing up into itself, a wilful withdrawing from defiling contact that has produced consequences still not properly understood and evaluated today. Society and culture lapsed into a kind of incestuous inbreeding. The war in Europe had other, more obvious consequences too, that had a direct effect on our community and most definitely on our family. The economy was suffering. There was increasing unemployment, inflation, lack of goods, and an apparently dwindling supply of food. And my grandfather made sure that we were made aware of it - personally, intimately and continuously. There were times I began to think that the hunger that always gnawed us was somehow my fault. That monster used to begrudge us the food we ate to such an extent that I used to miss meals out of condemnation and guilt. I say "meals" but only someone with a vivid imagination could really call them that. I no longer even expected to be able to still the hunger pains - they became a normal part of life.

The war, the stagnant suffocating atmosphere of small town life, the stuffy religious rituals and the brooding hatred in my grandfather's house fused into an oppressive, smothering nightmare. Even in broad daylight I felt as though I was living in shadows - a tangible darkness that clung to me. Yet it was the apprehension, the fear and even the stark terror I used to endure at night that combined to produce the defiance in me. Something inside me, small and uncomprehending as I was, begun to rise up and shout "No!" I was so strongly aware that I was Amber, unique, me, an individual. I was intensely conscious of being, of thinking and knowing. So often I would watch the other kids in the playground and feel bemused and not a little scornful of their naive games and laughter. I felt somehow superior in my torment.

Yet it was just as easy for me to join in and shout and run as wildly as they did. In fact I was popular with the others. Perhaps it was because I was so very small that they felt protective towards me. Perhaps they could sense the aching need to be loved and wanted. I know for sure that they were all most intrigued by my out-spokenness. It was unheard of in the predominantly Afrikaans-speaking community for a child to answer back when remonstrated by an adult. Respect, awe, even fear of adults and authority in general was ingrained in those kids. They were overwhelmed and I think a bit envious of the way I refused to be intimidated or cowed.

I remember clearly the shocked faces the first time I contradicted the English teacher. Well after all, she was wrong! I made her understand very clearly that as an Afrikaner she did not know my language as well as I did. The kids gaped at me in horror and then all the faces turned to the teacher to see how she was going to react. At first she was so taken aback she just stared at me in amazement. Then with eyes narrowing, she walked up to me and pulling my pigtails for emphasis, tried to impress me with her authority.

"How dare you talk to me like that? You do not use that tone with me. Do you understand? You will show respect and manners in future."

I jerked my head away and glared at her balefully.

"You listen, I didn't come here for you to pull my hair and act so big. I came here to learn. If you are not going to teach me properly then I'm not staying."

The incident went down in the annals of the children's history of that school. I was subjected to admiring looks, comments whispered behind grubby hands and a certain amount of disapproval too. It was as though I had drawn an unseen line in the dust and stated clearly that whoever crossed it was in for trouble. At first the other kids kept a kind of respectful distance and were very wary around me, but they soon began to accept me as I was.

"Oh that's just Amber. She's like that."

This became the prevailing attitude and instead of shunning me, they began to respond to that other, indefinable quality that has drawn people to me throughout my life. I have never been able to understand how it works, but for some reason, people would take to me and befriend me.

It was probably this that helped me not to break and give in, in the face of my grandfather's bitter cruelty. He couldn't stand the fact that I stood stiff against him. He redoubled his efforts to hurt and crush me. Daily I was called an "English bastard." I was the rubbish that my father had produced and then abandoned. I learnt to disappear when I heard his heavy step. Living in such a small community of course meant that he soon came to hear of my exploits at school. I had gained a reputation for having a fiery temper and some adults used to bait and taunt me as a game to watch my reaction. Then I suppose they went home and had a good laugh among themselves, in amusingly shocked tones. But I went home to face a thunderous grandfather, who had already wrapped the belt around his fist in preparation for the lesson he was going to teach me.

One of the things that never ceases to amaze and fill me with wonder is that through all the pain, the injustice and suffering, I have never lost my faith in God. You know, as a child in that world of hurt and desperate loneliness, I didn't see and understand like I do today, when I look back and analyse and learn to comprehend, to forgive, to let go.

How could a seven-year old possibly grasp the complex world of religion, of Afrikanerdom, of small-town South Africa and the pressures bearing in from the revolutionary awakenings thundered in by war and the collapse of an entire moral and ethical system? All I knew was that my world had shattered. And somehow, everything seemed to be trying to force me to believe that it was all my fault. I was being punished. I had done something so dreadfully wrong that my mother had died. I had been so wicked that my Aunt had to send me to my grandfather, that big monster with his black, bastard heart and his seething hatred.

I suppose that many of those people were sincere and upright in their hearts and genuinely believed that they were right and their life in order. But to me their religion was a sham and their behaviour a hypocritical lie. My mother had always taught me that God was love. There was no love in their conduct, just judgement, condemnation, censure and rejection. Or at the other extreme, pious faces and religious expressions of concern, but total indifference when it came down to the truth of loving one's neighbour as oneself.

Small town religion is generally just as narrow and bigoted as the society. Religion becomes just another platform for the notables. They twist it to become status, influence and power. So it becomes a dead ritual. They drain the real life and faith out of it and make it a hollow formula. Then they stick to those outer parades and facades and woe betide the one who challenges them, or dares to throw truth against them.

My understanding of God was not like what they tried to portray with their solemn, condemning voices and pompous Sunday behaviour. I never believed that they knew God like I did. He was never the thundering empty ogre they liked to make Him out to be. He has always been my special Friend.

He knows and understands me like no one ever has. I talk to Him about everything and though He has put me through a lot of pain and suffering I don't understand, I have never lost my clinging to Him. He is real to me and in all the torment and anguish of those years of fear, rejection and hurt, He has been with me in my loneliness.

I feel sorry for those who think they can only find Him in fancy churches and in the midst of heavy incense and solemn ritual. Frankly I don't believe He goes anywhere near those places. I feel sorry for them because most of them think they can con Him with their high-sounding words and magnanimous gestures. They are in for a shock. They think they are going to get into heaven waving their fat cheque and smiling their oily smiles. But they are going to find that the banks of Jordan don't except that kind of cheque. People forget that He made them in the first place. Do they honestly think He doesn't know everything they think and feel?

I know that I used to sit in the church and watch them, with their posh hats and special Sunday clothes. Even then I knew they were living a lie and even then I couldn't understand how they could think they were fooling God. Perhaps He just wasn't real to them, church

and God and all that were just another small town occupation, like
bazaars and picnics. It was just something you had to do because that
was the way it was.

That was how it was like in the town where we lived with our
grandfather. It always felt closed in. There was a feeling of
something menacing all the time, as though all you had to do was put
a foot wrong and judgement and punishment would descend. At first I
felt weighed down and crushed by this ugly weight, but then
something started to grow and rise up in me and it made me turn hard
and stubborn inside and fight back. Everything that was cruel, harsh
and negative somehow had my grandfather at its core.

He emanated hatred. Bitterness seeped out of him like pus from a
festering sore. There are huge portions of those early years that are a
black, gaping nothing in my mind. I have tried desperately to dig
back into those memories and bring them to the surface. I think the
trauma and intense emotions of those events have pushed everything
so deep I will never find it again. My subconscious has just blanked
them out altogether.

Here and there, like shadows of wind-driven leaves slapping across
crumbling walls I catch glimpses of an episode, a face, hear echoes of
a voice and inside me something trembles, shrinks back and the empty
void opens up into nothingness again.

It's strange how children always seem to learn the swear words
that no one dares even think at home, much less say. I learnt them.
On the playground, listening to the older boys and girls, I don't even
know where. But in my black despair and hopelessness they all meant
only one thing - my grandfather.

I know this hatred is eating in the very depths of my being and
bringing destruction with it, but it is as alive and intense today, over
forty years later, as it was when I lived with that monster. I don't
know how to get rid of it. The man is dead now, so it doesn't even
have any effect on him - not that it ever did I suppose.

He probably even took some kind of perverse satisfaction from my
grinding hatred of him. It showed him that his actions were effective,
that he was getting through to me, that he was hurting and breaking
me. I know that gave him fulfilment. But in my impotence and
childishness there was nothing I could do to hide the frustration and
the rage. So he would just observe and deep within himself, gloat,

and smile and think of other ways to torment, punish and crush his hatred into my being.

He was part of that small-town South Africa, but please understand that I don't mean by that, that he was fully representative of it all. I realise that there were countless little towns where the people lived in all sincerity and earnestness, attached to their traditional ways and believing their clear-cut simple principles and doctrines. The tragedy starts in the application of those simple outlines to the hideous complexity of real life and in the hypocrisy and lies that are the inevitable result. And it finds its full fruition in the innocent, uncomprehending lives that are ravaged by that apparently naive and "sincere" acceptance of what some revered authority proclaims to be right and wrong, good and evil. Small towns appear to breed this kind of heartless "morality". Or perhaps it was just the town that I was in - or the times.

The Second World War had shattered in, even on sheltered South Africa. My Dad was English, and he had enlisted. Thinking about it now, it was probably one of the factors that compounded my grandfather's rage and intensified his anger against this hated Englishman that had eloped with his favourite daughter. Dad enlisted, and then left. And when my mother died, he wasn't there. I suppose it was another black mark against him. Another "proof" to bolster my grandfather's bigoted hatred of all things English - especially my father, and of course, by extension, his children, and me in particular.

Communities tend to be clearly defined in small towns. And there is no boundary crossing from one to the other. There are distinctive leaders and "those in authority". They are not crossed or contradicted and never, ever challenged. It's like the dominee in some communities to this day. His word is law and judgement and that's that. For some reason I didn't understand, and still don't, it appears that my grandfather held some such sway in that little town of my childhood torment. I say "childhood" but it is a misnomer. I never had a real childhood.

That monster stole it from me. He embittered and twisted everything that was simple and beautiful. He fouled everything that he touched. From the day I walked into his house I sensed the dark brooding of his hating. It was a living thing that breathed and brooded in every room. Sometimes I felt that I could see it, a huge presence towering over him or rising dark and menacing in corners to leap across the floors towards me and slide its heavy shadow across the ceiling to try to cut off my retreat and engulf me from behind.

I think I hate him all the more today because of that very hatred that he forced into my life. I was frightened of him, in fact sometimes I was terrified he would kill me like he killed the cat. Beating me merciless with a piece of firewood while the blood splattered on the walls and carpet. But more than the fear, the hatred dominated me. It made me dig in my heels and fling the whole of my seven-year old existence in increasing rebellion against his hold. He brought the distrust and rejection into my life that have poisoned and stunted every relationship, every friendship, every attempt of mine to reach out into freedom and sunshine.

For some reason he seemed to be held in esteem in that small town. Like I said, small towns are closed-in communities. They adhere strictly and religiously to set ways of life and thinking and to try to break out of that mould takes more courage and character than most citizens can lay claim to. It was no different where we lived. Society was organised in a certain way and he had somehow built an unassailable fortress in it for himself. As long as he could keep up the facade no one would dare reproach him. I realise now that one of the reasons that made him direct all the intensity of his hatred and fury against me, is that I was breaking that lying mask down all the time.

I refused to be told what to say when and how. I spoke out. When it got too much at "home", I simply upped and walked out - ran out, as it happened, and I pleaded help from my friends' parents. Actions like this, unpremeditated and straight from the mouths of "babes and sucklings", shouted louder than any adult opposition would have. In fact it was their very attitude towards the innocence of children that in this case counted in my favour.

They could never have believed a child guilty of speaking out maliciously against an adult. If they had been able to get inside my head and see the pictures that I imagined of what I would like to do to him they would have been appalled.

CHAPTER THREE

Granddad's house was downtown and it wasn't particularly big or special, but it wasn't long before we moved to a larger place with huge grounds and lots of fruit trees. He must have been getting a pretty penny from the government for fostering the six orphans. Not that we ever saw a cent of that, or ever benefited from it. I still cannot understand what possessed him to demand that I and the others go to live with him. He hated us so bitterly. He resented our presence with every fibre of his being. Perhaps it was just the money. Maybe the people in the town had been talking and he felt that since they all knew that his daughter had died and left her children alone he had no option but to take us in.

Dad was away at the war. Those small town people must have known that he and my mother had eloped. Maybe that had brought some kind of shame or humiliation to the old man, it must have, especially since she was his favourite daughter. So he took it out on us - and especially on me. It infuriated him that of all the children I was the only one who refused to be cowed. I was the smallest, the only one with my father's brown eyes, the only one who stubbornly refused to speak Afrikaans.

I didn't understand a word of the language when I arrived there and at first he would speak only in Afrikaans or High Dutch. I didn't know what he was saying, but the sneer and scorn in his voice spoke louder than the meaning. Never did he bother to try to teach us the language, but from the first he demanded that we understand and speak it. I have always had a quick mind and I picked Afrikaans up quickly from the kids in the neighbourhood, but to him I would always speak in English.

"Bloody little English bastard," he would scream in fury, the veins standing out on his neck and his eyes blazing. I learnt to detach myself from the fear. I would stare at him impassively or let hatred and rebellion glare out at him. Then fascinated, I would watch his nostrils flare and see how his hands convulsed and the muscles in his arms and legs tense. For all my defiance I was taut and ready to run. He had big, heavy fists as I soon discovered.

Generally I would just stare at him with my mouth shut tight. But inside I was screaming at the top of my voice.

"My father and mother were English. And I'm English! And I'm going to stay English!"

I quickly discovered that he had no idea whether I really understood what he was saying or not, so I would just pretend I had no idea what he was shouting and screaming about. Eventually he would be forced to speak to me in English because no matter how much he beat me, I would not let him know that I understood him when he shouted at me in Afrikaans.

From the first he made it clear that there was to be no singing, laughing or playing in the house. The day after I arrived he summoned us all to the back garden. He had my precious suitcase in his hand. He made us fetch all our toys. I hid my doll under my pillow because I didn't trust him. But that man was a monster. He had seen her when I arrived. He marched me back to the room I shared with the others and hit me on the back of the head until I pulled her out. Back in the garden he put all the toys in a heap, he emptied my treasures out of my little suitcase. I was already sobbing and shouting at him, but he just ignored me. Then he poured some liquid over it all and watched with mocking satisfaction as it burnt to nothing.

I felt that black hatred run over into my being and I screamed until I couldn't breathe. I think I passed out, because I have no recollection of what happened after that. He never let the memory of that day die. Often he would taunt me, asking me whether my doll was in heaven, or whether she had gone to hell before me to let them know that one day I was coming too.

I was taken to school a day or two after I arrived. The numbers were so small that two standards generally occupied one room. I was bright and quick, so I finished standard one and two in one year. I was a voracious reader and absorbed rather than read books. My vocabulary grew rapidly and I knew much more than the other kids. It was an automatic response for them to expect me to answer the teacher's questions, because I was the "clever" one. The first day wasn't much fun though. The teacher put me in front of the class and I felt like I was on display.

"This is Amber. She is new here and I want you all to be nice to her and show her around."

I was so small I could barely see across the tops of the desks, one kid in the front was pulling faces already though. I ignored him.

"Come dear, you will sit here next to Petra."

Petra was not amused. She shifted over grudgingly as I eased in, shuffling along the scarred wooden bench and scratching my bottom in the process. My feet didn't touch the floor and my shoulders just made it above the desk lid. Mrs De Laney, the teacher, looked disconcerted.

"Good grief, you're such a tiny little creature," she half murmured and then taking the cushion from her own chair, shoved it under me. Snickers, whispers and muffled laughter scattered around the classroom like confetti.

I boiled.... I might be small, on the outside, but these smart-arsed-japies had better realise quickly who they were dealing with.

At break time I clambered down off the seat and followed the others outside. For a while I was lost. Someone shoved past me and mocked, "Get out of the way tich. I might step on you." For a moment I stared at his retreating back, then I swung my I lunch bag and hit him on the head. He stumbled forward and fell on his knees, grazing them as the momentum carried him onto his outstretched hands. "Tich yourself," I yelled angrily. The fury bubbled up in me. I had done nothing to this little lout. How dare he shove me just because I was smaller than him? I flew on him like a wild cat. kicking him and hitting repeatedly with the lunch bag until it broke and the contents flew all over the place. He was quick to start screaming and crying. Like all bullies he wasn't expecting his victim to retaliate. His anguished shrieks brought the teachers running. I was dragged off him, legs and arms flailing as I was lifted in the air, struggling and shouting through my own tears of bitterness and frustration. The other kids hadn't moved. Open-mouthed and round-eyed they watched the scene.

"What the devil is going on here?" demanded one of the teachers.

"Miss," one of the children gulped.

"Hendrik pushed her, so she hit him, then he fell and she hit him again, he started shouting so she hit him again, and now he's crying...."

"Yes Miss," he blurted with growing excitement.

Nothing this lively had ever happened and as the kids recovered from the shock they were starting to enjoy it - Hendrik was the class bully and they all loved seeing him on the receiving end.

I became an instant heroine. Hendrik was marched off somewhere, probably to wipe his messy nose and splotched face. I was given a talking-to; I refused to understand, but I did catch a glimpse of the amused smiles the teachers exchanged, so I realised with relief that the incident might not make its way back to grandfather's ears. When the teachers left I stood there forlornly, still sniffing and swallowing the odd heavy sob that surged up from the hurt inside to choke me.

I had thought that coming to school would be a wonderful paradise of escape and freedom from the brooding black abyss of my grandfather's hatred. The disappointment was crushing.

"Pardon me, Amber.... Amber.... Is that your name?"

I finally heard the timid voice that I realised had been hesitantly speaking for quite a while. I spun round and shouted in English.

"I don't speak your stupid language. What do you want?"

Taken aback, the girl stuttered, looked around for support and finding none, licked her lips and screwed up her courage to face this wild-eyed little harridan belligerently glaring up at her.

"Amber...I...you...your bread, it did fall on the ground," she fumbled. Holding out a soggy-looking sandwich, she continued. "You can have my sandwich if you want."

I was going to refuse angrily and turn my back on her. But somehow this gesture of kindness in my life of torment and resentment broke through the wall I was building around me and I stopped. My silence encouraged her.

"We are all very happy you hit Hendrik," she continued bravely. "He is not a nice boy."

That was the start of a friendship that was to brighten many of my gloomy hours. Elsabet lived just over the road from us with her Mum. She was older than me but always treated me like an equal. As we sat in the sun, sharing her sandwiches, I explained:

"I got angry when I saw my bread falling on the ground, and it was his fault, my grandfather doesn't give us bread and it was only because Aunt Miriam was there before him, that she could give me bread to bring to school and then I saw it all spoiled on the ground and it made me want to hit him harder."

"Do you live with your grandfather and grandmother, then?" she asked curiously.

"Yes," I said bluntly, then I corrected myself, "No, she's not my grandmother. She's Aunt Miriam."

Elsabet looked uncomprehending.

"I don't know where my grandmother is. I don't know if I have one."

I was just as confused, so it was no good her looking to me for an explanation. My elder sisters and brothers had just said that the woman who lived with grandfather was Aunt Miriam, because I had mistakenly called her grandmother and then reeled from the slap grandfather had delivered to the back of my head. Maybe my real grandma was dead. I remember thinking how crowded heaven must be if all the dead people from everywhere went there.

"Where's your Mom and Dad then?" Elsabet wanted to know. The old ache churned my stomach.

"My Mum's dead. My Dad's gone somewhere for the war."

The walls had come up again and Elsabet obviously realised it.

There were no more questions.

When I look back on those years now, I begin to realise that people were not quite so blind and indifferent as my little head had concluded. I think there was a lot of shocked talking behind closed doors about my grandfather and the way he treated us.

There was a great deal of disapproval and censure, but for some reason I still cannot understand, they were afraid to speak out publicly about it, at least for many years. I realise too, that my behaviour was instrumental in breaking down the walls of silence and hesitation. I had no qualms about speaking out about what that awful man was doing to us. That was probably adding fuel to fan the flames of hatred that burned in him against me. He considered me responsible for the change in attitude of the townspeople towards him.

When we returned to the classroom after break there was a different cushion for me. As I manoeuvred the thing so that I could see reasonably well and rested my elbows on the desk there was no laughter from any quarter. I had made my mark and no one was going to risk the retaliation they had seen Hendrik cash in. He certainly hadn't bargained for the lesson he had received. It was actually the end of his domineering days. Every time he tried to get pushy after that, somebody would warn him,

"Watch out Hendrik, we'll call Amber."

Then everyone would shriek with laughter and tease him cruelly. I arrived home that afternoon to find the monster sitting on the stoep. His head was lolled on his chest and it looked as though he was asleep. I climbed quietly up the stairs and cautiously started edging past him into the house.

"Stop right there!" his voice ground into me. "Who gave you permission to wear those shoes?"

I was startled. They were my shoes. What was he on about now?

"You take those things off immediately," he shouted, getting up.

I stood my ground and glared at him. I knew how this infuriated him but it was simply stronger than me, I refused to let him see the fear, I refused to give in to him.

"They're my shoes." I mumbled stubbornly.

"What? What's that?!"

His anger was crackling at the edges.

"I said they're my shoes!" I shouted back defiantly.

That was too much. He lurched up out of the chair and grabbed me at the back of my neck. Pushing and hitting me, he drove me into the house. When I fell down he grabbed my feet and jerked the shoes off.

"You'll wear the shoes when I say so!"

He thundered and stalked off into the shadows of the corridor to his bedroom, the offending shoes dangling from his meaty fists. I would see them again only on Sundays, when we went to church where he would sit with a holy, solemn expression and show the world what a wonderful Christian he was.

I sat there shaking, my teeth clenched as I felt the dry sobs racking my chest, but I would not cry. Aunt Miriam came tiptoeing softly from the background. Looking nervously over her shoulder she picked me up and whispered to me to go to our bedroom and lie down. Then she disappeared.

I limped off to my bed and lay face down, letting the pillow soak up the tears and hurt while the impotent rage burned in my chest. Quietly the door opened and with a finger to her lips, Aunt Miriam put a glass of water down on the floor next to me before slipping out again.

She was trying to be nice I suppose, but even today I think I despise her. I couldn't understand why she never defended us. She was like a non-person. Like she was afraid to live, apologetic that she breathed. When I think of her it's like there's nothing more than a shadow, always hovering uncertainly in the background, ready to dart away if it was discovered. She could have made our lives so much less painful, but she didn't. Perhaps she was afraid he would hit her too. Maybe he did. Still, I cannot help feeling scorn and contempt for her. I have always had to stand up to people and fight for myself and I can't understand those who won't. I will not bend and cow to arrogance and antagonism or people who try to manipulate and control me and I have nothing but contempt for those who give in to that.

She even tried to defend and justify him to me once.

"Amber, you must be more obedient. Grandfather really loves you and wants the best for you. You mustn't answer back."

The words that broke over my quivering little lips shocked that hesitation of a woman to such an extent that she literally backed out of the room. She never ever tried to excuse him to me again. Perhaps she felt guilty about what he was doing, because occasionally she would still slide a sweetie into my hand without the other children knowing about it, but she stopped trying to slip me food to take to school.

From time to time when grandfather wasn't around, she had given me the odd piece of bread to take for break. Mostly however, when the other kids ate their samies and fruit or sucked their sweeties I had nothing.

"Haven't you got something to swop Amber?"

"No; I don't need to eat as much as you," I would try to joke. "I'm smaller and don't need so much food."

Or would pretend I wasn't hungry. Elsabet knew the truth though and I suppose eventually it was just common knowledge, but being kids, we simply didn't make a big deal out of it. They all knew that my grandfather was cruel and wouldn't allow us to have bread for school. They took it for granted that I didn't get break samies. Elsabet often brought something extra for me and as time went on and other kids started to take to me, I suppose the word spread to their parents too, because on many a day some kid would bring me a fruit or sandwich which their Mom had sent.

That night Mum came to me again. I was crying quietly into my pillow so that my two sisters in the big bed with me wouldn't hear. It was dark and I was so afraid. All the shadows seemed to be alive and it felt like they started moving towards me when I wasn't looking.

Then to my horror I noticed a thicker shadow that was moving, and it was coming straight towards me. The fear stuck in my throat like a jagged bone. I could feel my breath cutting my lungs and my heart thudded so hard I thought my chest was going to explode. When the shadow came closer to me it was my Mum, her long black hair dangling smoothly down her back. Slowly and deliberately she walked towards the dressing table and picked up my brush. Then turning her head slightly to one side and the other she ran the brush through her long tresses, smoothing it over with the other hand. Brush...smooth, brush...smooth, her eyes following her movements in the mirror. She caught sight of my petrified face and smiled at me in the reflection. Then standing up, she glided over and touched me with the brush. That broke the spell.

The shrieks that ripped through the blackness must have woken the neighbourhood. Jerked out of deep sleep by my hysteria, my two sisters joined the screaming. I was berserk with fear, shaking and crying and yelling at the top of my voice.

Grandfather of course was enraged. Aunt Miriam drifted in and quickly slipped out again when his fury started shouting down my screams. Through my panic-stricken babbling, my sisters finally found out what had happened.

"It was Mum again, it was Mum," I choked out. "She was brushing her hair - with my brush, her hair, it was all loose and she was smiling in the mirror and then she touched me and she was here...."

The words tumbled out hysterically. With an impatient snort my grandfather caught hold of my own hair and yanked.

"Stop it! Stop it! You snivelling little English bastard. Shut your mouth. Stop it!" He jerked my head backwards till I was gulping for breath. "You just had a nightmare. Now shut up and go back to sleep."

He stormed out, enveloped in his dark dressing-gown.

I was still shaking and shivering and my sisters did their best to calm me down.

"Oh Amber, it was just a dream," Denise tried to comfort me.

"No it wasn't," I insisted forcefully. "It was Mum, I know it was her. She was here!"

Charlene held me and rocked me gently for a while.

"Amber, Mum couldn't have been here, she's in heaven, remember? It was just a dream, wasn't it?"

There was a doubtful undertone to her question.

This wasn't the first time Mum had appeared to me. Thinking about it now, I believe that Charlene was probably awake the first time and had realised that I was really seeing something, that I wasn't asleep and couldn't have been dreaming.

Eventually the panic lifted and I slowly started to drift into sleep.

"Denise," I heard Charlene whisper. There was a mumbled grunt in reply. "Denise," Charlene insisted with urgency.

"What is it?" came the irritated answer.

"Denise, don't you think that maybe Amber did see Mum?"

Denise was now even more irritated, but there was a hint of fear in her answer.

"Oh! don't be so stupid. How could it have been Mum?"

Charlene hesitated.

"Well, Amber was born with a caul, wasn't she? Maybe Mum is our guardian angel now and Amber can see her."

Denise's reply was inaudible, I must have been half-asleep by then, but I can remember wondering vaguely what a caul was. Strangely it gave me some kind of vague comfort, a feeling of being special.

I asked Charlene next morning.

"Charl, what's a caul?" She was unnerved.

"A what? I don't know what you're talking about," and she turned on her heel and left me.

That was enough to light the fuse, I would not rest until I knew what it was. No good asking my grandfather, he would use it as an excuse to beat me. Aunt Miriam was an even more hopeless case. So the next options were Elsabet and other kids at school. No one had ever heard of it, especially not the English word. So the only other solution was the teacher.

"Miss," I put my hand up. "What is a caul please?"

She looked puzzled.

"A call? Come Amber, surely you know that? It's like when I talk loudly, or shout. Then I call."

Some of the kids sniggered.

"No miss, that's not what I mean. This is something like a hat."

That thoroughly mystified her.

"What on earth do you mean, Amber?"

"Miss, my sister says I was born with a caul over my head and I want to know what it is."

At this there was outright laughter.

The teacher stiffened, "There will be order in the classroom! This is nothing to laugh about."

But she obviously didn't know what it was either, because she simply said I must have misheard, and that was that. Now I was getting angry. This thing was the reason why Mum visited me and maybe if I found out what it was she would leave me in peace and not frighten me so much.

But there was no one else to ask, so it was left to my imagination. It must have been over a year before I eventually found out, quite by chance. These appearances, or visions, or dreams or whatever they were, recurred frequently enough for the news to get around the school. I spoke about them a few times too, because of the awed response I would get. It made me feel important, special, like I was different from the others in a superior sort of way. One of the girls though, envied this privileged status and remarked petulantly.

"Oh! Don't think you're so special. My mother said you just had a fleece over your head. I think you're just a witch."

Like a flash I was on her. The suddenness of my attack caught her so unawares that she fell down and screamed. I pulled her hair as hard as I could.

"What do you mean?" I shouted, because it seemed to me this "fleece" was the same as the "caul" my sister had spoken of.

I frog-marched her to her house, pushing and shoving her from behind. As she ran crying in at the front door I confronted her astonished and anxious mother, "Mrs Botha, what's a fleece?"

Once she got over her initial upset and confusion, she must have seen my own bewilderment beneath the grim determination. She sat me down in the kitchen while she wiped her daughter's grimy tear-stained face and explained.

"A 'vlees'," she said, "is an Afrikaans word. Some people, when they are born, have a little skin over their face, like a little covering, that's all."

I still didn't understand.

"Why should it make my mother come to me?" I saw her hesitate. Then she smiled and with a light-hearted little wave of her hand she tried to laugh it off.

"Oh, that's just people being silly and imagining things. Now don't you go worrying about it. It is all perfectly normal and lots of people are born like that."

I was disappointed, but still not satisfied. She hadn't explained this "Vlees" thing properly, I was sure. It was only much later, in the course of my avid reading that I came across a character who had "second sight" because she had been born with a caul. I was electrified. Did I have second sight? The thought intrigued and also frightened me. It certainly would explain the feeling I often get of having been somewhere before, or of knowing what someone is going to say or do, or having that ominous foreboding of something bad about to happen.

At that stage however, it was added distinction to my already formidable reputation. I know the teachers had a really tough time to figure me out. There were days I would be soft, pliable, gentle and so sweet that I could feel they wanted to hug me. But then something would crawl over me and I could feel the rebellion surging up like a river in flood. Then out of nowhere these cutting, boldly antagonistic words would lash out at the one who had crossed me, teacher, adult, school, child, it was immaterial. No punishment had any effect. My grandfather used to shout as he beat me, "I will hit you until you stop crying," so I had learned long ago to choke back the tears. Hidings and beatings just made me stiffer and harder inside.

I had quickly perceived that people couldn't sustain my look either. When a teacher or some adult remonstrated with me about something I didn't think was just, I would stare at them. They became almost instantly unnerved. No one could hold my gaze. I know, to quite a few adults, I was a "child of the devil". This, the caul business and my ability to "see ghosts" led to a number of people giving me a wide berth - but in a weird perverted kind of way, they respected me. At least I considered it respect and it was important, because it proved to me that I was a person, I mattered, I counted, despite what my grandfather said and did to me.

CHAPTER FOUR

"Amber, where are you going for the holidays? Mom says we're going to visit family at the sea!" Elsabet was bubbling with excitement as we walked to school.

I peeked at her out of the corner of my eye... She was sincere, she wasn't provoking me. Holidays... what would I know about holidays? I wasn't in the mood for levity. My feet hurt. They were badly chapped and split all round the heels. Walking on the hot tar to school and back was agony. I was hungry. My grandfather had sent us to bed with a bunch of grapes and a slice of bread. I felt as though the hollow in my stomach was bigger than me. The sun was already beating on my head and I felt faint. I kept wiping a cold clammy perspiration off my face and forehead. Every now and again I could feel my heart suddenly thump rapid series of extra beats.

Elsabet babbled on. I was suddenly overwhelmed at the thought of having to spend every day at my grandfather's house without the escape of school. That sick feeling of dread started seeping up from my stomach, so I knew that something awful was going to happen.

During classes I couldn't concentrate. I kept feeling the hunger swell up in my stomach. At lunch time I just went home with Elsabet. She was a bit surprised but didn't query anything.

"Hullo Aunt Martha," I greeted her mother. "I'm very hungry, my grandfather won't give me any food, please can I eat here by you today?"

I can remember how my hands were shaking when I picked up the sandwich she made me. Never had peanut butter and syrup tasted so delicious. The problem of course is that peanut butter does not lend itself to rapid consumption! I almost choked because I was trying to eat it so fast.

"Wait child, wait, just stop a little and breathe."

Aunt Martha was wiping my face. I don't know where the tears had come from: from relief, from pent-up anguish, or from choking. In any case they were there, and she was obviously moved and very indignant. At first I thought she was angry with me and as she lifted her hand I cowered, thinking she was going to slap me. She was horrified at my reaction - I realised too late she was reaching for a glass of milk. Aunt Martha didn't say anything, but her lips were pressed very tightly together.

After lunch Aunt Martha gave us an apple and despatched us to the steps where we sat in the sun chewing. I sucked on the sweet juice and felt every drop and every crunchy morsel slip deliciously down my throat. She came down the steps with her hat on and her bag under her arm. She looked grim.

"Elsabet, don't you two go anywhere. I'll be back in a minute."

She was just turning her back when she caught sight of my feet. Her hand started up towards her mouth and then she stopped herself and looked quickly at me.

"Amber, what have you been doing to your feet?"

I was puzzled.

"Nothing Aunt Martha, just walking."

She bent over to get a closer look and then gingerly lifted one up to examine the cracked splitting flesh.

"Where are your shoes? You can't walk barefoot like this."

"My grandfather took them Aunty. He only lets us wear them on Sundays. Then I don't like to because my feet hurt to much."

She straightened up. The look on her face was inscrutable, but the "vibe" that wafted over me from her was delightful. I felt glee and rejoicing, because I knew that she was going to get back at my grandfather for me. I might have been only seven or eight years old, and in many ways perhaps very naive, but I had matured and grown wise in things that most children didn't experience till they were adults. I knew that my tiny stature inspired feelings of protection in adults, as long as I didn't blow it with my rebellion and stubbornness and as long as I didn't turn my glare on them.

The trouble was, deep down I knew that if someone did say or do something to grandfather, I would be the one to cop it. He infallibly blamed me for anything that ruffled his day. But at that moment it was worth the beating I knew I would get. Aunt Martha stalked down the street towards the Dominee's house. I watched furtively as Elsabet chattered on about the holidays and the sea. As she rounded the corner, the bubbles of glee in me suddenly collapsed into a little slimy puddle of misery and bitterness. I stood up.

"Please tell your Mum thank you for the lunch, I must go now."

I had an extra sandwich in my pocket that I was saving for bedtime. I should have eaten it when I had the opportunity. When I tiptoed into the house Charlene was waiting anxiously peering round the bedroom door. Her eyes were panicky and she motioned me to come quickly. But it was too late. The big voice thundered from the lounge.

"Why are you so late? Come here you!"

I tried to pull the sandwich out to give it to Charlene to hide, but as I managed to jiggle it free, he loomed in the entrance.

"What's that? What have you got there?"

As he stood towards me I started stuffing it into my mouth. It was my sandwich and he was not going to get it. Those big hands tore my fist open and then thumped me on the back till I had choked, coughed and spat every crumb out.

He took me by the shoulders and rattled me till the room spun.

"So now we've got a thief in the house too!" he bellowed. "But we've caught it! Haven't we?"

His malicious triumph thumped into my being with more force than his fists.

"Little bastard. I'll teach you to steal."

As he lifted his hand I shrieked at him.

"It is my sandwich, Aunt Martha gave it to me because you won't give us anything to eat. It is my sandwich and I didn't steal it!"

He stopped dead. Even in the gloom of the hall I could see the colour slipping from his face till he was a sick, grey colour.

But it wasn't fear, it was fury. His voice came out in a hiss, but the shock of my words had made him momentarily loose his grip and I shot out of the house so fast he had no time to grab me again.

I ran over the road back to Elsabet's house, breathless and trembling, but victorious. I knew I had beaten him on this one. He wouldn't dare follow me out into the road. Just then Aunt Martha moved into sight too, so it seemed that for once fortune was smiling on me. When she saw my bedraggled state and heard from Elsabet that I had already gone home but come back again, she must have put two and two together, because though she said nothing, she let me stay until late afternoon. Then taking me by the hand, she walked me home.

I felt the tension build up as we climbed the steps. My grandfather wasn't there. Aunt Miriam answered the knock and looking accusingly at me, invited Aunt Martha into the lounge while I was told to go and wash up.

They closed the door. How I wished I could hear what was being said. By the time I came from the bathroom, Aunt Martha was gone. When I wanted to walk onto the stoep, Aunt Miriam stopped me with a sharp command.

"Amber, go to your bedroom, now!"

She wouldn't look at me. As I hesitated her voice rose shrilly, and I realised she was frightened.

"I said, now!"

There was no supper for me that night, not even the grapes and slice of bread. Denise had some sweets which she had given me in sympathy. They were very curious to know what had happened, because they said my grandfather had stormed out of the dining room in a towering rage, shouting at Aunt Miriam about interfering women and witches and ministers who couldn't keep their noses out of other people's business. He had issued ugly threats about me that had shocked my sisters. I kept quiet. I felt it was none of their business. I knew already that they didn't really care about me. In fact it was clear that they bitterly resented the way I stood up to grandfather and rebelled.

I think they thought it was easier just to shut up and say "yes sir, no sir, three bags full sir". They would always give in to everything he said and did.

They were scared of him so they sucked up to him to gain his favour. I just refused to give him that satisfaction.

The days that followed were oppressive. I hadn't needed Aunt Miriam's whispered admonition to stay out of his way. I went to Aunty Martha's every day that week and I can still recall the taste of the soup, the hot bread she baked and the tangy juice of the apples she gave for 'after lunch snack'. But Friday was drawing closer. School was breaking up and Elsabet and her Mom were going to the sea, and my protection and security with them, at least that's how I felt.

On Saturday morning we were summoned to the lounge. I was trembling inside, but had my defiant face on. Charlene kept digging me in the ribs and whispering angrily.

"Amber, don't!"

But the opposition from my own sister just made me more stubborn. I was not going to give in.

He sat there with a gloating, self-satisfied expression on his face.

"Just because you think it's holidays now, does not mean that you can just hang around and loaf here in my house," was his opening remark.

"You don't live on handouts around here. You are not going to grow up worthless bastards like your father if I can help it. You will learn to earn your living."

The sermon continued in this vein. I switched off. His monologues were always the same. Hatred, resentment, scorn, derision - the antagonism and contempt he poured on my darling father and mother merely fanned the hatred I felt for him. Then there was a new note in his voice that made me listen again. There was a triumphant glint in his ugly eyes. He was obviously relishing his 'solution' to our free time.

"So the farmer will send his bakkie for you every morning early and you will harvest tobacco. Earn your keep. Learn not to scrounge - and not to expect to get everything for nothing," and at this his gaze poured naked hatred and rage into my soul.

I feigned indifference. He hated it when I refused to react to his taunts. His voice rose in anger.

"You will learn to appreciate what you get in this home," he threatened, glaring at me.

"You should be put in a workhouse, you're lucky you're not out in the streets starving. Where do you think you would be if I hadn't taken you in? What has your worthless father done for you? Just gone off. Shirked his responsibilities. What do you think would have happened to you if it wasn't for me?"

By this time my sisters and brothers were snivelling.

"Grandpa we are grateful, we know we're worthless and we know if it wasn't for you, then we would be lost," snuffled Charles, my second eldest brother. I turned my head in disgust and stared out the window. It infuriated him. I was brought back to the moment by a resounding slap on the side of my head.

"Did you hear me, you ungrateful little bastard?" he yelled.

I regained my balance and just stared at him, sending as much hatred and defiance down that look as I could muster. That was generally the point when my sisters and brothers would round on me, because otherwise he would start lashing out indiscriminately.

"Amber, you should be ashamed."

"Amber, who do you think you are?"

"Amber, stop it, behave yourself!" and so on.

Mollified and gratified by this demonstration of support for his opinions and attack on me, he would step back with a satisfied smirk.

"Yeh, well maybe there is even hope for some of you little bastards. But that one?"

He would curl his lip in disgust as he sneered.

"That one will end badly and she'll finish up in hell."

I was in hell already. I don't believe that any hell could be worse than the one I lived in for so many years of torment and anguish.

At the crack of dawn on Monday the farmer sent his bakkie for us. That simply started another phase, another aspect of hell. We had to pick tobacco. When the farmer was explaining what we had to do he looked at me very doubtfully.

"You now, what's your name? You look a bit small to me. Do you really think you can do this work?"

Before I had a chance to open my mouth my sisters and brothers had all chorused their protests, yes of course, we all could, we all wanted to work, we were all willing. I just looked small but I was really strong... grandfather must have really made some strong threats.

I suppose the farmer thought we had volunteered for the work. Or didn't care - as long as he got his work done. We were driven out to the fields on open carts behind tractors. I was given a box and a coloured woman showed me how to pick the leaves and pack them in the box. I was quite relieved, it looked easy - until I had been working for about five minutes. The leaves didn't always come away easily. My little fingers and hands soon began to cramp. Sharp pains stabbed into my back every time I bent down. It was harder to straighten up and bend down with every leaf. The box grew heavier. Eventually I was struggling to drag it down the row. My shoulders and neck was shot through with shafts of jagged pain and by the end of the first hour or so every single one of my nails had been torn.

The juice from the leaves was already staining my hands and arms. The sun grew hotter until it felt like a fire had been lit on my head. An old coloured man was working down the row next to me. He saw me struggling and slipping and trying to heave the box and he shook his head. He had a huge cloth that he wiped his face with, after a while he stood up, took the cloth and made a hat for me with it, knotting the corners tight so that it would fit. At first I thought he was laughing at me and I was getting ready to turn on him, but his eyes were sad and his face so deeply etched with wrinkles that the words died in my throat. I thanked him and I think he was taken aback, because I called him "Oom", I don't suppose any white person had ever addressed him that way.

After that he often walked back across his row to help me drag the box. As the day progressed my throat and mouth dried out like sun-scorched brick. There was dust and sand in my eyes, my nostrils and every pore of my body. My throat was so dry I couldn't swallow and my eyes felt scratched and gritty. I staggered to a more upright position and craned around to see where my sisters and brothers were. I could see nothing through the heat haze - and I refused to call them. So in desperate weariness I went back to picking.

When the sun was at its highest, the cart came round again. Some pickers had four, five and more boxes. I had barely filled one, which someone heaved on to the cart. Then I felt myself being lifted too. I wanted to cry with relief... it was over! But it was simply a progression to the next degree of torment.

The cart drove to a long shed which had rows of tables inside. The smell was awful. It stank of stale wine, unwashed bodies, urine and the all pervasive stench of tobacco juice.

Piles of leaves were stacked on the tables and we had to sort them, same size, same colour, and then stick them on needles, about sixty I suppose to a needle. We were paid a tickey a needle. The table was too high from the bench for me to be able to sit in comfort. My already pain-racked back was screaming with every movement. I tried kneeling on the bench so that my arms could reach above the edge of the table, but after a minute or so couldn't bear the agony. I tried standing at the table, but it wasn't long before my legs started to give in. The tobacco juice was black, sticky and smelly. It stained everything.

There was a toothless coloured woman next to me, sorting and filling needles so fast I could hardly see her fingers and hands. She had a dirty yellow "doek" around her head, pulled low down her forehead and she munched her toothless gums as she worked.

She held a bottle between her feet and from time to time would take surreptitious little sips out of it. By now the thirst was making me half-crazy and eventually I couldn't stand it anymore. The next time she lifted the bottle to her lips, I stretched out and asked for it.

She snatched the bottle away as anger flashed in her eyes, but then she hesitated, looked around and cautioning me to be careful, slipped the bottle into my anxious hands.

I had thought it was water, so I took a deep gulp and swallowed. The alcohol hit my stomach with a minor explosion and fire burnt all the way up through my lungs to my ears and eyes. Coughing, spluttering and choking, I nearly dropped the bottle.

Her eyes darting in all directions, she grabbed the precious stuff and hid it away again under the table between her feet while I hacked, spat and gasped. She cackled and garrulously rattled away at me in Afrikaans, of which I understood probably about one word in a hundred since she had a funny accent and used odd words. By the time I could breathe again, with eyes and nose still streaming, I asked her if she didn't have water. She stared at me uncomprehendingly, shook her head and explained that if I wanted water I had to bring my own.

So the day dragged on. At last the farmer stood at the door and called for us. I was so weary I could hardly walk. Someone grabbed my arm and push-carried me to the bakkie. I must have fallen asleep on the way home, because the next thing I remember is Aunt Miriam shaking me in the bathroom to make me wash. As soon as she had gone I put my mouth to the tap and started drinking, drinking and drinking. The cold water was like heaven. Eventually I could feel my stomach was full, but the thirst was not satisfied. The parched dryness seemed to have permeated every membrane and cell of my being. Then my body rebelled. Cramps racked my stomach and the precious water came shooting up in sour spouts.

Panic-stricken I looked for something to mop the floor with, but there was only my towel. My stomach ached, my throat felt as though thorn bushes had been dragged down it. And I was still thirsty. Desperate, I bent down to drink again, slowly now, one sip after another. The water stayed down, and this time started to soak the thirst away. I had learnt something.

When I got to the bedroom, there was a slice of bread and a bunch of grapes waiting for me. But I was so tired and so sore that I no longer even felt the hunger. My last thought as I drifted unhappily off to sleep was that at least I would have some money and would be able to buy food with it.

The days dragged past, an agony of thirst, hunger heat and pain.

When at last we had finished the farmer's fields I looked forward to peace and rest, but the next day we were packed off to a neighbouring farmer, and the torment started afresh. The juice burned into my nails and skin. It eventually took weeks to get rid of it. We never saw a penny of the money we had supposedly earned. Neither did we reap any of its benefits. If my grandfather bought food or clothing with it, we certainly never got any.

But he learned to regret it.

The first day we went back to school we had the usual "appearance inspection". We lined up while the teacher looked at our uniforms, handkerchiefs, nails, hair etc. My nails and fingers were black with tobacco juice.

"Amber!" the teacher was horrified.

"Just look at this filth! Aren't you a little pig!"

There was laughter up and down the line. That was it, I exploded. By that time I had picked up quite a few choice expletives and to the shocked delight of the other children, I let fly. When I had finished, she had no doubts concerning my feelings about thick-headed teachers, monster grandfathers, tobacco harvesting, tobacco farmers and a host of other related and unrelated topics that came bursting out like a dam had been breached.

"Amber, keep quiet! How dare you say that? Will you stop that!"

Eventually the torment of words gushing from my aching soul swamped her. I don't know how much she believed and how much she put down to childish fretfulness against an authoritarian grandfather, but the evidence of my stained and broken nails and chapped, cut hands was irrefutable. Not that it changed the way we spent our holidays. But it was another of the mounting accusations against the monster that was eventually to become the siege engine that would shatter those walls of hypocrisy and lies he had built around him.

A new teacher had arrived, a Miss Marais. She was young and she smiled often. On the first day she introduced herself and then said,

"I want each of you to stand and give me your name and age so that I can start to get to know you."

I yearned to like and trust her. but I had experienced rejection and abuse so often that I couldn't open up. So when my turn came I stayed seated, glared briefly at her and mumbled my name. She simply went on to the next person. But just before the end of the next lesson, as we were writing in our exercise books, I felt a hand on my shoulder. I started and jerked away, but the grip just grew slightly firmer.

"Amber," her voice was gentle, "I would like you to stay for a few minutes when the others have gone."

Then she carried on walking down the aisle, but I could still feel the warmth of her hand on my shoulder. She had spoken so softly I don't think anyone else had heard.

There was no way I was going to let others know that I had been singled out, so I dropped a few books, bent down, picked them up, fumbled, packed and repacked my things until the class was empty. Miss Marais was sitting quietly watching me. I fixed her with a hostile glare. She smiled and motioned me to her desk.

Reluctantly, and with as much antagonism as I could manifest, dragged my feet towards her and stopped rebelliously a foot or so away from the desk.

"No, not there, I want you here next to me. Come."

I was nonplussed. Hesitantly I inched towards her. Did she want to hit me already? As I came within reach she suddenly stretched out and put her hands on my shoulders, pulling me closer. I froze. Her face went sad.

"Amber, I'm not going to do anything to you, I just want you closer."

"Then get your hands off me."

But I had not calculated on this lady's insight. A little glint flashed in her eyes and her smile curled a bit.

"Why Amber, what are you afraid of?"

Stung I retorted, "I'm not afraid of anything!"

"Then you won't mind if I give you a little hug?"

By now I was totally disorientated. Her question made me gape at her. What did she want to hug me for? I started to pull back, but her grip was firm.

"Amber, there's no need to be afraid, I am not going to hurt you. I just want you to know that I think you and I can be friends and because I can see your loneliness and hurt, I want to give you a hug to help fill up that ache."

I didn't know what to do, I felt panicky, trapped, but at the same time there was a powerful surge of yearning in me. So I did what I

46

always did in crises. I went as hard as granite and just glared at her with my mouth shut tight.

"Amber, you do not fool me, dear. We'll get to know each other and then you will learn to relax and trust me more."

With that she gave me a hug anyway, despite my stiff shoulders and rigid body.

She was right, I did get to know her more, although it took a year or more. She was consistent - never grumpy one day and smiling the next. She was fair, and I sensed that she had a soft spot for me. I don't know why. I have often thought of her since and wondered what had drawn her to me. Perhaps she had been an orphan. Maybe they had warned her about me and she had decided to do something about it. She was persistent too, in a gentle way. Despite the rebuffs, she was constantly friendly towards me. As time passed, I learnt to relax my guard with her and eventually I was confiding in her, though it took a long time.

I actually enjoyed school more than most children probably did. I was bright and learned quickly. By now I had discovered the wonderful world of books and had become a voracious reader. I could lose myself in those stories, I would immerse myself in the people and events so that I lived with them. Then the dreary world of reality would dissipate and for a while I would be free and living all kinds of exciting adventures in fascinating countries and times. I would disappear into the bottom of the garden with a book and sit there until it was to dark to decipher the letters. That is where I also had my secret cache of food. It was something my grandfather never did discover and I used to relish my triumph over him in this treasure of mine on a daily basis - and especially when he had beaten me, as usual for something I hadn't done.

He was so miserly with food that I used to think he was trying to starve us to death. Maybe he hoped that we would just drop dead in the street. I know he would probably have preferred to beat us to death, but then they would have known he had done it, so he didn't dare.

My mother had made it so clear that God is love, so there were some things that you just never do, because it would upset Him so much - and one of those things was to steal. But I had to find some solution for the chronic hunger.

There was a small fruit and vegetable shop on the road to school. The owner was a funny, short little man with a strange accent and oily hair that always dropped over his forehead into his eyes.

But he was always very kind. I turned my sweet smile on him and like a lot of people, his heart melted towards me. He must have heard the stories about me, my vicious temper, the brazenness that adults accused me of, but it never seemed to affect him. He came out of the shop once while I was picking loose cabbage leaves up from where they had fallen under the crates.

"Hey, what you doing?" he queried, but not angrily.

I jumped.

"It's just old cabbage leaves, you can't sell these can you?"

He just looked at me, then shook his head and said,

"No, sure, you take if you want."

He went back inside, but I saw his face at the dirty window, peering curiously as I picked up the leaves and a few broken carrots that were lying in the dust.

In my secret place in the garden I had an old tin, I used to put all the little bits and pieces I found in water and cook them over a tiny fire, making sure there wasn't enough smoke to betray my hideaway.

Seldom could I wait until they were properly cooked. I learnt to cut them up small so that they cooked quicker and it also helped to make a kind of a soup with the water they boiled in. All the time I gloated over my grandfather.

"Hideous old monster, I won't starve to death, see - I can find my own food, I can cook it myself, and you can't take this away."

Sometimes the vegetable man would give me a bonanza. Soft, very spongy potatoes, or bruised, squishy tomatoes or even whole cabbages that had yellowed. Occasionally, as though he had overlooked what was in the box he handed to me, there would be a lush ripe fruit, or bright crisp carrots.

Inevitably, the holidays came round again. To me, they were an occasion for dread, not rejoicing.

When the other kids chattered excitedly about what they were going to do and where they were going, I disappeared, apprehensive that they would ask me.

This time it wasn't tobacco, but fruit we had to harvest. The farmer decided I was too small to climb the ladders, so I was put with others to the job of cutting the fruit in half and discarding the wormy ones.

It wasn't as bad as the tobacco picking, but my fingers were soon cut and gushed from the knife and my fingernails broken from pulling out the pips. There was a big guy who walked around and kept an eye on us.

"Come on you lazy bastards, stop loafing and put your backs into it."

He would shout, and sometimes hit one of the workers over the head or slap their ears. I hated him. He came and shouted in my ears the first day we worked there.

"Just because you're small, don't think you can get away with anything. If I catch you stealing fruit or messing around instead of working, you'll regret it. You don't come here and get paid for nothing!"

He loved his authority and really preened himself when he could yell at someone.

The next day my fingers were sore and I had difficulty holding the knife properly.

"Hey, you slacker! Didn't I warn you yesterday about taking chances?"

"Shut up you!" I flared back. "Who do you think you are, rubbish. Go and shout your mouth off somewhere else."

He was not expecting the retaliation and for a moment did nothing. Then he saw the other workers' amusement, and enraged he walked over and slapped my ears.

"Little bitch! You better work hard or you'll regret it."

And picking up a rotten apricot, squashed it onto the top of my head. He laughed and walked away.

The fury burnt over me so badly my hands were shaking and my heart thudding against my chest. I might only have been eight but I had already experienced the depths of resentment and bitterness. There was no way I was going to allow this animal to treat me like that. I waited, but for the next few days I only caught glimpses of him as he swaggered in other parts of the fields. But his nemesis also came.

Like so many, he overestimated his own power and authority - or underestimated my lust for revenge.

I was hard at work, totally absorbed in cutting, pulling out the pip and stacking the fruit. Then suddenly this slimy, smelly thing was pushed into my face and rubbed up and down with force, so that it squashed into my mouth and nose. Spluttering for breath I struggled to my feet, only to fall forward as gusts of raucous laughter swept over me. He shouldn't have done that. The huge wave of fury blotted out everything as it surged through me.

Grabbing the nearest thing I could, I whirled around and hit him with all my strength. The wooden crate splintered, there was an ear-splitting scream and blood everywhere. He lashed at me in white-hot anger, fortunately I ducked. He missed because he had only one eye to aim with. The other was a mess of blood and gore, the crate had connected with his forehead, eye and cheekbone.

Fortunately, the other workers were galvanised into action and managed to restrain him, otherwise I would have been mincemeat. Probably not even enough for a hamburger, but mincemeat none the less. I savoured the revenge.

"That'll teach you!" I thought.

Unfortunately, my grandfather thought much the same where I was concerned and when I got home that evening it was to find him waiting with the strap wound round his fist.

For two days I couldn't move from the bedroom, and when I did get up, I wasn't sent back to the fruit farm where my sisters and brothers were still working. But, it was an agricultural area and there were many other farmers looking for cheap labour...

There was one farmer who was not as bad as the others. At lunch time he used to have big jugs of water and plates of sliced bread waiting for us. He also didn't mind if we ate some of the fruit. One day I was carefully nibbling little bits of an apricot that I had secreted in the folds on my lap when his shadow suddenly stretched out over me from behind. I froze, and tensed for the slap.

"If you're hungry you can eat, Amber. Just don't eat too many apricots, especially if they're not quite ripe, because you'll get a tummy ache."

The back of my head was tingling from anticipation of the blow. It never came. He often used to walk over to me with a particularly luscious peach or apricot and drop it into my lap with a smile. I was suspicious at first, but I loosened up and started to answer his questions and chat.

"Well, Miss Muffet," he said smiling one day, "what wonderful things are you going to buy with all this money you're earning?"

He had a long thin stem of grass in the corner of his mouth and he sucked and chewed on it as he talked. I snorted with all my eight-year contempt at life and its injustice.

"What money? I don't get any money. My grandfather gets it and what he does with it, I don't know."

I sniffed importantly, like I had seen the teachers do and tossed my head. He sat very quietly for a while then taking the grass stem from his mouth, bent forwards and said softly.

"Amber, just look at me."

Surprised, I stopped cutting and stared at him.

"You say your grandfather doesn't give you the money?"

"No," I said with matter-of-fact resignation, "of course not. He says we have to earn our keep for him, otherwise we could be out in the street, or starving, but we starve anyway."

He looked at me again, curious, half-disbelieving, but intrigued now.

"What do you mean, starving?"

"Starving." I retorted indignantly and abruptly. "Surely you know - hungry, hungry all the time. He never gives us enough to eat, but he's always got meat and stuff and he makes sure the pantry stays locked too."

The self-importance was melting before the hurt, indignation and injustice welling up in me now.

"He doesn't think we're worth it. After all we're only English bastards. So he can earn money with us because we're like slaves. But he won't give us proper food. Maybe he's scared if we eat we'll get strong and do something to him."

He looked at me sharply and said.

"What did you get for breakfast today?"

I stared at him.

"Breakfast? I still had a piece of bread from what you gave me here yesterday and I had some apricots too," I confessed. "So I ate that."

"And for supper tonight? What will you eat?"

I shrugged my shoulders.

"I don't know. I suppose bread and some grapes again."

He looked angry, for a moment I thought he was cross with me, so I tried to make light of it.

"It doesn't matter really, we're used to it. I keep vegetables to cook too when he's not around, so it helps."

That only seemed to make matters worse. He got angrier.

"What do you mean, you keep vegetables?"

Now I was worried and getting flustered. I had blown it again with my stupid mouth and that meant another hiding tonight.

"Please, I'm sorry. I didn't mean any of this. Really. It's okay. Please don't tell my grandfather. He'll only get cross. He probably needs the money. I don't want the money anyway. Please don't say anything." I pleaded.

He insisted, "Amber what do you mean, you keep vegetables?"

Thoroughly miserable by now and badly frightened at the prospect of another thrashing, I kept my mouth shut.

"Nothing, I didn't mean anything."

I eventually mumbled as he kept repeating the question. He broke off, realising I think, what I was scared of. His voice grew gentle again.

"Amber, I won't tell your grandfather a word. Promise! This is just a secret between you and me. Honest."

I didn't believe him. I had spoken up too often in the past when some adult had spun that one, and had paid the consequences on the skin of my back. I wasn't about to make the same mistake. This man was different, he refused to give in. Eventually I explained about my kind vegetable man.

"Please," I begged tearfully. "Please don't tell my grandfather. Please don't tell him about the vegetable man, because I'm sure he'll go and thrash him too."

"What do you mean, thrash him too?"

It seemed to me that things were going from bad to worse. The situation was totally out of hand now.

"Does your grandfather thrash you?"

I nodded glumly.

"Why?" he demanded.

I shrugged my shoulders. I refused to get drawn into that one. I was also afraid that awful torrent of words and abuse would come frothing out again, so I kept silent. He sat pensively staring at me for a while, but when I sneaked a look at him, I could see he was not angry with me like I had thought. He was sort of absent. Then he got to his feet, patted me on the head and told me not to worry, everything would work out okay.

I was not very reassured. But when we went home that night, he pressed something into my hand and closed my fingers around it. It was too dark to see what it was but it felt like money. In the quiet of the bedroom that night, I slipped it out of my pocket. It was a whole sixpence! I was thrilled and overwhelmed. Up to then no one had ever given me anything more than a penny!

I treasured that sixpence for many years. It meant more to me than just money. Everytime I looked at it, I could feel the farmer's friendly pat on my head and hear him saying that everything would one day be all right. It always brought back memories of the warmth of his hand when he pressed it into my palm and the way he curled my fingers over it.

CHAPTER FIVE

I was probably eight going on nine when we moved. From my perspective, not all that much above ground level, the house looked huge - certainly much bigger than the one downtown. The grounds were big, and to my delight there were fruit trees in abundance - and there was more than enough room for me to find another secret hideout. My only distress was having to leave Elsabet behind. I would still see her at school from time to time, but it was nowhere near the same. We were not in the same class because she was older than me and it was awful not being able to escape from the prison of my grandfather's house, to sit in Aunt Martha's kitchen or relax on the steps in the sun. Their house was too far for me to walk now. I tried it once in desperation but the beating I got for coming home so late was so vicious I simply wasn't prepared to face it again.

I loved Elsabet so much, even though she was much older than me. She never talked down at me. She was a tremendous little athlete, running like a greyhound and she could jump higher than any other kid at school. Now I felt there was nothing to alleviate the grey misery of the oppressive afternoons. I was aware of a growing weariness inside me. The tiredness drained me, emotionally and physically. It seemed to cost such an effort to resist my grandfather's constant pressure. I felt like I wanted to lie down inside and sleep. I was tired of fighting, tired of standing hard and stubborn. His hatred had leeched life out of me.

I was dragging myself to school one morning like that. It was so cold that my breath made grey, messy puffs in the air ahead of me. I had tucked my hands under my armpits and scrunched my body as small as I could against the freezing wind. My feet had hardened by now, but even they were white with cold. I had my head down and my eyes screwed into tiny little slits, so I nearly bumped into the two girls standing waiting for me to reach them.

"Hello Amber," one of them greeted.

She was Rita, the younger of the two. Funny enough she was also something of an athlete: a very fast runner. I remember watching athletics at school and wishing I could run so fast - then grandfather could never catch me! I smiled at them but as usual the suspicious questions out cautious fences around me - what did they want?

I was known for my short and fiery temper and there were a number of kids, not to mention adults, who used to think it was amusing and would go out of their way to bait and taunt me. Then when the expected outburst rewarded their efforts, they could go and talk in shocked tones to one another about how brazen and arrogant I was, and what a "demon" and other similar judgements and condemnations. But I was not so blind that I didn't perceive how much they relished their entertainment". Today I can only conclude that that was the only lively high spot they could look forward to. So now, in retrospect I don't even begrudge them their cruel mocking and teasing. Now I just feel sorry for them. Throughout the bitterness and sorrow of my own life I have noticed a strange "law" at work - impartial and relentless. For want of a better name I call it the "law of seed and harvest", or the law of sowing and reaping. In the story of "Tom and the Water Babies" there was a lady called "Be-done-by-as-you-did" and that sums up the operation of this "law". With time I came to realise that those who mocked and derided. those who judged and condemned would one day taste the pain and the lonely rejection of their own deeds.

"The mills of God grind slowly, but they grind exceedingly fine." Often I use to weep and cry out against the injustice, but now there is a quiet resignation and peace in me, because I know that a time will come for justice to be meted out to those who so liberally lorded it over me and others.

I have seen it happen too often to believe it is mere coincidence. Now I know. as I have experienced in my own life, that you will reap the words and actions that you sow. You will harvest the hatred, the rejection, the pain and anguish, just as you will the joy, the concern, the care and love.

Well Rita and Rebecca had been waiting for me. They were among those who took to me and developed a kind of protective air. Rita in particular became one of my dearest friends and little by little they filled up the aching hole of loneliness that Elsabet had left.

Sometimes Miss Marais would ask me to stay behind after class and for a while she would talk to me, ask me questions and try to make me laugh. During those heavy weeks that I still remember with a feeling of grey suffocation, she was very concerned about me.

"Come Amber, you haven't been yourself for a few days now, what is the matter?"

It seemed such an effort to speak, such a senseless burden to even think, so I just shook my head tiredly and stared at the floor. I was at the bottom of a dank hole. There was hardly any room to move and there was no way out. The opening was along way above me and only dead light filtered through hopelessly, making the gloom even thicker around me. Maybe if I curled up small enough inside. then I could disappear. I could see Miss Marais was trying to reach down to me, but if I took her hand she would only try to pull me up and out again, and that meant the whole awful roundabout would start up again. I didn't want to go on. I was tired. I just wanted to lie down and stop.

She bent down towards me and lifted my chin in her hand. It was so soft and it reminded me of my Mum, how she used to pull my head up gently by the chin when she was combing and plaiting my hair. I could feel the tears welling up into my eyes and everything blurred out of focus. Miss Marais pulled me to her and just held me while the dark heavy sobs crushed out of my being. In between the tearing gasps for breath my words broke out in shattered lumps.

"Miss Marais, what right has he got to beat and punish me? I'm not his child. Who lets him keep on hitting us? He hasn't got the right."

"Amber, it will all come right. One day, you'll see, it will stop. His turn will come. One day it will all be over."

"I want my Dad so much. Why doesn't he come back for me? If he were here my grandfather wouldn't dare lift his hand to us."

"Sweetheart, maybe he doesn't know where you are. Or maybe he doesn't know what your grandfather does. You know maybe his commander won't let him come now because he still has things to do in the war."

She would do her best to soothe and comfort me and it would soothe the jagged edges of hurt, but the brokenness inside was still there - sharp and splintered.

It was Easter so it meant church every night for two weeks. To me it seemed so senseless. What was the point of going to church every day for two weeks? My mother had taught me that God is love, but I couldn't see any love in that church and certainly none in my grandfather who insisted that we go. If being a Christian depended on what he demonstrated then I would have become a Buddhist long ago. I couldn't understand why we had to go to church twice on Sundays either - surely once was enough? So going every day for a fortnight was even more incomprehensible.

Church to me was torture. I was to tiny for my feet to reach the floor so I sat in increasing discomfort not daring to fidget because it would earn me a thrashing, not understanding even a tenth of what was said and feeling the pins and needles get worse as the service went on. Sometimes mercifully, I would fall asleep. Then Charlene would dig me viciously in the ribs to wake me up when the congregation rose to sing. Often one or both of my feet had gone numb, so I would stumble and sometimes fall and grandfather would glare at me.

I once asked Aunt Miriam why we had to go to church and she explained that it was so that God could take our souls when we die. That really flummoxed me. The only sole I knew was the one under my feet and I really couldn't understand why God should want that. Especially now, because since my grandfather had taken my shoes away my soles were always cracked and dirty. So one Sunday coming back from church I said in all innocence.

"Grandfather, can I rather give God some other part of my body?"

He stared at me uncomprehendingly.

"What the devil are you talking about?"

Impatiently I repeated, "Can I give God something else, my hand or my arm or something. My sole is all hard and cracked since you took my shoes. I can't give him that."

As usual the answer was a backhander and an insult. I had no idea what I had done to deserve that slap. Later, when I did understand, the murderous hate rekindled in me. As so often, I promised myself that one day I would be above him. One day, when I was grown up I would go back and show him that I had succeeded, that he had not managed to destroy me, that I was better than he had ever been.

During the special Easter services, there was a time when people would stand up and pray. Some seemed to go on forever, their voices booming impressively or droning on monotonously in the echoing church. Others spoke so softly you could hear only a gentle buzz or timid murmur and I would open my eyes and stare in the direction of the voice to try to see who it was. Then Charlene would bump me so that my hat would slip over my eyes. Disgruntled, I would fold my hands over my eyes again and concentrate on keeping awake.

One day about half way through the service I decided it was my turn to speak to God. My grandfather had laid in to me for something I hadn't done, as usual, and the anger was still seething. In a moment of stillness I got to my feet and in a loud, high pitched voice prayed with all the sincerity of an unjustly suffered wrong and an aching heart. I didn't know that only grown-ups were allowed to talk to God, but even if I had known, it wouldn't have stopped me. I already knew that God was a lot more interested in truth and sincerity than in long-winded religious prayers.

"Dear Jesus, please teach my grandfather not to hate us so much and not to beat us for something we didn't do. Amen."

I could feel the silence. It got so thick I could feel the weight pressing on my head. I sneaked a look at my grandfather. He was as white as the hymn sheet in his hands. And it was shaking with his rage. "Oe, Oe," I thought, but at the same time there was a deep, delicious thrill of satisfaction. I knew I had got back at him. Often enough I had heard adults talk of that "out of the mouths of babes and sucklings" verse and with all my heart I wanted them to know from me what he was doing. I didn't want just rumours and stories. I wanted them to know the truth, I wanted them to see and know what he was doing to me, I didn't want just gossip that would have stayed at the level of conjecture and wondering. They had to know what that monster did behind closed doors.

I wanted to get at him. I wanted his lying smile wiped off his face, I wanted all his friends to see and know what he was really like. When he went and played "jukskei" with them in the town square. I wanted them to see the ugliness, the hatred, the viciousness. There was to be no room for doubt.

Someone cleared their throat. The sound reverberated and people shifted uneasily. The Dominee stood up and started praying. I can't remember what he said, but it was the one short prayer that I wished could have rather lasted all night. I knew what was waiting for me when I got back home.

I wasn't mistaken either. But as I lay on the bed with my body throbbing and burning, I took comfort in the memory of how people had avoided him when we left the church. Some had just looked at him and walked hurriedly off. Others had mumbled a rapid greeting. Only the Dominee had shaken his hand, and he had looked hard and long at my grandfather, until he had had to turn his eyes away.

It was another shot at that wall of "respectability" he had erected, another block that fell crumbling under the onslaught of truth. Sadly, it was another reason for his hatred of me and more incentive to thrash me into silence and submission.

He seemed to look for ways to get at me, because beating me no longer seemed to give him as much satisfaction as before. I would refuse to cry and that stole something from him. So he took it out on other things, things that I loved, because he knew that would hurt and shatter me inside.

The chickens were the first to suffer. Just as I came home from school a few days later I heard this awful racket from the back garden. As I raced round the corner, I was confronted by an awful sight. My grandfather was standing with an axe in his hands, laughing, and a chicken was running round in terror. But to my horror, it had no head, and its blood was spattering all over the place. I screamed hysterically and shut my eyes, but it was useless, that scene was branded into my brain. For days I couldn't go near the backyard because the whole thing would be enacted before me again, and I was convinced the place was drenched in blood. Only after it rained would I venture back.

The monster killed every single chicken like that - waiting until I was there to see it. And he would stand and gloat over me, laughing at my horror, swinging the dismembered head from his bloody fingers.

"Look Amber, the eyes are already shut, but he's still running around!"

How I hated him then.

I knew every one of those chickens. They used to lay eggs in the garden, and Aunt Miriam would send me to go and look for them. I knew all their hiding places and sometimes when I could see they wanted to hatch the eggs, I would tell Aunt Miriam I couldn't find any eggs. I will never forget the first lot that hatched. I had crawled carefully under the bush to check up on the broody hen and had been met with a very threatening squawk and huge ruffled-up wings and feathers. Cautiously, but quickly, I had backed away and then stopped, thrilled when a little yellow head had peaked out from the black wing.

"They've hatched!"

I shrieked in delight. All six eggs had hatched, but one little chicken was scrawny and weak. It had funny eyes, as though it couldn't lift the lids properly and kept stumbling onto its beak when it tried to walk.

I found it dead and stiff in the grass the next day and wept sad tears over its bedraggled body.

"Aunt Miriam have you got an empty box for me?"

I pleaded and gentle as always, she had found a box and a small piece of an old pillow slip.

Tenderly I had wrapped the rigid little corpse in the cloth and laid it in the box. Then digging a hole I had given the poor chick a proper funeral, marking the grave with flowers and a twig cross.

Now that monster was killing all my little chicks off, one by one. I took to staying at school in the afternoon. Miss Marais caught sight of me just as she was leaving and walked over, "Hello Amber," she said quizzically, "Why are you still at school?"

By now I had no qualms about letting everyone know all the facts.

"My grandfather waits until I come home Miss Marais, and then he chops the chicken's head off so that the blood squirts all over the place and he makes sure I see it. I can't stand it..."

My breath stuck as the sobs burst out. She sympathised, but it didn't help.

The pigs were next. I loved those fat squealy pigs. I used to sit and tell them stories. I called them "Grunt and Grunt" because of the noise they made. He slit their throats and let the blood just pour and pour. I never knew there could be so much blood in a little pig. The noise they made was awful - the shrill squealing was like spikes in my heart and stomach. When I turned and ran crying into the house he just laughed and mocked me.

Jimmy was also very upset. He cried a lot and though I was just as miserable and hurting, I swallowed my tears to try and comfort him and calm him down. When we went to school the next day though, he looked pale and sick and he said he felt funny. He didn't seem to be able to walk properly, as though his body had suddenly become too heavy for his legs. I had to take him right to his desk and then before I went to my own class, I told his teacher that he wasn't feeling well.

It was during break that they sent for me. Philip came running up, eyes bulging and cheeks rashed from excitement.

"Amber, the head says to come quickly. It's Jimmy - he's got sick."

An awful sick feeling hit the pit of my stomach and I felt nauseous. Jimmy was my little brother and I loved him with a fierce, protective love that at times was probably possessive. I was at the head's office in seconds. Jimmy was lying on the bench, grey-yellow, with sweat filming over his face and his eyes tightly shut. I panicked and fought viciously against the hands that restrained me.

"Amber, keep still! And don't go near him. He's going to be all right, but if you go over there in this state you'll upset him and make him worse!"

That calmed me down, but I was still burning with anxiety.

"Why can't I go near him? If I hold him he'll be all right. He's always all right when I hold him."

I thought of the times his agonised crying would stop when I sneaked into his bedroom at night and hushed and cuddled him to sleep. He would grab me desperately around the neck or chest and grip tightly. Then little by little his hands would relax till eventually his arms slipped down and he fell asleep.

I knew that if I could just sit by him and hold him, he would be all right.

"Jimmy is very sick dear. We're just going to take him home now and your grandmother will put him to bed. You and your sister must also go now because the doctor has to come and make sure you don't get Jimmy's sickness."

This sounded bad. For once it didn't look as though they were trying to blame me for it either, though no doubt the monster at the house would use it as an excuse to beat me.

They took us home and Jimmy was carried into the boys' bedroom, but after the doctor came, they moved him to another, small room, closed the door and told us not to go anywhere near him. I'm convinced they didn't know at first what was wrong. As soon as the coast was clear I tiptoed to the room, quietly turned the knob and edged in, closing the door softly behind me.

"Jimmy, Jimmy - it's me, Amber."

He lay there, totally unresponsive.

"Jimmy, it's Amber, it's me Jimmy. Jimmy wake up!"

He was awake - I think. He lay motionless, staring up at the ceiling with wide, sunken eyes. I was shocked - what was going on?

"Jimmy?" I touched his shoulder and shook him softly. He didn't even blink. Now I was frightened. His eyes stared blankly into nothing. I couldn't take anymore. My mouth was dry and my heart thumping loudly in my ears. I went to look for my elder sisters.

"What's wrong with Jimmy? Why can't we go into his room?"

They didn't know any more than I did, but knowing me, Denise shot a warning look in my direction.

"Amber you stay out of there. You'll only make things worse for everyone if you disobey grandfather again...as usual," she added with cutting resentment, and then turned her back on me with rancour. I pulled a tongue in her direction and went to find Aunt Miriam.

"Amber, not now, go away, the doctor says he mustn't be disturbed and I've got things to do, go away!"

The frustration of being treated like this curled deep inside but there was nothing I could do about it.

I tried Miss Marais at school next day but she was none the wiser. The morning was endless. I kept seeing Jimmy's eyes staring sightless at the ceiling. I began to worry that he would die too. When the final bell went I ran all the way home. If I was with Jimmy then death wouldn't dare take him - I could save him. All I had to do was be there, or hold him. Aunt Miriam met me at the top of the steps.

"You stop just there. I don't want you in the house this afternoon and don't even think of going near Jimmy's room. Doctor says he has to rest and be quiet. You'll make him sicker if you go and upset him."

There was a determination in her voice I had never heard before. Something serious was happening. Jimmy wasn't strong like me.

How was he going to manage on his own? He had never even slept in a room on his own before. How could they just leave him there in the dark with no one near him?

Frantic and feverish with worry, I slipped into the room. The smell hit me first. Rottenness, something dead and putrefying. It was a sick, heavy smell and it made me want to puke. But it wasn't coming from Jimmy - it was lurking somewhere in the dark of his room. The hair rose up on my arms and the back of my neck. Jimmy lay on his back like the last time I had seen him, eyes open, but sunken even deeper back into his sockets than before. His skin was yellow and there was a white-yellow slimy fur on his lips. I had intended to come and hold his hand, but I couldn't even bring myself to touch him. I stood there swallowing and choking back the nausea then to my horror I heard the door behind me open.

It was Deryck, my elder brother, but it might just as well have been Grandfather. He was furious with me and yanked me out mercilessly, pulling my hair till some of it came out in his hand.

"Don't you ever go back in there again. Do you hear?"

He emphasised his words with slaps and punches. Grandfather got to hear of the escapade and thrashed me so thoroughly I made triple, quadruple sure no one would catch me again. But it didn't stop me from going to visit Jimmy. He was my little brother. I knew he couldn't lie there on his own all the time with just Deryck and Aunt Miriam going in there.

All his hair fell out. I didn't know whether to laugh or cry when I looked at his face. He was all bony, like a skeleton, with his eyes sunk so deep I was afraid they would drop right into the back of his head. One day I clucked up enough courage to search for his hand under the blanket. But it was like holding a chicken's claw. I don't know if he knew I was there.

"Jimmy," I whispered, "Jimmy. Can you hear me?"

I stood on tiptoe and gently leaned onto the bed to peer into his eyes. They were open, but completely lifeless.

"Jimmy?"

There were little flecks of dried spit at the corners of his mouth and it didn't look to me like he was breathing. Ugly, cold fear crawled from my stomach into my throat. The stench of petrification was making me sick. I wanted so desperately to talk to him and now that I had managed to elude the watchdogs he couldn't talk. Hot tears pricked into my eyes. I tried once more, gingerly putting a finger to touch his cheek. His head lolled to the side and terrified the wits out of me. His eyes were blank, unseeing. They were sunk so deep into his skull.

"Maybe he can't see past the eye sockets," I thought, and tried to stretch taller so that he could catch sight of me. But it was useless.

Once outside, the fear and hurt overwhelmed me. I sat with my back to his door and let the tears flow. Aunt Miriam found me there, a sodden little heap of misery. She shot a quick look down the hall, then seeing there was no one around, kneeled down and gave me a long sympathetic hug. I was so surprised I stopped crying. I could smell the perfume she always put on - it used to float melancholically in the air behind her. I pulled away and stared at her in astonishment. Almost abashed, she struggled to her feet and said awkwardly.

"Don't worry Amber, Jimmy will be all right. Come away from here now before someone sees you."

Then with a kind of embarrassed expression, she turned and walked away.

Jimmy had typhoid fever and it had soon assumed epidemic proportions. I wasn't allowed to go to school. The first day Aunt Miriam told me to stay at home I climbed over the fence and went to visit Rita's mother to find out what was happening. She told me that they were going to close the school, because more kids were getting sick. We were under quarantine and not allowed to leave the yard. It was almost like holidays, except that we didn't have to go and work at the farm. I was very grateful for this quarantine thing, even though it meant I missed my friends terribly. At least grandfather wasn't allowed to make us go and work.

For the first time since my mother died, we had time for ourselves. Of course we still had to do the usual housework every day, scrub the floors, polish them, sweep, wash and iron, but we had become proficient and finished the task quickly. I had long since learnt that if I pretended exhaustion or even "overlooked" certain of my own jobs, one of my sisters or brothers would do it. They were scared of getting punished if my grandfather saw something undone. I suppose it was a way of getting back at them - not very nice perhaps, but I don't really feel guilty about it. I would shoot off to the bottom of the garden, or go to one of my secret places and melt into the world I had created for myself. There I would live with the people in my books, experiencing their adventures, feeling their emotions, dreaming their hopes and ambitions and rejoicing in their happy endings.

When my mother was still alive, there was always music in the house. She played the piano and I quickly picked up the tunes and learnt to tinkle them out while she sang. Both she and my elder sister often had friends around and while someone played, there would be laughing, singing and dancing and I was always in the middle of it. I loved music, loved singing and was an excellent dancer.

These talents were soon noticed at school and I was immediately chosen to perform in the school concert. To my delight the teacher taught me a whole lot of new dances, Waltzing and even the Charleston! These "holidays" were ideal opportunities to practice.

I would make sure there was no one around to watch, and then singing to myself I would twirl around among the grasses and between the bushes and trees. Sometimes I would spin till I got dizzy, so that when I stopped the world kept on whizzing around in a blur of bush, trunk and branches, till I collapsed in a giggling heap, panting and laughing with delight.

I think it was during this long quarantine that so much of the foundation was laid for the aloneness that was to form my life. There were times when loneliness swamped that little private world and I longed bitterly for my friends, but it was during these months that I learned to be alone with myself, no one took any notice of me or cared about me, so I learned to fill my own time. I read, I talked to myself, I played in my own adventures and stories, I danced and sang. I would go and round up the pigs and tell them tales, or chase the chickens till they were so tired I could pick them up and stroke their feathers. We had again acquired two pigs, some four or so chickens and a goat. Eventually I had read all my books, so I borrowed my sister's school books and read those too. Every afternoon I did homework from my books and then for fun, worked on the exercises in my sister's books too. While there were things I didn't understand, there was so much that opened up new realms of knowledge to me. Again, I was discovering a wealth of wisdom and experience that lay in books.

The quarantine seemed to drag on forever. We had to drink some weird medication every day. Nowadays I suppose it would be considered some kind of sangoma brew, but the old people then had great faith in it. What was in it, I don't know, certainly herbs soaked in enough brandy to make you gasp for air after you had tossed it down - under Aunt Miriam's watchful eye. I must have been tipsy a great deal of the time!

Then just as Jimmy began to get better, Deryck succumbed to the fever. He complained one evening of being terribly tired and he looked pasty and sweaty. I woke up at night to the sound of doors slamming and feet running down the passage.

"Tell him to hurry!" called Aunt Miriam and her voice had crying in it.

I drifted off to sleep. Agitated discussion woke me up again just as the light was dribbling grey and pale through the curtains. I edged off the bed to peep out the window. The doctor and my grandfather were walking down to the gate and I could hear their voices trailing eerily in the morning mist but couldn't distinguish what they were saying. For a moment I panicked about Jimmy, but then from that deep knowing inside came the assurance that he was all right. As quietly as I could, I padded down the hall to find out what was happening. Jimmy's door was ajar, so I cautiously peeped in. Deryck had been moved in with him, so I knew that the fever had struck again.

We were not allowed to go back to school until Deryck had recovered completely. The first day back was strange and exciting. Everyone had grown - some of the girls who had had long hair now only had a downy fluff. Others had hair cropped like a boy's. Many of the children were still bald, or only just sprouting fuzz. Those of us who still had hair found it very funny! The kids looked so different and so skinny. There was cruel teasing and a few fights when some took exception to the mockery, but we all quickly got used to it. Jimmy was the wonder of the school for a few glorious days of fame. His hair had been thin and blonde before the fever. When it grew back, it was thick black and curly. I teased him mercilessly, telling him he wasn't really Jimmy, that while he was sick they had come and exchanged him for someone else, but I stopped very quickly, because he would become terribly distressed and then I felt awful for upsetting him like that.

Sadly, there were a number of faces missing. Annetjie walked into the class with her eyes fixed on the floor and sat down in a hopeless heap of misery next to her twin's empty desk. Hendrik's place was vacant. When the teacher called the register, there was no answer to several names. She would lift her head at the silence, look around the class over the top of her glasses, shake her head sadly a few times, make a mark with her red pen and then read the next name.

It's amazing how tragedies can fade into normality in a child's world. The school concert that the fever had postponed was to be held soon. In the excitement and exhilaration of rehearsals and preparations, the fever, the deaths the long months of quarantine were forgotten. The teacher had made me a beautiful little fairy dress that stood out so crisply and daintily. I was entranced when I put it on and saw myself in the mirror. Transformed! Fairy Amber - the good fairy, I told myself, who would grant wishes and turn people's sorrow into happiness. I danced a few steps, eyeing my reflection delightedly - I looked beautiful, graceful, a real fairy! I lifted up my arms and pirouetted, turning my head over my shoulder so that I could watch myself all the time. And then my world collapsed.

My panty. My one and only, formless and no longer white panty. As I twirled, half my bottom appeared in all its minute glory as the shapeless panty flapped wearily to one side. It was the last one left of the few I had brought when we came to live with my grandfather. Not only was it a dirty-white hue, it had no elastic round the legs, and blessed with little holes. I was painfully embarrassed and darted looks everywhere to see if anyone had noticed. Then with my back towards the wall, I inched over the bench and sat down.

"Amber where are you? Time for you and Rita to do your duet."

I shook my head glumly. She looked at me in surprise.

"What's the matter? Don't tell me you have forgotten the steps, you were dancing beautifully yesterday!"

"Teacher I'm feeling a bit faint. Can't I just sit for a while?"

She hesitated, then nodded and clapping her hands for attention, shouted for the wood elves and gnomes to do their piece in the meanwhile. Rita came to sit next to me.

"Amber, are you all right? Why are you crying?"

I was angry that she had seen the tears. I spent weeks and months dancing in the garden, feeling like I was flying, loving the steps and the rhythm and the feel of the ground whirling under my feet - and it was all for nothing. I had this beautiful dress and I looked so lovely and now it was over. The disappointment and hurt were overwhelming.

"I'm not crying!" I blurted. "I'm angry!"

Rita was taken aback.

"Has someone done something to you? Has your grandfather said you can't be in the concert? What's happened?"

Rita was my friend, I knew she wouldn't laugh at me, but it still took such a determined effort to tell her the truth.

"Rita, it's my panty, I haven't got another one, and this one's all full of holes and floppy and when I pirouette you can see half my bum."

She was very sympathetic and put her arm around me. But it was her mother from behind me who saved the situation. I hadn't realised she was there - in fact if I'd known I would never have spoken up. I didn't trust adults and there was no way I wanted her spreading the story about the town so that everyone could mock and laugh at me.

"Don't you worry Amber," she said firmly, putting her hands under my arms to lift me up. "I'll make sure you get a couple of nice new, white panties that fit and then you can show everyone how beautiful the wood fairy is!"

A rush of gratitude and relief flooded me and for a moment I didn't know what to say. Then I leaned forward and kissed her.

"Oh thank you Mrs Joubert - thank you so much!"

She was moved and turned her head away, but I saw the tears in her eyes.

The great day came. I was so excited I couldn't stand still for a minute. Everyone was getting agitated with me, because I wanted to be everywhere and see everything. When my turn came I launched into the dance with my whole being - I became a fairy. I was one with the music, I was flying and free and so happy. The exclamations and "ah's!" from a delighted audience gave me wings and my heart was bursting with joy! I didn't want to stop and when the music ended and the applause exploded I was smiling so much my face began to hurt! The teachers waiting in the wings were full of praise.

"Amber that was beautiful!"

"What a magnificent performance - they loved you my dear!"

The other girls crowded around too, though some of them were the usual cats.

I basked in the glory of that dance and praise for the rest of the concert. I didn't want to take the costume off! When it was all over and the magic of the fairy dress had been carefully stored away. I walked to the school gate to find my grandfather and Aunt Miriam waiting for me. His face was as black as the mountain after sunset. I quailed. What had I done wrong now. The light and the sparkle died. The old death rose up into my chest again.

"And where did you get those pants you are wearing?" he demanded.

I was speechless. Miserable old monster, what business was it of his? Regaining my composure I just glared at him.

"It's none of your business. You certainly didn't buy them for me, did you?" And I started singing...."God save our gracious King, long live our noble King...."

The purple-red colour surged from his throat into his face and his eyes started to bulge with rage. I could see the muscles in his arms twitching again. Aunt Miriam put a restraining hand on his arm and smiled and nodded at some acquaintances.

"Good evening Sir, Ma'am."

"Yes, wasn't it a glorious way to spend the afternoon."

Grandfather had a fixed smile as the people stopped to congratulate me.

"Amber, you were such a lovely fairy. I didn't know you could dance like that. Well done, it was beautiful!"

I crowed inside, smiled and curtsied. I could feel grandfather's fury reaching white-hot point but I loved to see him discomfited.

"Gee grandfather, maybe I should have told them that someone else gave me a panty to wear, and they must thank that person, because otherwise they wouldn't have been able to see me dance!"

I shot a quick sidelong glance at him. Maybe I'd already overdone it and he would hit me now. I moved out of range a bit and carried on singing the anthem. He hated anything even remotely English and if there was one tune that infuriated him and drove him into a frenzy of murderous anger and hate it was the English national anthem. So I would sing it on purpose to needle him - especially if he was launching into one of his tirades against me and all English bastards.

Then I skipped on ahead as though I didn't have a care in the world, but I worked on going faster and faster so that I could get home before him and find a good hiding place that he didn't know yet. But even that was useless. The longer he looked the madder he got and the worse was the hiding I ended up getting. That night was no exception. But even the pain of the belt couldn't dissipate the joy and the fulfilment of that glorious afternoon, and for weeks and months afterwards I would relive it, and the memory would brighten the gloom of the dark shadows in and around me.

CHAPTER SIX

I shot up straight in bed, my heart was pounding so hard it hurt to breathe. High-pitched screeching and awful gut-piercing yowls vibrated through the walls and the air itself. It was so fear-charged and frantic that its intensity filled my own blood. Deafening bangs and thuds thickened the noise and then on top of it thundered the rage-red curses flooding from my grandfather's ugly mouth. Shouts, yells, terrible crushing and hammering sounds - and all the time the inhuman, panic-stricken yowling. The sleep - thick mist of awakening was cut to ribbons - confused, frenzied and terrified out of my wits. I screamed till the sound tore my throat.

Someone grabbed my shoulder and pulled me down onto the bed. My eyes were stretched so far open I could feel the tightness of my skin - I couldn't breathe, but my mouth was wide open. I was choking and gasping and jerking for air. Denise yanked me up again and slapped my back till I raked in a hoarse, grating breath. Then she pulled me to her and pushed my head into her shoulder to drown the frightened sobs.

"Denise what's happening, what is it, what's happening?" I cried hysterically.

She just held me tighter and shushed me while she also stared tensely at the door. The pounding was irregular, my grandfather's heavy body was clumping around in the lounge as he swore - and the awful yowling pitched into high shrieks. Then there was a particularly blood-curdling cry, a wet thump and then a series of mushy blows.

The silence hung thick and tense. We sat petrified in the darkness. The tears were pouring down my face and I was struggling for breath. But Denise had her hand over my mouth to drown the sobs. Then there came the familiar heavy tread as my grandfather walked out of the lounge. A door slammed. A violent trembling was shaking through my body. Someone was coming to kill us all. I knew they were breaking the doors down. I was half-crazed with fear. It was dead still outside, but I was convinced they were lurking outside the door, waiting for us to go to sleep so that they could burst in and murder us all.

Trembling and shivering uncontrollably, I could feel the panic building up deep down, it was draining all my life into a deep pit of horror and filling my being up with black terror.

Charlene had run to the door and locked it. Then after a whispered consultation with Denise, she had softly opened the window and climbed out. Denise shoved her pillow under the bedcover in Charlene's place and then tried to get me calmed down again. By now I was close to hysteria. Charlene seemed to be gone such a long time. Eventually her shadow slipped across the windowsill and she climbed back. I couldn't see her face properly, just the black shadows her eyes made in her face and it looked awful. She climbed back into bed. I tried to ask what was happening but when I opened my mouth only hoarse breath came out, my voice got stuck somewhere and I couldn't speak. Sobs were still shaking my body and the panic was spreading up into my chest. I don't know whether it was exhaustion or whether I just passed out, but the next thing I remember is screaming at the top of my lungs while Denise held her hand over my mouth.

"Amber, you're dreaming! It's OK! Wake up, wake up it's all right! You're fine, we're here, it's all right."

Confused images and echoes jumbled in my head. I was convinced they were breaking down the door and coming for us. I struggled against Denise's hand. Then Charlene's face appeared right above me. Together they managed to calm me down. Then Charlene explained what had happened. Her breath was also coming all jerky and weird and her voice was shaky.

"It was just a cat. Some cat got into the house. It must have found a window open and climbed in. Grandfather found it and killed it. All that thumping and shouting was just him chasing the cat around the lounge."

I started crying again. The panic that had started in the depths of my being lurched up like a slimy monster and reached long tentacles into my throat. I couldn't stop shaking. I got up and staggered out of the room, but I couldn't walk properly. I kept bumping into the wall as I headed crazily towards the lounge. There was blood everywhere. On the floor was a mangled, bloody mess of torn flesh and fur, next to it was a jagged piece of firewood, covered with blood. Angry voices rose from somewhere inside the house. Something inside me just snapped and with a yell that broke from the black depths in me. I hurtled out the house. It was a nightmare. It had to be a nightmare. I heard my sisters vaguely calling me. Screaming hysterically I raced on, oblivious to the stones and thorns.

I stumbled up the steps of Rita's house. I fell at the top and crawled to the door, hammering and crying like a maniac.

"Rita, Mrs Joubert! Let me in. Rita! He's going to kill me. He's got a piece of wood and he's going to kill me!"

In my frenzy I was convinced my grandfather was pounding after me with the bloodstained piece of wood in his hand, his face congested with hatred. The door was flung open and I fell heavily inside. Strong hands picked me up, but I was so crazed with fear that I struggled desperately and viciously. But the grip didn't loosen and eventually, totally drained, I went limp and just let the crying foam out of my body as tears streaked down my face.

Rita and Rebecca were standing awe-struck in the door, staring uncomprehendingly at the scene. Mrs Joubert put me to bed with a cup of something hot and sweet. She sat next to me and held my hand, smoothing my hair down with her other hand. In snatches and tremors, the story tumbled out. I saw her lips go tight and at times the muscles in her jaw would jump.

There was a knock at the door and I started -

"That's my grandfather. He's going to come and kill me too, Mrs Joubert. Don't let him get me, please!"

But when she came back. Denise and Charlene were with her. They also looked grim. I had never seen Denise with such a strange expression on her face.

"It's all right now Amber. You can come home."

My voice started rising shrilly as I began to refuse, but Denise was adamant.

"Grandfather's not there. He's gone off somewhere. We've already buried the cat and Aunt Miriam is cleaning all the blood away now. You have to come home now Amber."

Something in her voice quieted me. There was a new thing happening here that I couldn't understand. I could sense that Denise had undergone something dramatic and that a change was looming. She was so different, not in appearance, inside. I could feel as though something had broken, she was somehow another person, there was a hardness, a determination I had never perceived before. A little awed, I allowed them to pull the blankets back so that I could get out of bed. I flung my arms round Mrs Joubert and whispered thanks in her ear, and then followed my sisters home.

When I came back from school the next day, Denise and Deryck were gone. They never came back to that house and grandfather never uttered a word about them again. It was as though they had never existed.

Denise had started working for people somewhere so she had somewhere else to go. My grandfather walked around for a long time with a vicious burning in him. I always knew when he was in the house. I could feel the air grow thick and heavy. At first I felt funny after Denise left, for a while there was something missing, and I realised that I was going to have to fend for myself a great deal more than previously. My grandfather obviously couldn't get back at Denise, so he vented his frustration and rage on us, especially me. I presume she must have been able to speak about him with a great deal more freedom than before, so the talk in that little town really began to buzz. Rita's Mom was at the house a few days later when I came back from school; she had a very pleased smile on her face. In fact she looked decidedly smug. Aunt Miriam was just seeing her off at the gate and my grandfather was standing in the door, glaring after her. I could see the ugly black hatred in and around him, like a slimy mist trying to heave its weight off a swamp. I could feel his anger from where I stood. Mrs Joubert greeted me with a huge smile and a quick hug, shook Aunt Miriam's hand briefly and left.

I hesitated at the gate. There was no way I was going any closer until I knew what had happened and could prepare myself. Peering quizzically at Aunt Miriam, I waited for her to say something. She wavered as she looked back at the monster waiting at the door then nervously, almost out of the corner of her mouth, she explained, with a hint of accusation in her voice.

"Mrs Joubert has invited you to go on holiday with them when the school breaks up."

Her words tumbled over each other so fast I almost didn't understand.

When I did grasp what she had said, I was scared too, just in case it wasn't true. I stared at the monster looming in the doorway. Slowly, the realisation seeped in to me, and I could feel the delight starting to lift a cautious head. He wouldn't dare say no! Mrs Joubert was the church secretary! She was also the Dominee's sister. He was trapped! I crowed with delicious triumph.

Cornered! The monster was cornered! Throwing fear and caution to dry out on the fence, I skipped into the garden with a huge grin smeared from ear to ear.

He thought he was going to intimidate me.

"You! You've been going round begging like the rubbish little English bastard you are - asking people to take you on holiday, huh?"

I stopped at the bottom of the steps and glared up at him. I had always stood my ground and now that Denise had gone, a new defiance had been growing in me. He was not invincible, he was not all powerful and I was not going to allow him to keep on treating me like dirt.

"I've asked no one anything. People in this town are not blind and deaf you know. They can see what you are doing. They're not so stupid as you think."

Then as he lifted his arm to hit me, I moved back a few steps and added with a new confidence.

"And if you hit me, I'll make sure they know that too, and why."

The colour started to blotch his cheeks with reddish purple. He clenched his fists and then to my surprise, suddenly turned and lurched into the house.

The taste of victory was heady, sweet and oh so buoyant. But once in my room, I felt the triumph drain away and slip between the floorboards. I was alone again and misery, rejection and bitterness came seeping in like some mephitic gas. I fished in my secret place under the foot of the bed and pulled out the scrap of paper I had written my father's address on. No one knew I had found it. I suppose because I was so small or because no one thought of me as a person, of someone who could feel and think for herself, they often spoke above me as though I weren't even there. But I had ears, and a very good memory.

I heard my grandfather and Aunt Miriam talking often enough and eventually through careful eavesdropping, had found out where my father lived. That afternoon, somehow the black dejection overwhelmed me and despite the warning voice from inside me somewhere, I wrote him a letter.

"My darling Dad,

Please can you come and fetch me now? Denise has gone and so has Deryck. Grandfather doesn't like me and he is always hitting me for no reason because I'm small and love you. He doesn't give us food and I have to ask my friends' parents to eat with them. He makes us work on the farms and takes the money. I didn't even have a panty for the concert. Then Mrs Joubert gave me one and he hit me. He killed the cat with piece of wood. I'm scared one day he will try to kill me like that too. Can you please come soon? I can clean house for you and even iron. I miss you so much and Mum too. Sometimes she comes to see me at night, but then I scream because it frightens me. Why do we have to stay with grandfather when he hates us so much? Please come soon.

I love you Daddy
Amber

It took me almost all afternoon because I kept making mistakes. Then I would rub out and try again. I wanted him to have a perfect letter. I wanted him to see that I was clever and doing well at school. I wanted him to be proud of me so that he wouldn't mind if I asked him to come fetch us.

At school the teachers were all amazed when I came back after the typhoid epidemic because I was so much more advanced than the others. I had worked and read my sister's books and I knew all the lessons the others hadn't even started yet.

"You're a real bright penny, aren't you?"

The principal had beamed as she patted my head and congratulated me.

"We'll have to see about giving you some harder books, won't we?"

In fact Miss Marais had given me other text books and reading books to keep me occupied and interested while the others worked over lessons I had completed months before.

I liked the idea of being a bright penny. It made me think of my own beautiful pennies. Some of the farmers had discovered that my grandfather didn't give us the money we had earned, so from time to time they would press pennies into our hands just as we were going home. I didn't like these sad dirty little coins, so I would spend hours polishing them, till they shone like burnished gold. It was wonderful to be called a bright penny. It made me feel like I meant something, that I had a right to be there after all, and not only that, but that I was special, that I was different from others in a good way, not like a bastard or a piece of rubbish.

I put the letter under my pillow, so that I could take it to school the next day. Then I would buy a stamp and an envelope on the way back from school and post it.

That night there was a huge fight. From somewhere Charles had finally dragged up the courage to confront my grandfather and he said he was leaving too. I have never seen my grandfather so angry. From purple-red he went white. He was clutching the table and I was tensed up on my chair, because I was convinced he was going to upend the table on to us. I was ready to leap the moment he moved.

When he started talking, Charles was very nervous. He swallowed often and it looked as though his tongue was sticking in his mouth. He was twisting his hands in his lap. But then when grandfather sneered at him and called him a sick little white rat, he suddenly got angry and started shouting. Soon they were both yelling at each other. I suppose it was like with Denise.

Grandfather pushed too far and something inside Charles gave way.

All the anger, all the hatred, all the years of rancour and smarting against injustice erupted. I'm sure if Charles were bigger he would have tried to hit grandfather with something. Aunt Miriam was also pale, but with fear, not anger. She put her hand on grandfather's arm, to calm him I suppose. He jerked like he'd been burnt and threw her hand off with a violent gesture. I thought he was going to hit her and I had my hand on a glass, ready to throw it at him if he did. But he was too absorbed with trying to crush Charles with his ugly thunderous voice. Charles and Jimmy were frozen. I kicked Jimmy and showed him to follow me and the two of us slipped away. No one even noticed.

I took refuge in the bedroom, I knew from bitter experience that my grandfather would attack anything he could get his hands on when he was in such a mood. Throughout the night there was shouting and other loud bangs. Next morning I was worn with constant waking and lying listening, drifting off and jerking out of sleep. The three of us were late leaving the house because of the uproar, with grandfather still shouting and thumping from one room to another.

I forgot the letter. When I came home, he was sitting on the stoep, and the letter was in his lap. It's strange how things work out. Any earlier and I think the things he said and the beating he gave me would probably have broken my spirit and closed every door of resistance, defiance and hope for ever.

Coming when it did, after Denise and Deryck's departure and Charles's belated resistance, it just strengthened the determination in me that this man would never, ever break, crush or stop me.

While he was hitting me, all I could feel was the white hot fury, the hatred, the defiance and rebellion rising up in me, with a force and intensity that drowned everything else. He only stopped with exhaustion. He was breathing heavily and I was thinking, "Drop dead you bastard. You will get no more satisfaction out of my tears ever again."

I just stood there and looked at him.

"It's easy to hit the littlest one, isn't it? You think I can't hit back. It's not that I can't. It's just that I don't even want to touch you."

I saw how my contempt pierced him, like a molten tube sliding down his throat and puddling in his belly. He was totally at a loss. He didn't know what to do or say. He looked so stupid that I laughed, in spite of the pain that was now throbbing in my body from his blows. The next thing I remember was a powerful blow that threw me against the door.

Then nothing!

When I opened my eyes, a cracking pain slashed into my head, I moaned and with closed lids lay and listened carefully. I was in bed - mine. I hoped. It felt as though there were an axe imbedded in the back of my head, but when I tried to roll my head to the side to relieve the pressure, the pain stabbed right down my neck, into my eyes and shattered through my brain. I moaned again. Then I heard the door open and involuntarily I winced. But it was Charlene with a glass of water and an aspirin.

"Aunt Miriam says you must drink this," she whispered, examining me with a worried, scared look.

"Are you all right? Your head was bleeding so much I got a fright."

Gingerly I touched the spot where the pain pounded. I was half expecting to find a hole, but it was just a lump of clotted blood and matted hair.

"I hope he got a fright, the ugly monster." I said and closed my eyes against the vicious stabs of pain. But that incident decided me. It was like signing a solemn contract in blood. From there I knew there was no going back, no compromise and no weakening. As far as I was concerned the man was dead. He was not going to stop me, intimidate me, break me, or hurt me ever again.

From that time I was in open rebellion. I flaunted my antagonism and defiance. I no longer drew back from asking people whether I could have meals with them and giving a detailed explanation for the reason for my request.

Charles left, after the heated argument, I suppose my behaviour together with all these events were the final proof the towns people needed. They spoke openly about my grandfather's treatment of us, now. They often invited us out for holidays and I spent more time away from the house than in it. At first he tried to retaliate, but somehow the fire seemed to have burnt low. He looked older. Maybe the hatred was starting to crumble him inside. Whatever it was the number of beatings diminished. It was almost as if it became too much of an effort, or he didn't get the usual sadistic pleasure from them. I no longer feared him. My hatred and contempt for him were too great. Thinking about it now, I believe that the scorn he sensed pouring from me was unbearable for him and he simply couldn't work up the energy he needed to overcome it.

It was the end of a phase. But it was only the start of another, different kind of unhappiness and suffering.

CHAPTER SEVEN

"Oh come on Amber, for goodness sake, do you want me to go down on my hands and knees and beg you?"

Charlene was impatient and irritated. Her best friend Deborah had invited her to go on holiday. but grandfather had found a way, he thought, to stop us from accepting invitations like that. He put his sanctimonious, pious face on and said,

"Oh Mister, Misses, we are really so thankful and so grateful for your very kind offer. It is so thoughtful and kind of you to invite Charlene, but shame, you see it really isn't fair on Amber if her sister goes on holiday. So thank you again from the bottom of my heart for your generous invitation, but I really can't accept it."

And he smiled his triumphant, greasy smile, while he looked so noble - as though he were making a huge sacrifice.

But this time he came short. Mrs Carey, Debby's Mom, was not a woman to be trifled with like that. She stared at him with open contempt, and leaning forward threateningly said in a firm, "don't-mess-with-me" voice.

"Then Amber must come with Mr Baker."

Perplexed and uptight my grandfather stared at her. He didn't have an answer prepared for that one, so he had hissed his thanks again through tight lips and saw Mrs Carey to the door.

Charlene had giggled behind her hand and dragged me into the bedroom with her. But I had been less than responsive.

"I don't want to go, Charl."

She had stopped dead and then turned on me.

"Don't be such a selfish little brat Amber. If you don't go then I can't either."

"Of course you can. You've just got to stand up to him and make him let you go." I had countered, but she didn't have enough spunk for that. It was easier for her to round on me.

The Carey's were going to a farm and I did not have happy memories of farms. The places were odious to me. Anyway Charlene and her friends never wanted to play with me because I was so much younger than them and so small. I was a nuisance, and they let me know it. I got in the way and they made no bones about it. Charlene pestered on and in annoyance, I marched out of the bedroom. My grandfather was on the stoep and he had a smug little smirk twitching his lips. He didn't say anything but I knew what the monster was thinking. I went straight back to the bedroom where Charlene was sitting disconsolately on the bed.

"It's O.K. then Charl, I'll come with you. When are we leaving?"

I spoke as loudly as I could to make sure he would hear every word with crystalline clarity. When I went back outside he was gone. No way would I give him the satisfaction of thinking that he had got the better of us. At least a farm holiday would mean that I wouldn't have to listen to his ugly voice fouling up the air. And if they wanted to make me work I would simply find a place to hide.

As I expected, once we got to the farm Charlene and Debby made like I didn't exist. In fact Charlene shouted at me to get lost when I tried to hang on. So I just gave up and decided to explore the place on my own. The second afternoon I was sitting on a slope, watching the coloured labourers moving down the rows, picking or weeding or something. I felt so sad, and so lonely.

Distractedly, I pulled at the grass, putting little stems into my mouth from time to time. Then I started singing to myself, and for some reason the tears began to slip down my cheeks, I hugged my knees and let the sobs rack and tear my body.

"What's this then? Why are you crying?"

I got such a shock I screamed and trying to scramble to my feet - fell flat on my face. Strong hands picked me up and dusted me down. Through the blur of tears I saw a tallish figure, all in khaki with a big hat.

"Hey, what's up kid? Why the tears?"

I just sniffed and wiped my nose on the back of my hand. He pulled out a huge handkerchief that smelled funny, like dust and tobacco, and wiped my face and nose with it. Now I could see him clearly. He was very sunburnt and had deep wrinkles around his eyes and mouth. When he took his hat off there was a mark round his forehead and his hair was pushed flat. It looked funny and I giggled.

"There now, that's better," he grinned, "so why were you crying?"

This was an adult. A strange one too. I clammed up and got non-committal.

"Oh it wasn't anything, I just stubbed my toe," I shrugged. "Thank you for your help, I must go now."

I started to walk away when his big hand descended on my shoulder.

"How can you stub your toe if you are sitting down?"

His eyes were amused and at first I thought he was mocking me. The ire started to steam up and I was just about to make some defiant crack when I realised he wasn't trying to be nasty. The sparkle in those eyes was soft and friendly. I concentrated on getting my hackles down.

Eyeing him cautiously I searched for an answer. He spoke first.

"They've left you alone because you're too little, haven't they?"

I wavered, then nodded dumbly.

"Well," he grunted as he bent down and picked me up, "you're not too little for my company, so let's go and look at the pigs."

He swung me onto his back and showed me how to hold on around his neck and grip his body with my legs. I was ecstatic and a bit frightened. No one had ever piggy-backed me before and it was a wonderful feeling!

He started jogging and I couldn't breathe properly because I was laughing so much. Every step bumped air out of me and I had to yell to him to stop so I could get my breath back. He was also laughing.

"What's up now? Never ridden a horse before? You have to breathe with the trod young madam, time your breathing now!"

And off he went again. Whooping with laughter and delight I didn't want the "ride" to stop. It was the weirdest sensation, bumping up and down and seeing things from that height, over his head and over his shoulders, so that the whole world seemed to be jumping and skipping up and down!

By the time he stopped I was breathless. He was panting and sweating and laughing like a child. He sat down next to me and solemnly put his hand out.

"Mike's the name - what's yours?"

"Amber," I replied, sticking my hand into his where it disappeared in his huge fist. To my relief it emerged again still in one piece.

"Well Amber, I would be honoured to have you grace my hours with your presence," he said seriously and loftily.

I was bemused - he talked funny! When he saw my face he burst out laughing.

"That means you're welcome to come with me, sunshine. I would enjoy your company."

Did he mean it? The suspicion and doubt welled up in me. What did this guy want from me? Why was he so friendly? Maybe he was only mocking me because the others had left me alone. He must have caught a glimpse of the emotions confusing me, because for a moment his face went sad and serious, then he smiled and patted my arm.

"You think about it. We'll go up to the house for tea now and then I have to go down to the fields. If you want to, you come with me and I'll show you what the workers are doing down there. Then if you like it, tomorrow you can come with me when I do the rounds."

I relaxed a little, still somewhat unsure.

"Rounds? What are rounds?"

I had visions of him cutting wheels out of wood.

"That means do all the jobs and go to all the places I have to supervise," he explained, again with a little grin.

"Why do you call it rounds then?"

He thought for a moment.

"I suppose because basically I go round in a circle - starting off from the farm house, going to different places on the farm and then coming back to the farmhouse again."

I nodded wisely, it made sense.

It was the start of a wonderful holiday. Mike and I became good friends. At the crack of dawn each day I would wait eagerly for him to come and fetch me. That first day still sticks in my head as a kind of fairy-tale come true. The sky was a deep indigo and there was just a sore red strip on the horizon when he knocked at my window.

"Amber? Come young madam, the birds are waking up and we must get moving!"

Still half asleep I struggled through the mist of waking in total disorientation.

"Amber! It's Mike, get dressed, sunshine - I'll wait for you on the stoep."

By the time I had got there he had poured two mugs of steaming coffee from a flask. I had never tasted anything so delicious. It was black, but thick, sweet and unlike anything I had ever drank before. It mixed with the smell of early morning, cold earth and wet dew. It merged with the sleepy twitter of the stirring birds and the dawn cock-crow that cut piercingly through the crisp air. It warmed me from inside where I huddled next to Mike, drawing the comforting warmth from his body. I think I could have sat like that forever. I was quiet and at peace, and there was such a gentle, deep happiness in me.

Then Mike heaved a deep, contented sigh, drained the last of his coffee and shaking the remaining drops out of the cup, stood up and stretched into the morning air.

"That's it, little one, the day begins! Drink up and let's tackle it!"

It was a fascinating day, full of new sights and smells. Mike made everything exciting - he made farm life seem like an adventure, a challenge and it was obvious the farm labourers liked him. Wherever we went they greeted him with waves and nod. He introduced me and that same respect and friendliness was passed on to me. I loved it. I almost wanted to go and hug them. I had seen the cows in the distance, but now Mike took me to the shed. At first I was scared. They were huge so close up. All I could think was that if they shifted their feet and stood on me, they would crush every bone in my foot. I'd never get my foot out from under that hoof. I clung to Mike's leg. He just laughed and gently prized my fingers loose.

"They won't hurt you Amber, even they aren't that stupid."

That made me laugh, because I thought of my grandfather - he was that stupid! So Mike was saying that cows had more brains than my grandfather

"Come, I'll show you how to milk them."

I was fascinated. I stared in amazement as his hands and fingers moved deftly on the animal's teats, squeezing and pulling, and the milk spat out in a steady stream. It smelt warm and so different from the milk in bottles.

"Now you try," he said and pushed me towards the pail.

I swallowed hard. I didn't want him to see how nervous I was, so close to those hoofs and swishing tail. The cow must have sensed my apprehension, because it turned round to look at me and shove its curious face in my direction. I jerked back, it had such huge eyes!

Its jaw was grinding round and round and up and down and it just looked so weird I burst out laughing and the fear fell into the straw and got trampled under the cow's hooves. Then it was exciting. I grabbed hold of the teats and pulled and jerked, but nothing happened. Disappointed, I looked at Mike with an accusing expression. He was trying not to laugh.

"Slowly and smoothly, sweetheart. Look, let me show you."

And he put his big strong hands over mine so that I could get the
feel of it. I got such a surprise when the milk suddenly came spurting
out that I yelled and would have let go if his hands weren't over mine.
Then gradually I got the hang of it. By the time the holiday came to
an end I had become an expert. Mike had endless patience with me.
Even when I made mistakes and did things wrong, he never shouted at
me.

Mike was my big friend, I followed him everywhere. I hung on
his lips. I wanted to do everything perfect to make him proud of me.
I sat next to him at the big dining room table and I think I talked non
stop. The people who owned the farm were very rich, but they had
remained spontaneous, simple-hearted and genuine.

They had none of the pretentious arrogance that rich people often
affect. They were sincere and generous and treated us all alike. Mike
was the farm manager and he ate with them like one of the family. I
couldn't get over the variety and quantity of food.

We had arrived in the late afternoon, so our first meal there was
dinner. When I saw all the food on the table I was bemused and
uncertain. Mrs Roelofse, the farmer's wife, dished up and when she
put the plate in front of me I couldn't believe it.

"Mrs Roelofse, is this mine?"

I thought I had better make sure, because I certainly didn't want a
beating from her husband, he looked much stronger than my
granddad.

"Yes, Amber, why? Is there something wrong?"

I shook my head and decided I had better make double sure, just in
case.

"Is it all mine? Can I eat all this?"

She looked puzzled and glanced towards Charlene for clarification.

"It's yours Amber, all of it. Why, what's the matter?"

I shook my head bemused and overcome. All this food at one
meal! It was more than we used to get for three or four days
altogether. Charlene just looked embarrassed. But now Mrs
Roelofse's curiosity was piqued.

"Why do you ask?"

I glanced at Charlene to get some cue from her, but she was
staring at her plate.

By now everyone at the table was looking at me. So I took a
breath and explained.

"My grandfather only gives us a slice of bread for supper. He would never allow Aunt Miriam to let us eat food like this."

There was a shocked silence.

Mrs Roelofse looked at Charlene for confirmation, but she had her eyes fixed firmly on her plate.

"When I ask for more food, he says I'm a pig. So I go to my friends' house for food, but even there I've never had so much for a whole day."

Charlene was redder than the sunset had been that evening.

"Shut-up, Amber," she hissed at me.

But it was too late. I had seen a chance to get at my grandfather. So in between mouthfuls I regaled them with stories about the way I sneaked food from the pantry, collected old vegetables from my vegetable man and pinched sweeties from my Aunt Miriam's secret place in the cupboard. I soaked up the attention. But Charlene was not in the least amused. That night she poked me in the ribs and stamped me a few times in a temper, warning me never to speak about things at home again. I'm still not sure what her case was - perhaps she was jealous, or maybe she was afraid that the old monster would get to hear of it. Anyway I ignored her. I was certainly not going to exchange my grandfather's dictatorship for hers.

The days drifted past in a glorious haze of happiness and freedom, and then one morning early I had another of those awful visions. I was lying in bed just as the blackness of night was cracking into dawn. Then as I gazed out of the window, a beautiful lady came drifting in. She was dressed a in white dress like a bride - it seemed to float around her, and she had a veil over her face. She came towards me, but her feet were not actually on the floor, but just above it. My heart jumped, stopped and then started sounding till I could feel the throb stabbing in my chest, throat and ears. I closed my eyes, but she touched me and when I opened my eyes again, she lifted her veil. To my shock it was Mike's face! I drew my breathe in so sharply I stopped breathing and she lowered her veil. Then it was a lady again, but when she lifted the veil it was Mike.

Confusion shot through my terror and thoughts churned through my head like foam. Maybe I'd gone mad after all. Maybe the way grandfather had treated us had turned me crazy. How could this woman become Mike? She touched me again and this time I screamed - and kept screaming. I heard feet running towards the bedroom, the door burst open and Mr Roelofse and his wife rushed in.

In gasps and sobs I told them what had happened. Mrs Roelofse hugged me to her and smoothing my hair she tut-tutted me into some semblance of calm.

"It's just a nightmare, Amber. Don't you worry. As soon as the sun is up and you have had some nice hot breakfast and a cup of milk, you'll feel much better."

While we were eating, the phone rang. Mr Roelofse came into the dining room with a strained expression on his face and called Mike. Then he gave me a long, strange look and calling his wife, they both left the room. I began to feel apprehension and unease heaving inside me. When the couple came back she was pale and there were tears in her eyes. She didn't look at me. Mike was away for quite a long time. When he came back his eyes were red and swollen. They went to him with obvious deep compassion. Mr Roelofse took his hand while his wife embraced him and they all wept together. No one said anything. I watched this with widening eyes, growing fear and a cold, sick feeling in my stomach. Mike gave me such a weird look, it terrified me. I must have done something wrong. I must have caused some terrible tragedy or disaster. Now they were all going to turn on me. Mike wouldn't let me come with him anymore. They would give me a thrashing and send me home. Dear God, what had I done wrong?

I began to tremble inside, and then through his tears, Mike said, "Amber, how did you know?"

I hadn't the faintest clue what he was talking about.

"I didn't do anything. I'm so sorry Mrs Roelofse, I don't know what I've done wrong, but I promise I didn't mean it. Please don't punish me. Please don't send me home."

The words bubbled out of me in panic - stricken gasps. But there was no accusation in their words and stares, only sorrow, bewilderment and something that seemed almost timidity. I began to cry.

Eventually I learned that at the same time the woman had appeared to me, Mike's sister had died. I was appalled. It all seemed to me that every time I loved someone or something, it was taken away from me. As though I was the cause of tragedy. As though I wasn't allowed to be happy and to love. That was when I became fully aware of the feeling of impending loss that had always lurked vaguely around in my being. It was the first time I had been able to identify it. It has never left me since. Whenever I start to reach my hands out to grasp a long desired hope, a cherished aspiration, a precious dream, this monstrous thing heaves its ugly head out of its dark hiding place and threatens me with its murderous leer. So I draw back. Sometimes, it seems to me, too late.

Like it was with the typhoid epidemic. At times I had wondered if perhaps there was a shortage of people in heaven or something.

The church bell was constantly tolling its mournful death - call over the town as one funeral after another was held. And it was always the people that I loved. It never seemed to be strangers, or those I disliked.

Now looking at Mike's devastated face, all those fears engulfed me and I burst out in regret,

"Oh Mike! It's all my fault! I'm sorry, it's all my fault!"

Nobody knew what I was talking about - how could they?

But the agony and the fear laid deep foundations in me that day.

Now, whenever I am tempted to open up to a new friendship, savour a wonderful relationship, the barriers let me go only so far and no further. I feel I can't risk it - I can't risk them.

I'm afraid they will only be snatched away from me. And then it will be my fault.

That was the end of the holiday. We still stayed there a few days, but Mike left. I suppose he had to go to arrange his sister's funeral or something. Anyway, I never saw him again. But I never forgot him. I never forgot the first time he had found me crying. I used to lie at home at night and re-live the tractor rides, the trips to town for sweeties, the cow-milking and all the other things he taught me. Then, where no one could see me, I would let the tears of regret and despair pour unhindered down my face.

CHAPTER EIGHT

During our absence things had been happening in our town that were to change our lives dramatically. We walked into the house with the usual trepidation. Whenever we came back from friends my grandfather would be particularly obnoxious - as though he was trying to make up for lost time. But his sneering face was nowhere to be seen. Aunt Miriam welcomed us with affection, but she looked nervous and even more timid than usual. I wondered briefly what was going on, but in the excitement of returning and going to find friends I soon forgot.

I wanted to go and see Denise, buy some sweeties and then do the 'rounds' - Mike's face flashed into my head and for a moment I paused as the sense of loss stabbed me. What was the good of thinking about him? It was just another person I seemed to have brought bad luck to. I shook my head to rid it of the thoughts.

There was nothing I could do about it. So I pushed it all down deep where the other sadness, hurt, sorrow and resentment lay. I had a secret place under the bed where I had been hiding my store of pennies - each one of them like burnished gold - treasure of dedicated care and attention - and most of them earned with sweat and blood! I pulled the handkerchief out with utmost care and unwrapped it. Carefully I took the five pennies lying there in shining glory and added them to the other one in my pocket. Then I headed for the cafe where Denise worked - at last I had enough for those special sweets I had eyed so long.

I came rushing in with my hair flying and face flushed.

"Lo Denise! We're back - grandfather wasn't there so I came straight away. We had a lovely time, but Mike's sister died so he had to go away before we left. We had so much to eat and I milked two cows - it was lovely! I even rode on the tractors."

The news tumbled out and it seemed I couldn't talk fast enough. There was no one else in the shop so Denise didn't have to keep going away to serve like so often happened.

I reached up to pull myself level with the counter - it was high for my tiny body, and one of my precious pennies was squeezed out of my fist. It made a dull thud on the floor. My heart dropped with it. Oh no, now I wouldn't have enough for those special sweets.... I fell to my knees, feeling the despair rise up to engulf me. No! Oh please don't tell me I've lost it... I couldn't see it anywhere, tears began to well up, that - and despairing. By now I was crawling around on the dirty wooden floor, scrabbling around in the dust choking back my sobs. Denise was highly embarrassed as well as angry.

"Amber get up off the floor!" She looked around anxiously, worried that someone might come in and see me I suppose. I didn't care. I had looked after that penny, shined it, worked for it, polished it - it was my penny and now it was gone. It wasn't fair! The injustice of it was hurting me now too. I lay down flat on my tummy to try to see under the counter and my dress caught on something so that when I moved it tore. The desperation and injustice were becoming a frenzy in me. I dug around so frantically that I ripped some nails and then scratched my hands open on something sharp. Weeping with loss and disappointment I ignored Denise's angry hissing. That penny was mine. Without it I couldn't buy what I had been longing and saving for, for such a long time.

Then strong hands lifted me up. I looked up with my teary, dust smeared face. I didn't know the man at all. He wanted to give me a penny he had taken from his pocket, but I brushed his hand away and dropped to my knees again. I didn't want his penny. I wanted my own penny. Lying flat on the floor I stretched my arm as far under the counter as it would go and peered into the murk with screwed up eyes. Then I saw it! Shining in the forgotten dust for years of neglect. It was there! Frenziedly I grasped and tore at the dust, till at last my fingers closed on the precious coin.

When I got to my feet the tears slipping down my cheeks were tears of relief and joy. I had my penny back. I tried to smile at the gentleman who stood looking at me with complete lack of understanding.

"Thank you for your penny 'mister' but that was my penny under the counter and I couldn't leave it there in the dust. It was my penny you see... Mister."

He didn't see... and I didn't know how to explain.

My head throbbed where I had bumped it. My hands were soiled and bleeding and two fingernails had been torn off to the quick. I knew grandfather was going to give me a solid beating for the torn dress, but it didn't matter. I had spent hours rubbing that penny with sand to take the dirty brown colour away and make it gleam like gold.

If I hadn't retrieved it I think I would have wondered for years why I had left it and not looked for it. I know the man wanted to give me a substitute for what I had lost, but it would never have been the same. It wouldn't have meant the same. It wouldn't have had the same value. I could wash away the dirt, and the scratches and bumps would heal. My nails would grow back and the blood would soon dry, but I would never have been able to leave my shining penny there in the dust of abandon.

Denise was angry and impatient.

"I don't understand you Amber, you're just silly. For goodness sake, you were going to spend the stupid penny anyway so what difference does it make whose penny it is?"

She slammed the sweets down on the counter for me.

She was right, she didn't understand. Nor was it worth trying to explain. I stood on tiptoes and tried to reach up over the counter for my sweets, which were placed spitefully just out of reach. I suppose Denise wanted some kind of revenge for the humiliation she thought I had caused her. But the gentleman picked them up and handed them to me. When I thanked him, he patted me on the head and together with sweeties, pressed his penny into my hand too, and winked. I stared at him with my mouth open. Sometimes I didn't understand adults at all.

Like the teachers said at school, I was a precocious kid, I suppose because I used to read so much and because I had, had to stand up and fight for my rights against my grandfather and my older brothers and sisters. Being so much smaller than everyone else I had to be constantly aggressive to stop people from taking advantage of me, or shoving me aside. But I learned quickly that for some reason I couldn't explain, many grown-ups as well as children would take to me. I always had lots of friends although I could never get really close to anyone. There was something thick and solid inside me that would make me go rigid and stand-offish if someone tried to overstep that imaginary line of protection. Then I could get waspish and make some biting comments that would frighten them away from further attempts at too much intimacy.

Though I could generally sense when someone was being sincere or not, there were some teachers I just could never fathom: like Miss de Villiers, the singing teacher. I loved singing, I had a lovely voice and music was one of the joys of my life. It always made me feel light and carefree and the notes used to dance in me, scattering the darkness and gloom that often hunched there. From the time I had entranced everyone as a wood fairy, I was a natural first selection for every concert. Woe betide the teacher who would even think of looking at someone else first! I made no bones about the fact that I was the one for a particular role or song.

"Miss de Villiers, I'm here, I'll sing that song," I had stated most adamantly. She was taken aback by the monumental cheek coming from such a diminutive body. A giggle from the side of the classroom brought her back to herself.

"We'll see Amber, I haven't decided who is going to play what role yet."

"Miss de Villiers, that song is mine. I will play the role of Greta."

Her eyes widened at this unheard of audacity. But by now I was dug in. I had a very stubborn streak and there was no way I was going to allow anyone else to have that role. I wasn't quite sure whether she was serious or not when she went on, glancing doubtfully in my direction.

"Well, I don't know Amber, I think one or two of the other girls would be very good as Greta, perhaps we should hold an audition."

I flared up, half in panic.

"Miss de Villiers, no one can play Greta or sing like I can. No one else wants that role - do you?" I appealed to the class.

Round eyes stared at me apprehensively and a chorus of No's bounced around the classroom.

"See?" I said triumphantly to Miss de Villiers, but I was speaking to her back.

Thinking about it now I realise she had probably been teasing me and was just having a quiet chuckle at my expense, but it was a very serious matter to me at the time. All the same, I couldn't figure her out. Surely it was obvious that I was the best singer?

Didn't she know how I cherished that role? How on earth could she even presume to think that someone else could do it?

I always wanted the most important role. I believe that the teachers soon realised that it was useless offering me a secondary part because I would obstinately refuse it. I loved the applause, I loved it when people cheered and clapped for me - it thrilled me when they were all quiet and absorbed and it was my voice that was filling them with music and light! It made me feel special - I was wanted and for a few brief moments, I was loved and appreciated. I could never get enough of it. Surely the teachers understood how important it was to me?

It was that year that Miss de Villiers apparently thought she was doing me such a big favour.

"Amber, you have a lovely voice and we are going to need you to help the little ones to sing."

I looked at her warily. Where was this leading? Was she trying to set me up so that the main singing role could go to someone else? I said nothing and kept my face blank.

"You're the best singer in the school and the little ones in the concert are going to need your help with the songs and the parts they sing and act in."

I kept my face impassive.

Somewhat exasperated by my lack of reaction. Miss de Villiers continued.

"Isn't it wonderful to be able to contribute like this and help others Amber? You have a gift that can bless others - aren't you excited about that?"

I just kept looking at her blankly, because I could feel that this was going in a direction I was not going to appreciate.

"This year we want you to be the guiding singer."

"The what?"

"There are a number of scenes where the little ones will be acting and a main singer will be accompanying them from back stage."

I didn't let her get any further.

"Miss de Villiers, I don't sing back stage. I sing where people can see and hear me. I don't want to be just a voice. People have got to know that it's me, Amber, that is singing."

And no amount of persuasion, flattery and cajolery could make me change my mind. When she left I don't know whether she was irritated or amused, but I was agitated. How could these people just reduce me to a voice? Didn't they understand anything?

The agitation became indignation as I reflected on the matter, so by the time Miss Marais called me I was a bundle of taut upset nerves.

"Amber dear, we need your help."

I looked glum and uncooperative. She smiled.

"No one else can sing like you. No one else can hold a tune and no one else can make their voice rise up so sweetly and strongly. And we need someone like that so that the little ones aren't afraid and nervous."

Surely Miss Marais wasn't going to side with the others? My look was accusing.

"So what I want to suggest is that we tell everyone in the audience, who is singing backstage so that everyone knows that the lovely voice guiding and helping the little ones is yours. Wouldn't you like that?"

I brightened up, that was better! Not just an anonymous tune, but Amber's song! Yes, that was acceptable. Thinking about it now I suppose it must have caused considerable amusement among the teachers, though perhaps there was more than one or two of them who would gladly have throttled me.

But when the big day came I was ready behind the scenes.

"Ladies and gentleman, a special announcement before the beginning of this act. Our main singer, Amber Waverley will sing the background song from backstage. Though you can't see her, we thank you for your applause and appreciation."

There was a ripple of murmured comment from the audience and then silence. My heartbeat quickened as I waited for the introductory notes - then I opened my mouth and poured out my soul in the lilting, joyous tune that carried the little ones confidently and happily into their scene.

The applause was thunderous and I could feel the tears of happiness pricking my eyes. I knew they were clapping for me and I wanted to burst into song again, and dance for them, dance until the pain burst into shreds of light and sing until the shadows were swept away by the carefree melody of innocence and childhood that I had never been allowed to touch for more than a few brief moments of glorious freedom and joy.

Aunt Miriam didn't come to the concert. She had been very quiet since we came back from the farm and we didn't see her much.

Grandfather had grown more morose and bad tempered than ever and I kept right out of his way. I rarely went home in the afternoons now. Often I would sit in the classroom and do my homework and Miss Marais would come in. Little by little I confided in her. In bits and pieces the truth came out. The more I grew to hate my grandfather, the more willing I became to let people know what he was doing. The more I spoke out, the less I feared him.

Sometimes Miss Marais would look at me as though she didn't believe what I was saying. The first time I saw that look I wanted to get angry, but I wanted to cry at the same time, and because I didn't know what to do I just clammed up. Then I bent my head and carried on doing my homework. To my anguish the tears of hurt oozed through my squeezed up eyes and dripped onto the page. Miss Marais saw them. I think that's when she realised that I wasn't exaggerating and the full horror of my story started to seep in. I fully believe that she was instrumental in the truth getting known, certainly at school and almost just as surely among the town "notables".

One evening I was dragging my feet home when I saw a huge commotion in the yard. There were people there and angry voices shouting at one another. I wanted to turn and run but then Charlene appeared out of nowhere and quickly pulled me into the house through the backdoor. Her eyes were wide with fright and her face was tear-stained.

"Aunt Miriam's very sick. Grandfather won't let them take her to hospital. She's lying in bed and the room is all dark."

She didn't live long. I don't think she wanted to. I felt very sorry for her because she hadn't been unkind, just weak. I don't believe grandfather liked things that were weak and sick. I remember when first Jimmy and then Deryck had typhoid he did nothing to help them. He never even went near their rooms, much less help to look after them.

I believe he hastened her death. Oh not physically, like poisoning or beating her or something like that. He wasn't that crude. He just let her know he was sick of her hanging on to life.

"Let go! And be done!" he shouted once as he slammed out of the bedroom.

I remember those words and I remember his face as he stormed down the passage. God forgive me, but there are days I hope with all my heart that he is having to pay for all the destruction and evil he caused to many people.

Aunt Miriam's death was like her life had been, a shadow, an apology for the disturbance. I can recall almost nothing of the funeral. Just snatches, ladies dressed in black who held my hand or hugged me, people shaking grandfather's hand, flowers and the smell of the hot earth of her grave.

I do remember how sombre the house seemed when we went back, just the three of us and grandfather. It loomed empty and threatening and it seemed strange to me because Aunt Miriam had never really taken up that much space, not physically or any other way. But the lightly restraining presence was gone, and now there was nothing to stop my grandfather from doing exactly what he wanted.

Our circumstances grew desperate and the worse they got, the more brazen and defiant I became. Charlene was often reduced to tears because of my rebellion.

"Don't! Amber don't!" she would scream when I stood up to the monster or answered him back. She would claw at my arm and I would shake her off because she would hinder me from jumping back when he lifted his hand to hit me.

One night I felt I had reached the end of my tether and I started writing to my father again. But there must have been a curse on me or something, because for the second time, I forgot that wretched letter in my room. As I walked back from school next day, I suddenly heard crying. Puzzled, I stopped. It was my voice. I listened, cocking my head slightly to one side. There was no doubt, it was my voice and I was crying, bitterly and full of pain. Now I was getting scared. It was broad daylight, I was in the middle of the dusty street, there were people walking just ahead of me on the side of the road, and I could hear myself crying. Somewhere in the distance it was true, but it was my voice.

I felt weird, hollow inside and frightened. There was no one at home when I arrived, so I went straight to my bedroom to do my homework. I was sitting cross-legged on the bed with a book on my lap when the door burst open and the huge angry figure towered in the door.

"You won't learn, will you?"

His voice was full of hate. I started to move backwards towards the edge of the bed. Before I could leap off and shoot through the window he lunged forwards and grabbed my leg. Screaming and kicking I thrashed around on the covers, grabbing the edge of the mattress and trying to land a foot in his face. As he pulled, the mattress came up with me, but with a swift yank he jerked me loose. Then the beating started.

He was breathing heavily as the blows fell, wherever his hand or fist could find a point of contact.

"Don't... you... ever... try... that again!"

The punches, slaps and blows punctuated his commands.

"You will never... ever... try... to write... to that bastard... again. Do... you understand?"

When he had finally tired of beating me, I lay crumpled on the floor. After he had left I pulled my knees up to my chin and just hugged my legs, trying to swallow the sobs and tears. I refused to give him the satisfaction of seeing me cry. What right did that bastard have to hit me? I was not his daughter. I lay there, trembling and shivering till it was pitch dark. Then slowly I staggered to my feet, clutching at the wall for support until I could stand without falling. I stood for a while until the room stopped spinning.

That was it. I had had enough. Without a sound I left the house and walked away, as far as I could from that house and that town. Two days later while I was sitting weary, thirsty and totally hopeless at the side of the road, a police van pulled up. A woman in uniform got out and walked towards me.

"Hello, are you Amber Waverley?"

I just stared at her.

"Amber? We've been looking for you for two days now. Your teacher reported you missing when you didn't come to school."

I said nothing.

"Come dear, we're going to take you home."

As she put her hand out to me I leapt up like a cobra.

"I'll never go back! Leave me alone! Don't touch me!" I screamed. "I won't put a foot in that house while that monster's there!"

I think it took her a while to calm me down. She assured me we weren't going to my grandfather's house. I made her promise, swear, that she wouldn't try to make me go to him. Then I let them drive me back.

I stayed with a family who had children at the school. They were among those who had always felt sorry for me, their mother had often sent me fruit or a samie for break and I had been on holiday with them for a few weekends too.

Though I could feel they were genuinely concerned for me, I couldn't relax. Inside I felt tight, brittle, I was so tense that I would jump and scream at any unexpected noise or movement. I expected that monster to appear at the door at any moment and demand that I go back. I pictured him dragging me down the road, hitting me with a piece of firewood till I was bloody and dying. Every time there was a knock at the door I would start trembling and look for somewhere to hide.

Then one day when I came back from school there was a lady waiting to see me.

"This is Mrs Lewis, Amber. She's just come to talk to you. I'll leave you two together and go and make some tea."

I sat down and sized her up. No more sweet Amber now as far as I was concerned. I had often been accused of being brazen, well then I might as well be it. I was tired of being pushed around and beaten up for nothing and I had drawn my "This-far-and-no-further" line in the dust in front of me. Mrs Lewis began to question me about my grandfather. I glared at her.

"Why don't you ask the people in this town? They've all stood and watched it for years. They know just as much about him as I do."

She persisted, but without being ugly about it.

"What do you want to know for?" I wanted to know. "What's it to you?"

My rudeness didn't faze her in the least.

"I'm from Social Welfare, Amber, and we would like to remove you to a place where you, your sister and brother can be properly cared for."

I might have been old for my age in many ways, but I was also still very naive in others. I had no idea what Social Welfare was or meant and no inkling of the chain reaction I had unleashed by running away. It had been the final element in an explosive mixture that had caused it all to fizz and bubble up in the face of the townspeople. Now I realised that it was probably the final proof that some genuinely concerned people had been waiting for.

I still don't understand though why they took so long about it. If they had acted earlier our whole lives might have been so different.

If they had had more courage, if they had confronted my grandfather, if they had taken us into their homes... if... if... if.

It was the end of one phase and the start of another. Mrs Lewis eventually accompanied me to the house, together with the people whom I was staying with; I refused point blank to go there alone. She helped me pack my things. When she held the pitiable small suitcase in her hand she looked at me with big, sad eyes.

"Is that all, Amber?"

I nodded. That was all. I turned and walked past my grandfather who was waiting on the stoep. I didn't even glance at him. I never saw him again.

CHAPTER NINE

The station was exciting - there was so much noise, with people jostling and rushing, porters shouting, the steam blowing in huge hissing billows and the clang and clatter of the train doors and windows being slammed open. I felt wonderfully free and my heart was thudding with this new adventure. I couldn't understand why Charlene looked so subdued. Didn't she realise that we had left that awful man behind, that he wouldn't be able to hurt us again. I looked happily up at Mrs Lewis, her blonde hair caressing her cheek as she bent down to pick up my little suitcase. She was so lovely, the station was wild fun, the train a gorgeously snorting beast and we were heading for a new life. I thought it was magnificent. From time to time though Charlene was shooting me venomous looks. At last, irritated I snapped at her.

"Charlene why do you keep looking at me like that? What have I done now?"

"You stupid little fool," she spat, "we've got to go to an orphanage now, and it's all your fault. Orphanages are like prisons. You think it was bad with grandfather? Just wait till you've been in the orphanage for a while, you'll long to be back with grandfather again."

I stared at her with total disbelief. Back with grandfather? Had she gone stark raving mad? Nothing, absolutely nothing in the world could be worse than living there. My mind could simply not conceive of anyone else as bad as him, as for someone who was worse it was just impossible. I shrugged and decided not to pay any more attention to Charlene. I was not going to allow her to spoil these thrilling new experiences.

I sat close to Mrs Lewis when the train pulled off. It jerked and lurched and heaved slowly out of the station. I watched the windows slowly move past, then as the train gathered speed we left the buildings behind and I saw the houses slide past, faster and faster. The train whistled and I jumped. Mrs Lewis smiled and put an arm around me. But I couldn't sit still for long, trees and poles were shooting past now and I wanted a clearer look. Kneeling by the window, I wanted to stick my head right out.

"Careful Amber, you'll get soot in your eyes and that is very painful." Mrs Lewis cautioned.

And none to soon, just as I turned my head towards her, something flew into my eye with a burning sting.

Fortunately it was right in the corner so the sudden rush of tears flushed it out. I didn't have to be told twice and after that I was very careful about sticking my head out of the window.

Mrs Lewis made sure we didn't go hungry. I had never tasted some of the little snacks and sweets she produced. If the journey to the orphanage was this good, then I couldn't see that the orphanage was going to be all that bad. I dismissed the nagging little fear that Charlene's poisonous accusation had insinuated in my heart and threw myself whole-heartedly into enjoying this journey into a new life.

Before long the compartment was too small for my exuberance. I was fascinated with the sliding door and kept going in and out till Mrs Lewis began to lose patience.

"Amber, if you want to go out into the corridor, then go out but don't bother the other people there, and don't go into anyone else's compartment, and in three minutes I want you back here."

I shot out like a rabbit heading for open fields. This was unbelievable, a whole new world to discover while another was clacking past outside! The smells were strange but nice, dust and polished wood, leather and sooty, musty smells, then warm, sweet coffee from the waiter edging his way down the corridor. I leaned against a window that was half-open and soaked in the fascinating and beautiful scenes. I loved seeing the objects close to the train flash by in a blur, while further away they drifted past in a stately glide to the clicked-clack, clicked-clack of the wheels.

I began to sing and soon I was dancing and skipping up and down the corridor. Occasionally Mrs Lewis would call me in and have me sit down, give me something to eat or drink and chat. I can't really remember what she spoke about to Charlene, she spent most of the time talking to Charlene, who sat there looking glum and miserable. Before long I would be jumping up and down again, until Mrs Lewis, probably out of pure exasperation, would let me out into the corridor again.

The orphanage was a huge double-storey building, with a balcony all around the top floor. As we drove up the horseshoe-shaped driveway I caught a general view of a lovely big garden. As the car stopped in front of the stairs, a tall lady came out of the glass doors and stood waiting at the top of the steps. If she hadn't been wearing a dress, I wouldn't really have known whether she was a man or a woman. Big-boned with a hook nose, she immediately doused the bubbling excitement that had been welling up in me. I darted a glance at Charlene. An awful apprehension began to prick inside, what if she were right? What if this was worse than my grandfather's house? I hung back now as Mrs Lewis went to greet this grim-looking woman. She turned and motioned for me to come.

"And this is Amber."

The cold eyes surveyed me, an unfeeling up and down, like I was a second-hand dress that was not quite fit for re-sale. My heart dropped and all my previous decisions came flooding in again. If this place tries to make me bend to rules and regulations that are unfair and unjust they can forget about keeping me here. I felt the hard wall rise up roughly inside.

This old bat would see that I could be just as cold and unfeeling as her. I met her almost indifferent stare with one I hoped would convey my own warning. Inside, the building looked bigger than what it seemed from outside, but it wasn't cold and scary.

"Come girls," said the hawk-nosed woman, and she led us to a room just off the entrance.

"Now just open your suitcases and unpack. I want everything laid out neatly here, and double-quick please, I don't have time to waste."

There was so little to unpack that within a few minutes it was ready for inspection. Mrs Lewis exchanged a "What-did-I-tell-you?" look, with the big fat woman and shook her head as if to say she just couldn't understand it.

The big woman's expression didn't change.

"Well, we're not going to go very far with that, are we?" she queried.

"Come along, and we'll see if we've got your sizes."

Charlene and I trotted docilely after her big-boned figure as it marched purposefully into another room where there were big cupboards. Methodically she pulled out the items one after another until I began to think it was Christmas, Easter, New Year, holidays, surprises and wonders all rolled in one. School shoes, church shoes, Wellington boots, school uniforms, aprons, underwear. I felt ecstatic! We were also given marker pens and labels and it was the most tremendously new and exciting thing to write my name on so many labels and stick them on things that were not second-hand, that were whole, and that fitted!

Mrs Lewis went to the dormitory with us.   She smiled at my flushed, happy face and sat us down on a bed.

"Mrs Crawford is the principal here," she explained.   "I think you are going to be very happy, as long as you obey the rules, do what you are told and learn to co-operate with the other girls.   Some of them are orphans, some have only one parent, some have been put here because their parents aren't able to look after them.   No one is better or worse than any other here.   When the school starts, you will be going to the girl's school and I'm sure you will make lots more friends there too.   Work hard, do your best and you will find that everything will work out well for you."

She showed us the lockers where we could keep our personal, private things and then took us all over the house.   There were only two or three girls there and I was surprised.

"Where are all the other girls then?" I wanted to know.

"The rest of the girls will be coming back next week before school starts.   Some of them still have family to go to for holidays, others are invited out by friends or other people.   Don't worry, you won't be alone here!"

That night I lay in the dormitory and stared up at the ceiling. Light from the street was flickering and snaking across the walls and it was very quiet.   There was such confusion of feelings, I couldn't figure it out.   Relief, apprehension, excitement, fear - a definite sense of lightness, as though the black oppression from my grandfather had been blown away.   At the same time I wanted to cry, but wasn't sure why.   One thing I knew for sure, I wasn't going to allow anyone to push me around here.   I didn't care who it was: principals, matrons, adults, children, they were all going to know that I was not going to be messed with, that I was not going to put up with injustice.   Those who tried to step on me because I was small were in for a shock. They would find out very quickly that I was a tough handful that they would wish they hadn't picked on.

During the next few days, the children started coming back to the orphanage for the new school year.   I was very wary and stand-offish to begin with, because I didn't know what to expect and the old fear of rejection and fear of hurt were building preparatory barriers of protection.   I quickly learnt the routines and schedules and found with a deep inner relief that the girls were very different from the ones I was used to. There was no vying for position. There was very little cattiness. The older girls tended to take responsibility for the littler ones and I soon understood how everything was always shared.

There were eight little kids, then the primary school children and then about ten high school girls. The "home girls" as we called them, formed a special category on their own. They had either completed schooling and were waiting to be placed in some form of employment or were unable or unwilling to study further. The senior in charge of the group I was in was really helpful. She was strict, but I suppose she had to be, otherwise old "Dragon" would let her have it.

The Principal, I found, was commonly known as "Dragon." She was a weird mixture of contradictions. As unfeminine as they come, flat as a board and it seemed to me, totally void of any humane feelings. Yet she herself had an adopted daughter and she did unexpected things, like play tennis magnificently and teach us too, encourage us to sing and play the piano. But then, as though to compensate for these lapses into kindness and humanity, she would dispense random slaps, without any reason, as she walked past some child or moved down a row of us. I never could figure her, I still can't today. In my more bitter moments of resentment, I would imagine her having to wear a board that said, "in case of rape, this side up." Because she was really so incredibly flat-chested.

The hatred, suspicion and rebellion that my grandfather had implanted in me lay just below the surface, ready to flare up at the slightest provocation, and initially I had several run-ins with some of the girls and even with the Dragon. Little by little though, some of that harsh aggression eroded away. I found that the other girls actually respected me as an individual, a person in my own right. When I was uptight or miserable I discovered to my amazement that there was genuine understanding. They didn't mock me, they didn't try to push me into talking or explaining. I had become very sensitive to the sincerity of people's words and actions and I could feel that these girls were not pretending.

One day I was lying face-down on my bed, crying my loneliness and misery into the pillow when I felt the bed sag under someone's weight.

"Go away!" I shouted. "Leave me alone!"

There was no response, I kept crying, but my tears no longer had the freedom to flow while someone was sitting there watching me.

Now anger started to drip in to the unhappiness and eventually I couldn't stand it anymore. I whipped round and lunged for the intruder, wanting to push her off the bed and make her go away. She had obviously anticipated the move, because she sat just out of reach.

Foiled and frustrated, I glare at her and was opening my mouth to swear when she just shook her head at me. Surprised, I shut my mouth and stared at her .

"Amber you are just making it so hard for yourself. Look, I know you hurt and I know you have gone through a lot, but it's also time you realised that you have to let go of those things and make the best of what you have got."

"What do you know about what I've gone through? What do you know? And what do you care?" I shouted aggressively and spun my back on her again.

For a while there was silence while I contemplated my own horrible lot and the unfairness and injustice of my life.

"Nobody knows what I have had to go through. Don't tell me you understand. You can never understand what has happened and how I feel."

This normally provoked the 'understanding' and mollifying response: "But I do, dear," and similar sick platitudes.

There was just silence from behind my back.

"What makes you think you can understand? Who do you think you are?"

I could feel a tinge of uncertainty creeping into my antagonism.

This was not going like it should. There was still silence at my back.

"How can you know what the hurt is like? How can you know what I feel?"

Silence. This was too much for me. She should have been stung into some kind of retort by now or come out with the usual phrases trotted through for such situations. But nothing. I turned round to look at her. She was just sitting there looking at me, her eyes were full of tears and hurt, yet, full of compassion and understanding. Unnerved and totally out of my depth I didn't know what to do.

"Amber," came the soft admonition, "you must remember that you are not the only one in the world who has suffered. I might not know exactly what you have gone through and how you hurt. Maybe nobody knows or ever will. But that doesn't mean that they haven't also suffered. And maybe even much more and much more intensely than you. Your pain doesn't make theirs meaningless. You are not the cantor and fulcrum around which the world revolves."

I stared at her, feeling shame and confusion prick my face and not knowing how to react.

"The first thing you will have to learn is that the world owes you nothing. A lot of us come here having been hardly done by, not having the same advantages as others, but we expect the world or people or whatever to be kind and nice to us and give us stuff for nothing, because we have had a hard time up to now we will never get anywhere in life. We will spend the rest of our lives waiting for that recognition, that restitution, that hand-up. It will never come Amber. You must learn that if you want to do anything with your life you have to do it yourself. Stop blaming others. It doesn't matter who is to blame for where and what you are now."

I glared at her here, with fury and violent disagreement, opening my mouth to object. Her look was enough to make me close my mouth.

"I know that sounds rough. I know it sounds unfair. But if you keep looking for someone to blame for all the mistakes and everything that has gone wrong in your life, you will never ever fix anything. You will make your own life bitter and twisted. You have to stop looking at whose fault it is. You have to now take the responsibility to fix it. You have to decide you are going to make something of yourself, go places, be someone - in spite of what has happened to you. Maybe even to prove to others that you can do it, that you are worth something."

She was making sense. In my proud rebellion I didn't at first want to receive her words, because I took relish in hating and blaming those responsible for my misery and hurt. This new attitude was going to require a one hundred and eighty degree revolution in my thought process.

"You are not alone in here Amber. And every single one of us is hurting in some way or another. Every single one of us has gone through awful experiences. You accuse me of not being able to know and understand what you've gone through, but have you taken the trouble to wonder what I, or any of the others could have suffered? Do you even care?"

I couldn't bear her look anymore. I knew she was right. I didn't know how to handle this approach. If she had condemned and hit me it would have been easy. I would have been able to reject her words and scorn her and carry on being antagonistic and aggressive and "touch-me-not" - while the loneliness and hurt festered like a rotting abscess inside. But her words were sliding in through all my defences and bringing truth that I found uncomfortable but couldn't refute.

"We're all together in this thing. If we fight one another then life here is going to be a worse hell and pit of torment than any deprivation or misfortune could make it. We have to help one another, realise that we are not alone nor the only person who matters."

No one had ever spoken to me like this before. And she was only a few years older than me too. I was picking at the bedspread, and the tears of anger had become remorse as I began to realise what a little rat I had been. The bed bounced slightly as she stood up to go. I looked at her, regretful and probably a little pleading too.

"I'm sorry I was so horrible. Please will you...." Somehow I couldn't get the words past the flood of sobs that surged out of unknown depths in me. She walked over very simply and naturally and held me until the crying finally started to die down into isolated, jerky sobs.

"It's okay Amber, it's okay."

CHAPTER TEN

The first day at school was a series of strange and new experiences. Getting there was one of the traditions I found so stupid. I came bounding down into the drive with great excitement. I had a new dress, bright shiny school shoes, one of the seniors had helped me brush and plait my hair and my stomach was delightfully full of breakfast - still an unheard of luxury for me at the time. Everyone was milling around, talking and laughing, I looked for the girls I was supposed to be going with. Then someone shouted an order I didn't hear, everyone started lining up in ranks.

"What on earth is this?" I wondered.

The little ones shuffled stiffly into position, suitcases in one hand, hats firmly on their heads, staring straight in front. Behind them the primary school girls were jostling and arguing. Jenny looked around, craning her neck to see where I had got to.

"Amber, your place is here, come quickly."

As I moved beside her I saw that the high school girls were all neatly in rows and files, most of them looking bored or indifferent. There was a senior in front and when she saw that everyone was in place she shouted,

"Okay, everyone ready, let's go," with that she took the lead down the drive towards the nursery school.

This was not my scene. I did not like regimentation, it reminded me too much of the soldiers who used to come marching down the road from the harbour when I was still a little girl. For some reason I had a naked horror of those uniforms and when I saw the ranks coming I used to scream with fear and hide under the bed in panic. They had to use a broomstick to poke me out of there once the soldiers had passed by.

I broke rank and decided I would go and walk with Charlene, who was in a row somewhere in front of me. But before I had gone three steps there was a senior next to me with a warning look.

"Amber, no nonsense please. Get back into your row and stay there."

Jenny gave me a disapproving look too. I realised immediately that trying to rebel against this tradition was useless. Docilely I walked in line, but that didn't stop me from running off at the mouth.

"This is stupid. Why don't they just tell us to march, then we can be proper soldiers! I feel so silly. What do they think, this is some kind of parade?"

And I griped and complained until Jenny shouted out in exasperation,

"Oh Amber, shut up! It's the way we go to school and that's that. Moaning about it will only make it worse!"

I puffed my cheeks out with a disgusted sigh and trudged on. At the nursery school the little ones peeled off and filed into the building. We marched on. I relieved the tediousness by imagining that I was walking along banging a drum or sounding off a trumpet. Shortly afterwards we arrived at the primary school gate and were delivered safe and sound by our senior. The high school girls carried on alone.

It was only then that I realised that it was an all girls' school. I found it awkward and strange. The boys' school was just across the road from us and later on I discovered that we went there for athletics. There were a lot of curious stares and much whispering when we trooped into the classroom. I soon found that there was very little mixing between "normal" girls and "orphanage" girls.

I have never been able to understand the attitude that prevailed towards us. There were obviously exceptions and I made quite a few friends with the "normal" girls, but on the whole they treated us like some kind of inferior being. The commonest insult was "government loafer." This flummoxed me. The girl who first flung that at me was very disappointed by my reaction. I didn't know what she was talking about, so I just ignored her. I'm still not sure what they were thinking about with that epithet. Did they think it was my fault that my mother was dead? The way the "normal" kids behaved, you'd think we had killed our parents.

Most of the other girls were scared of us because we stood up for one another so fiercely. They soon learned not to pick on one of us, because the others would arrive in a flash and pitch in tooth and nail to defend the luckless victim.

Small towns are claustrophobic little communities, where everyone knows everyone else's affairs. The forties were hard years for everyone, and those who suffered more, envied and resented those who felt the pinch less. Those who dug their heels in determined to fight and come through the hardship and lack no matter what, despised and reviled those who didn't. A vicious envy crept through their actions and words like a venomous serpent, infecting their children with the poison of frustration and impotent anger. Children merely repeat what they absorb in the home. But that doesn't mean the words hurt less.

In a small town, everyone knows who the kids in the orphanage are. Some were there from broken homes. Some because they were genuine orphans. Some because their parents couldn't make ends meet and the orphanage was the only solution. Others because the parents had decided it was the government's fault that they were struggling, so the government should pay. They didn't even try to fight back. They didn't bother to struggle on like the 'righteous and virtuous' ones. So, piously and sanctimoniously, these self-righteous Pharisees called them and their children... "government loafers". After all, they were bravely standing, and suffering through determined clenched teeth, soldiering on... So they resented the unprincipled who found an easier way out, not realising, or simply not caring, that it wouldn't be the adults who felt their scorn. We did!

It is a truism that children are cruel. That cruelty is all the more vicious because it is applied with the intention of hurting and cutting as deeply as possible. I didn't know nor understood what a government loafer was - except that I was constantly having it rubbed in my face. I began to feel that it was because my mother was dead and somehow they were telling me it was my fault.

The teachers made no distinction between us and I learned to appreciate that. In fact, if anything, they tended to favour us a bit because we worked so hard. It's not that we were exceptionally brilliant, but in a way I think we were trying to show them that we were just as good and better than the "normal" kids. Most of us shone at school because of this determination not to be left behind or considered inferior. When one of us was struggling with something, others immediately came to help.

I experienced a unity and concern here that made deep inroads in the distrust and suspicion that my grandfather had forced into my life. I became part of a family that stood together, fought together, cried together and laughed and rejoiced together. That doesn't mean to say we didn't argue and fight like other kids, because we did. But somehow there was never any lasting rancour. We shook hands and made up and things went back to normal, with no spite or malice to sour relationships.

They very quickly promoted me from standard five to six because I
was so advanced for my age. They also learned that I was a rebel. I
used to flare up so quickly in the face of what I imagined a wrong. If
it seemed to me that a teacher used an accusatory tone of voice or was
high-handed with me, then I would answer back so brazenly that the
rest of the class looked on stunned in shocked silence. It was
something I simply had no control over. Sometimes the words would
be out, cutting the air and turning it a dull red before I realised it, and
then the regret would already be churning in my stomach, but it was
too late.

My reputation for devil-may-care daring was held in awe by some,
grudging admiration by others and frank disapproval by others, but it
left no one indifferent. The others soon began to put me up to things
because they loved to watch the teachers' reactions, and revelled in
the situations that were created, but they weren't prepared to pay for
the consequences. As usual, the teachers didn't know how to handle
me. I would take to some and really go out of my way to work hard
and please them. As far as they were concerned I was the sweet,
willing Amber who could never put a foot wrong. But some teachers
just rubbed me up the wrong way. I would just let the rebellion and
stubbornness sweep up out of me and stare at them. Once I had dug
my heels in, that was that. No amount of punishment could make me
budge. My grandfather had beaten me so much I think I simply
became inured to it. It had no effect on me except to harden the
resistance still more.

Sometimes at night I used to cry in my pillow about this defiant
rebellion, because it would surface when I didn't want it to. People I
wanted to like and be liked by I began to push away from me. It was
like I couldn't really get close to anyone. This thing would react
inside me and make me curl back into myself, close up and pull away.
Though I was friendly with many of the girls, I could never get really
intimate and trusting. I always felt as though there was a space
around me. It was fenced with barbed wire and had a "No trespassers
allowed" sign up.

And I sat in the middle of it, alone! Scared to reach out in case I
was slapped away. Scared to love in case I somehow brought harm to
the loved one.

I enjoyed school. There were opportunities and challenges that I
loved pitting myself against. I took up tennis and despite my tiny size,

became quite a formidable player. Dragon played tennis very well and I sometimes think that I excelled to show her that she was no better at anything than I was.

That first day at school is clearly etched in my memory. I was very quiet and watchful, taking everything in, listening to everything, sensing the atmosphere and picking up the positive and negative feelings that swirled around the classroom. At break time we were all given milk and vitamin sweets, and the children separated into their groups and circles of friends.

Fran was a dark-haired girl who sat behind me in class. She walked over and invited me to come and sit with her and her friends. I was going to refuse, but after a slight hesitation, shrugged to myself and thought, "Well why not?" and walked over with her.

They were too inquisitive for my liking, so after fielding the first few questions I turned my glare on them.

"So what am I here? The new monkey in the zoo? Have I got to pass some kind of examination before I can sit with you? Why don't you just mind your own business?"

I got up in anger, but another girl with mousy hair grabbed my skirt and started laughing.

"Gee are you touchy! Just relax, no one's going to eat you. If you don't want to talk, that's your business. We didn't mean to get you upset."

I jerked my skirt out of her hand and shot a look heavy with suspicion at her. But then I sat down again, somewhat mollified. We eventually became quite good friends. They would bring samies and sometimes sweets to school for me. This was highly preferable substitute for the orphanage porridge which I detested. The stuff would stick to my palate and when I tried to swallow it, bile would come flooding into my mouth. It felt like all the muscles in my throat were working backwards to hurl the stuff out again. I wasn't a very big eater in the first place - I think my stomach must have shrunk at my grandfather's house.

During break the girls started telling me about the teachers. "You'll love the chemistry teacher, he's a real doll, and he blushes a lot!"

They all burst into giggles.

"He gets embarrassed when the girls stare at him. We don't really know why, but we think it's because last year one of the standard nine girls fell in love with him. She used to wait for him after class and try to walk home with him!"

Hilarious cackles greeted this memory and Fran rolled over on to her back in delight.

"He got so embarrassed by the whole thing that he would run out of the class five minutes early to avoid her!"

"What happened then?" I wanted to know, amused by the pictures I was forming in my own mind.

Gales and shrieks of laughter - then Fran choked out: "His classes made so much noise in those five minutes that the Head came to find out what was going on. Of course one would say anything, so she summoned him to her office. Shame, we saw him there waiting when we came out of assembly."

At this they all yelled with laughter again.

"What happened?" I insisted.

Penny with the mousy hair continued.

"When he came back to class they said he was all flushed. For days he shouted at them when they just so much as whispered and he was very jumpy."

"And the girl?" I asked.

They sobered up a bit. Fran shook her head in dismissal.

"Oh! she's just stupid. They put her in Miss Clarke's chemistry class. She failed and last year she left for some other school."

Chemistry was the first lessons after break. My curiosity was fully aroused now. All new girls had to sit in the front, so I had an unimpeded view of the unfortunate and unwilling lover boy. I was a bit disappointed when he hurried in, he looked very ordinary. I had pictured a dashing, handsome actor-type, who would sweep the pupils off their feet with his deep voice and flashing eyes. But he had a slightly high-pitched voice too and he seemed clumsy. He always seemed to bump into the corner of his desk while he was explaining something. I couldn't imagine why anyone would fall head over heels in love with him.

Turning these things over in my mind, I didn't realise that I was fixing him with a penetrating gaze until I heard sniggers from behind me. His face was slowly turning red and he kept looking down at his hands. Then apparently steeling himself to confront the situation, he suddenly lifted up his head and pointed at me.

"You, the new girl, what's your name? Do you have a problem?"

I stood to my feet, demurely.

"No sir," I smiled sweetly, and waited, watching him slowly lose his composure.

The girls were loving it. I could feel the delight dancing around the classroom.

"No, yes, well... sit down then," he flustered, "and pay attention!"

I remained standing,

"And my name is Amber, sir," I smiled again.

He stared a moment, surprised.

"What? Oh, yes your name, Amber is it? Well Amber, sit down and concentrate now."

"Yes sir." I said and as daintily as I could, I sank down into my chair, and fixed him with an adoring gaze. By now the girls were choking back their laughter. I had become an instant heroine. Mr Phillips was disorientated. He couldn't remember what he intended doing and in rummaging through the mass of papers and books on his desk, he knocked a pile of exercise books over. I leapt out of my seat and enthusiastically 'helped' to pick them up.

"It's all right thank you Amber," his voice was agitated. "Go and sit down."

"Oh Sir," I said plaintively, "I only wanted to help."

Looking downcast and miserable, I fidgeted with my fingers and then looked up at him with a downy soft, imploring expression.

Thoroughly rattled he almost shouted.

"Yes, well, thank you, no - just go and sit down. Thank you, no it's all right..." while the class collapsed in giggles and snorts. Immensely pleased with myself, I turned to go back to my desk, showing him a hurt, dejected little body, while a huge grin faced the delighted girls. He fumbled through the rest of the lesson, glowing alternately pink and red as he caught sight of my unwavering gaze. I loved it! It was almost like being back on stage and listening to the audience's applause. In fact after the lesson, the girls crowded around, laughing and congratulating me. Eventually though, Mr Phillips trained himself to ignore my fixed stares, so we had to find new ways to unsettle him.

After school I began to learn the orphanage routine. Everything was regulated by bells. There was a hotel right next door and I was surprised they didn't lay complaints about that relentless bell.

Lunch was not a big meal - in fact, in those first years, none of the meals were. I think the hard times were pressing on everyone, and places like orphanages and similar institutions probably felt it most. People had less to donate, money was tight, so we simply went without a lot of things that nowadays people assume as their rightful due.

The sawmills delivered scrap wood which we had to saw to make fire for the boilers. The hotel would phone in the evenings and notify Dragon to send the girls for the left-overs. They would walk over with huge pots and urns that four or five of them would struggle back with. The pantry and storeroom were kept locked, not that that stopped the raids - all it did was heighten the challenge!

We had four tables seating us in the dining room. By now all the children had come back and after the obligatory silence for Dragon's grace, there was quite a lot of talk and chatter. A glass of milk stood at each girl's plate. To my surprise I saw a number of girls carefully pour their milk into a little bottle or tin with a screw-on lid. Puzzled, I watched to see what they would do with it, but during the course of the meal was distracted and forgot about it.

The girls on kitchen shift had to wash the dishes while the rest of us trooped off for study period. I didn't have any homework and quickly grew bored, so I slipped off to find Charlene - and walked straight into the Dragon.

"And where do you think you are going young madam?"

She cracked me on the side of the head and grabbing me by the shoulders, marched me back into the study room.

"I've got nothing to do," I protested. "I wanted to find my sister."

Her eyebrows rose in mock surprise.

"Nothing to do? Well we can fix that very quickly."

Still holding my shoulder, she push-marched me to the kitchen. The girls were just finishing the washing and drying.

"Belinda, give Amber a pail and a brush. She has volunteered to scrub the floor in her spare time."

So I learnt that the heresy of having "nothing to do" would incur a merciless penalty. I was seething with resentment.

"I might just as well go back to my grandfather's house. You treat me just like he did."

Unperturbed, Dragon delivered another slap, almost absent-mindedly, and replied calmly.

"I'm sure we can arrange for your return. In the meanwhile, you will learn courtesy and manners. You will most certainly not answer back so rudely. So when you have finished scrubbing the floor, you may help Susan and May saw wood, until you have seen the error of your ways and come and apologise."

I spat.

It was not an auspicious start. I ground my teeth but kept my mouth shut. This Dragon was in a position to make my life really miserable and there was nothing I could do about it. I swallowed hard on the rebellion and after I had finished the floor I went to knock at her door. It was slightly ajar and there was a mirror hanging on the wall opposite the door. I caught sight of myself - tiny but still boiling and puffed up with indignation. I took a deep breath, smoothed my hair down with both hands and then turned my head slightly to examine my profile. It looked to me that I had grown older since I had left my grandfather's house - and prettier too, I smiled at my reflection. Then I brushed down my bodice and dress. I was starting to develop too and I took pleasure in my neat little figure. Turning sideways, I tried to see how I looked when a dry voice echoed from around the door.

"You may come in now Amber."

I flushed, the old Dragon, she must have been watching me all the time. I stalked in aggressively, and then remembered in time that I had come to apologise. Another deep breath. I was about to speak when I thought I saw amused lines at the corner of her mouth. I was so surprised I stopped in mid-word. But when I looked again I thought I must have been mistaken. Her lips were as flat and straight as her body.

"Well?" she prompted. I mumbled over an apology.

"Considering you are new here Amber, I'm prepared to give you a chance. You are dispensed from sawing wood, but I expect you to use your time profitably. And in future there will be no cheek from you. Is that understood?"

I nodded.

"I said, is that understood?"

"Yes Mrs Crawford."

"Then you may go. Learn the rules and respect them and you will settle in quickly."

She motioned towards the door. As I went out, I glanced at myself again in the mirror. This time I was sure, I did look older and prettier than when I was at my grandfather's house!

Belinda was in the same dormitory as me. She took me in hand and explained the shifts and duties. We all took turns at doing all the work in the orphanage. Some of it was hard and dirty work, especially for someone as physically small as I was, though I kept priding myself on my strength. I might have been tiny compared to others, but the work on the farms and in my grandfather's house had built up unusual stamina so that I often surprised the girls with my capacity for work.

While some of the older girls helped the littler ones to bath, others helped in the kitchen, preparing the meal, setting the table, cutting bread, making the fire and so on. Belinda and I were on the bread-cutting detail which I had expected to be a breeze. By the fiftieth slice of bread I had long since changed my opinions about the ease of bread-cutting. The slices had to be a certain thickness, any thicker and either some children would have to do without or Dragon would slap you up for carelessness. Any thinner and they would crumble into bits. It was a nightmare. My height didn't help matters either, because I had to stretch up as well as exert strength downwards to cut and my back and arms were aching from the awkward angles. Cutting crooked was another sin punished with head-ringing slaps. So by the time we had finished I didn't want to see another piece of bread as long as I lived.

We had soup from the hotel to eat with our bread, and a tiny little pat of butter. During supper, Dragon announced that there would be singing in the hall afterwards and I brightened up a bit. I considered myself to have a wonderful voice and thoroughly enjoyed singing and dancing.

As I lay in bed that night running through the day's events in my head I came face to face with the conundrum of what Dragon was to become for me. I never could really figure her out. She contained so many contradictions in herself. There were times during those years that I felt genuine affection for her, but then something would turn it into seething hatred. She would give the most unexpected mercy and yet deal out the most unrelenting punishment. She could be so harsh and unfeeling, yet she played the most wonderful music and loved singing. She thought nothing of slapping even the little kids for

116

absolutely no reason whatsoever, yet she could be strangely kind in giving favours and privileges.

She was an excellent tennis player and I couldn't fit that in with the stern, flat figure leading evening prayers. She seemed to pick on me because I was rebellious and answered back, and yet I could feel that somehow I was a pet. She boasted to others about my knitting ability and gave me easier work to do. I don't know, maybe she felt sorry for me because I was so small, or maybe she also felt the pull of that strange thing within me that makes people want to be nice to me. The fact remains that I could never fathom her out. One would never know whether she was going to be nice today and treat you kindly or come down like a ton of bricks for some real or imagined transgression. Perhaps that was her way of controlling us, keeping us in constant uncertainty.

I was drifting off to sleep when a strange, intermittent noise began to echo through the dark silence. Bemused I lay still and listened. Gurgle, slop, gurgle, slosh - muted, wet sounds churned in the darkness. Like interrupted waterfalls, starting and stopping. There was whispering from some of the beds, and all the time this strange liquid chop and gurgle. Cautiously I slipped out from under the blanket and inched over to Belinda's bed. The same noise was coming from her direction. Peering into the murk I whispered.

"Belinda, what are you doing?"

A shadowy figure beckoned me.

"Making butter," she said softly as I clambered on to her bed.

"Making what?"

She showed me her little bottle of milk. She had added salt and like many of the others in the dormitory was shaking and shaking it, churning the milk into butter. In the watery light flickering in from the street lamps I could just discern tiny little blobs in the liquid.

"See? Tomorrow I'll be able to put it on my bread."

I was impressed. This was almost as good as learning to milk cows! After a brief whispered conversation, I crawled back into bed. Orphanage was not a joke and it wasn't a comfortable life, but it was a huge improvement on life with my grandfather. As I thought of him the huge wave of hatred surged through me and engulfed my whole being. I felt tears of resentment, hurt and rejection well up and all the loneliness came flooding through with them. I didn't want the older girls to hear, so I pulled the blanket over my head and pushed my pillow tight against my face until I cried myself to sleep.

CHAPTER ELEVEN

I jolted awake, struggling to breath. My throat was dry and my tongue was sticking to my palate. I felt like something huge was mushing down on my chest. Opening my mouth I tried to call out but there was no voice. The fear fluttering in my stomach thickened into a rising. heaving panic. I couldn't move. Though I was screaming frantically in my head, there was no sound. With incredible effort I dragged my head up off the pillow and there sitting at the end of bed with red, burning eyes fixed evilly on me was a huge black dog. His tongue was lolling out of his mouth and while I stared in horror he pulled his lips back over sharp yellow teeth, spit and slime dripping onto the bedclothes. My breath jerked out in sharp sobs, I still couldn't make a sound. I closed my eyes - maybe it was just a dream. When I opened them again, he was still there, staring fixedly at me. The dog was panting heavily. He shifted his weight and the muscles in his shoulders shivered.

"Amber, what s wrong?"

My panic-stricken sobs must have woken Belinda. I turned my head in desperation and could just make out the shape of her body as she leaned over on one elbow. At last my voice jerked out:

"The dog... the dog..."

Belinda sat up, "What dog?"

I looked back at the foot of the bed. The creature had gone.

Trembling and quivering I tried to explain.

"Belinda it was huge, and it was sitting there slavering and staring at me, its eyes were all bloody."

She gave me a hug, and then smoothing my hair down, made me lie down. Covering me with the blankets she sat next to me till the sobs had died away.

"It was just a nightmare, Amber. You see there's nothing there now. You had a bad dream. Don't worry. Just lie down now and go to sleep. Nothing can get you here anyway, because we're all together."

But every time I closed my eyes I could see the glowing red eyes and the long yellow fangs. Belinda crawled back into bed. I waited till I heard regular breathing and then carefully crept out of bed and tiptoed to Charlene's bed.

"Charl, Charl," I whispered urgently.

She grunted half asleep. I shoved her to make room and slipped in next to her. Mumbling disgruntedly she moved over a bit and fell asleep again. I lay awake for a long time, staring at the ceiling looking at the street light make misshapen shadows on the walls. When I eventually dropped off from utter exhaustion, the birds were just beginning to peep and chirp.

I walked around like a zombie that day. Nervous as a cat. I jumped when people spoke to me. School was sheer hell, because I couldn't concentrate and when the teachers spoke to me I didn't understand what they were on about. When they asked me what was wrong I just stared blankly at them. Their voices seemed to be coming from another planet.

It was the start of the old nightmares again - visions, apparitions, dreams whatever they were. Sometimes my mother would come drifting in to the dormitory and stand by my bed as though she wanted to say something. Other times I would see my grandfather coming after me with a piece of firewood so that he could beat me into the same bloody mess he had made of the cat.

My screams would echo right down into the entrance hall and Dragon would come running. Being yanked out of sleep with such blood curdling yells would set some of the other girls off too, so there would be an ascending chorus of screams, moans and crying that Dragon and some of the seniors would have to calm down.

The first time it happened, Dragon thought I was doing it on purpose. I don't suppose I could really blame her, because I had already established myself as a rebel, who could not be broken with punishment. She came hurtling in to the dormitory, gown flapping and hair sticking out from underneath her night-cap like spikes.

Grabbing me by the shoulders she shook me till my eyes were hitting the bridge of my nose and my teeth were clattering against my forehead.

"Stop that! Amber you stop that right this instant!" she shouted angrily.

When I had managed to swallow the cries and could breathe over the pounding in my chest. I tried to talk. Dragon shone her torch in my face. She must have realised immediately that I was not play-acting. The light blinded me so I couldn't see her face, but her grip on my shoulder relaxed and her voice softened with genuine concern.

"Amber, keep quiet now. It's all right. I'm here. You just had a dream, it's all over now."

I tried to talk, but she hushed me and made me lie down. She told one of the seniors to bring me a glass of water with some sugar in it. She held my head while I drank it. I was still shaking, so she tucked the blankets around me and tried to calm me down. Much later when sleep was eventually making my eyes heavy I turned my head and saw her big, flat figure standing by one of the windows. I think she must have stayed there till I fell asleep. I was quite surprised, it was not what I would have expected from this cold creature, this was just another of the puzzles to add to the mystery of this weird woman.

The following week it was my turn to help saw the wood. We had this big old saw with a handle on either side; it was almost bigger than I was. Belinda showed me how to hold the handle and then shouted at me to begin. It was agony. The wretched thing kept bending and I couldn't control it. I had both hands on the handle and pulled and pushed till my knuckles were white and my fingers cramped. The muscles in my back and arms ached and the wood just refused to let the saw cut into it. I could feel the frustration drive angry tears into my eyes and that made me even more tense and irritated. Belinda was losing patience with my clumsiness. I wanted to scream and kick the thing, and throw it on the ground in fury, break it, but I had to keep trying to saw.

"You better get used to sawing. No one gets off. And if we don't saw, then there's no hot water. That might even still be okay now in summer, but just wait till winter and then see what it's like. You think it's difficult sawing now, wait until winter."

Belinda was heartless and for a while I hated her, but she was also right. There was no excuse, I just had to do it.

I learnt to saw, but it was never easy for me, small as I was.

Belinda hadn't been exaggerating when she spoke of approaching winter either. I will never forget the torment of sawing wood in the winter. Your fingers and hands freeze so that you can't feel them. They go white and even when you press the flesh, there is no red mark to indicate the presence of blood at all. Sometimes it was impossible to hold the saw properly it would slip off the wood or out of your hands. One or two of the girls had some real nasty cuts and bruises from that hideous implement. The wood froze as well and seemed to go as hard as rock. Or it would suddenly roll to the side and fall on your feet. More than a few of us used to be reduced to tears by that job, but I suppose it was better than toilet detail.

The ablution block was way down at the bottom of the garden and the smell was awful. I hated going there, I was always afraid there would be somebody waiting behind the door to grab me so I would never go there alone. And I never ever went there at night. It didn't matter how desperate I got, I would just grit my teeth and wait until morning.

The little ones were also petrified of going down there in the dark, but they didn't have the same will power or resistance as most of us. A lot of them were still very tiny and they often used to wet their beds. Then next morning they would get a hiding.

I couldn't stand to hear them crying. I used to run away where I couldn't hear them any more. It would drive me crazy.

What was the matter with Dragon? Couldn't she realise that no amount of beating was going to make them stop? It was only making them worse, because the fear of the hiding just added to the fear of the dark and increased the pressure on them. I could never understand why Dragon, and adults like her took so much pleasure and spent so much time beating and slapping the kids. It was such a stupid waste. So many of us would have loved her and looked to her for guidance, gone to her for counsel and support. Instead we grew to resent and hate her, distrusting even the times she was kind, because she was so inconsistent in her moods.

Debbie and Grace made up for her a little bit, but I think even they were intimidated by her and we didn't really get to see them much. They were in charge of the kitchen and did all the sewing for the orphanage. Most of their time was spent in the sewing room. They were sisters and emanated a gentleness and softness that was all the more noticeable because of the harshness that cracked out of Dragon. Sometimes I think that she should have been in Germany during those years, she would have made an excellent *SS officer*, or Nazi commander of a concentration camp.

Sometimes so out of the blues, she would do something so unexpected and kind and I would be totally disoriented. I began to think that maybe she had been dropped on her head as a child and it was taking her a long time to recover.

One of the most senior girls there had a long scar on her face. She was very morose and bad-tempered and I used to give her a wide berth. To my surprise, so did Dragon. One day when we passed this girl in the corridor. I nudged Belinda.

"Linda, who is she? Why doesn't she ever smile and why does Dragon avoid her like that?"

Belinda shushed me nervously and looked over her shoulder. When she was sure that we couldn't be overheard, she whispered.

"Audrey is bad news, don't you go near her or annoy her, because she'll flatten you with one hand."

Seeing my sceptical expression, she continued, insistently, "Really Amber, she gave Dragon a beating when she hit her for something."

Now *that* was really incredible! The doubt must have been leaking out from all sides, of the look I gave Belinda.

"It is true Amber, you ask anyone and they'll tell you."

"Did you actually see her beating up Dragon?"

"Well... no, but some of the girls did."

"Who?"

"I'm not too sure," Belinda admitted, "but I know some of them did."

Further enquiry revealed that none of the girls at the orphanage actually witnessed the rumoured beating so I never did find out if it actually took place. It was a fascinating conjecture though and when I was really upset with Dragon I used to picture the scene over and over again, with variations. Sometimes I would be the one slapping her around, but as dreams go, that one didn't actually work too well, because I always had to be standing on a chair or table or something, otherwise I wouldn't even have been able to reach above her waist.

I might not have been able to retaliate physically, but my tongue made up for what I lacked in size. I had a very quick mind and with my razor sharp tongue could deal very effectively with anyone who tried to take advantage of my height, Dragon included. She would stiffen and without blinking an eye would slap me so hard I would go flying. Then the punishment would come.

"Toilet detail, Amber, and bed without supper."

It took her a while, but she learnt that no amount of beating ever had any effect on me. Toilet detail did. Yet I considered the orphanage my home. Of course there were times I would sit and dream, imagining a real home with a mother who loved and cuddled me, silk sheets, caring brothers and sisters, nice clothes, a room all to myself, outings and delicious things to eat. But it was still so much better than life with grandfather. There were no bars or locks on the doors or windows, there was a big garden, I had friends there and at school. To me, running away made no sense at all. Where could one run to? What could you run away from anyway? You always carried yourself and your problems with you.

I remember coming back from school one afternoon to find a police van parked in front of the orphanage. I came to a dead halt. For a sickening flash of recall, I saw the police van in front of my parents' house and the two policemen holding my father down as he struggled on the road before being flung into the van and carted off. I didn't want to go a step further. The girls in the rank behind me had to shove me forward.

"Oh come on, Amber."

They pushed impatiently till I stumbled a few steps forward. With my heart in my mouth I edged through the door and ran up the stairs to the dorm as fast as my shaky legs could pump. There was no one there. I shot out to the senior dorm to find Charlene. No one! Panting and gasping for breath I headed for the study room, Charlene looked up irritably as I clutched the side of the table.

"What is it now Amber? Can't you take things normal like everyone else? Why do you have to treat everything like a drama?"

Her sarcasm hurt, like it always did, burning deep holes into my being.

Wide-eyed I blurted, "But Charl the police are downstairs!"

"So what? Have you murdered someone so that they've come to fetch you?" she sneered.

Then looking up to see the tears of hurt, she softened a bit and grudgingly explained.

"Tracy ran away last night and they've just brought her back."

There was a sombre atmosphere at supper. Tracy wasn't there. She had been locked in the punishment room. We were given a sermon by Dragon about how we should be grateful for the orphanage, about how other kids like us had to go out and earn a living, stay in the streets, die of hunger and so on. It was a dull grinding bore that no one took seriously. Once my senior had come to sit on my bed and talk to me. I can still hear her words and I know how they affected my life. Again I stared at Dragon uncomprehendingly. Why didn't she realise how little it would take to

124

really help us? Couldn't she see that the lecture was not only useless but counter-productive?

I looked round at the girls. Some had obviously switched off.

They had heard the same *fol-de-rol* before. Some pretended to look earnest and contrite, but you could see what was going on behind the mask. Others were openly thinking exactly the same things-

"Stupid Bitch... grateful?... for what?... being slapped around?... half starved?... cleaning toilets and sawing wood?... having to stare at your ugly face every day?" and so on.

The language reflected in the expressions of others was considerably less refined. They were clearly letting Dragon know what they thought of her and what they suggested she do. I wanted to giggle. I knew the laugh was already in my eyes and I struggled to stifle the chuckles. They came out like a snorting cough. I looked down at my plate and quickly shovelled a forkful of something into my mouth.

Dragon had frozen. She glared stonily in my direction.

"Amber, what is that you find so amusing? Kindly share your mirth so that we might all have cause for some hilarity."

Some of the girls were already trying to hide their smiles, pushing food into their mouths, or hiding their faces behind serviettes. I looked at Dragon with all the sweet innocence I could muster and pointed at my mouth, which was decidedly too full to reply.

"We will wait until you have emptied your mouth of that obviously much too large spoonful crammed into it." she sniped contemptuously, but her scorn was lost on the other girls. They were too busy trying to stifle the giggles caused by my brave and manful attempts to chew quickly, while I kept my earnest gaze fixed innocently and as sincerely as possible on the harridan at the head of the table.

Unfortunately I stole a glance at Belinda to see whether she was impressed with my performance. Her face was purple with the effort of not laughing. She caught my eyes as she was drinking water to drown the giggles. It was too much. She spurted into the glass and then all over the tablecloth, coughing and hacking with laughter and fear as she realised all too late what she had unleashed onto herself.

It started a chain reaction. All around the table girls were snorting and laughing, pretending to cough into their napkins, or choke on something. "Dragon" was not amused, I kept my face innocent and sweet, as though I didn't know what they were all on about. But that old broad was not taken in, in the least.

"Order! There will be order! Stop that noise! Calm down and behave yourselves, or you will go to bed without supper for the rest of the week!"

Her voice whipped through the room like a wasp sting. Girls straightened their faces, pursed their lips tight to clip the smiles and stared fixedly at their plates, hands, tablecloth, anything to stop them from looking at either me or Dragon.

"Belinda, you will go straight to the dormitory. Your table manners are disgusting and until such time as they have improved, you will be on kitchen duty."

She turned a baleful glare at me.

"Amber..." she hesitated.

I realised immediately that she had forgotten what she had wanted to get on my case for.

"Yes Mrs Crawford?"

I smiled politely. It was one of the rare occasions that I saw her flustered. She slammed the table with the flat of her hand so that the plates and glasses rattled.

"It's time you girls learned to grow up and behave yourselves! You're acting like a lot of childish little babies with no understanding of the seriousness of life. *Dismissed!*"

She rose angrily to her feet, we hurriedly followed suit, whether our plates were empty or not, and wasted no time getting up to the dormitories.

The laughter that burst out up there was raucous but muted. We didn't want to tempt fate too much. Once again I was the heroine of the hour. I basked in the glory. I felt I could hug myself with delight!

Saturday morning we had to be up just as early as the other days. During the week we had to finish washing, scrubbing and cleaning before we went to school. but on Saturdays it was garden work.

The grounds were big and the work was hard. I quite enjoyed it though. I loved seeing things grow and I used to derive pleasure from digging and sowing and watching things come up. Dragon used to pitch in there with us. The first Saturday I saw her with work clothes and a little spade I was flabbergasted. I would never have thought she would stoop to such menial labour. She never missed a Saturday.

Even when she didn't actually dig and weed with us, she was there to slap us around, just in case we missed her I suppose.

At lunch we put all the tools away, some of the older girls left to go and work at the sport stadium. We sold cold drinks and sweets there to earn a bit of money. The rest of us watched them go with envy and then trudged off to finish the study period.

Saturday evenings were the highlights of the week. We were allowed to stay up later and often "Dragon" would call us to gather around the piano and sing. Some of the girls would write to family or friends. Others would read or sew. There was always a quiet, gentle atmosphere then. I remember those evenings it was as though there were a soft light enfolding us.

Sometimes we would sit down in groups and chat and laugh about all kinds of things. The older girls would tell us about funny incidents that had occurred in the orphanage before we came. Later we would often use this time to plot our next escapade. Occasionally Debbie and Grace would join us and they always brought an added gentleness and lightness.

The little ones would sometimes drop off and the older girls would carry them up to their beds. The rest of us would sit savouring every minute, trying to drag the time out to the last second. The girls in my dormitory tended to fall asleep quickly once they were in bed, so I didn't have long to wait before sneaking out. I was still scared of the dark and most nights I would creep over to Charlene's dormitory and slip into bed with her. Then just as it started to get light, I would tiptoe back to my bed before anyone found I was missing.

Now, several decades later. I'm still afraid of the dark. People say that as you mature, you grow out of your childhood fears and phobias. I didn't. I still dream of my grandfather beating me to a pulp with that bloody piece of firewood. I still smell the toilets and go ice cold with fear at the thought of what is waiting for me behind the door. I still hear the little kids crying from the hidings.

Perhaps one day, when I've written it all out and brought it all out from the bitter depths of hurt, loneliness and rejection, it will start to fade. Perhaps when the last chapter is complete and the book is closed, the door on the past will close too and I'll be able to put the light out at night, and sleep without dreams.

CHAPTER TWELVE

It was a perfect footprint, clearly - and accusingly - marked in soup, the edges only slightly smudged when the foot's owner had bent to clamber through the window. The silence was tense. Dragon stood ram-rod stiff in the pantry where the offending footprint provided damning evidence of unlawful entry. We had to file past the table to behold this proof of our perfidy.

"Thieves!" Dragon had hissed. "Do you know that breaking and entering is a crime that can land you up in *jail*."

Her eyes had burned black and glinted with anger. The tittering in the back rows had been quickly stifled when she stiffened and whiplashed the rows with a razor-like glare.

"It is not a laughing matter."

But it was very difficult for us to take it seriously. Raiding the pantry was an important part of our lives! It was a deliciously dangerous undertaking with hugely satisfying rewards. The successful perpetrators basked in a glow of hero-worship and appreciation for days and every one of us benefited from the proceeds. Even the littlest ones had their share.

Standing there with straight shoulders and earnest gaze, I remember the first time I had found out about the raids and midnight feasts.

I had been woken by loud whispers and somebody bumping my bed. The momentary fear had been quickly dispelled when someone shook my shoulder and shoved something into my hand.

"Here, Amber, wake up - take this."

An apple! Then another figure had come along and dropped a handful of something else on the bedclothes.

"Quickly, take this and put it away somewhere," and the figure had passed on to the next bed. I groped around in the semi-dark and my fingers found a number of little objects. I gingerly picked one up and brought it up to my nose to smell it - heaven! I couldn't believe it - sweet and fruity, slightly rubbery to the touch - dried peaches and apricots as I later found.

What was going on? Sitting up and peering into the murky shadows I whispered the question to Belinda. The answer came through a happily chewing mouth.

"Pantry raid."

My first midnight feast was a wonderful experience. We sat in trepidation of discovery and great excitement at the largesse being distributed. Several of the girls had raided the pantry and the variety of "*merchandise*" made our digestive juices ecstatic! We were very tensed up, giggling nervously and very much afraid that Dragon would erupt into the dorm. But at the same time there was such bubbling delight, such joy at the successful raid, triumph over the locked doors and windows. We couldn't find high enough praise for the intrepid raiders who grinned with great satisfaction and pride.

Donations were made to the orphanage from companies as well as individuals and we had no qualms at all about lightening the weight of these stocks in the pantry. They were ours. We had a right to them. When they weren't given to us, we simply went and took them. And it was such a challenge to find ways past those locks!

This particular night we had orange juice and dried fruit as well as apples and rusks. We gathered on one another's beds and talked in conspiratorial whispers, then as excitement mounted and the party progressed, the volume rose without our realising it. Soon the laughter was ricocheting around the dorm and some of the littler kids were raising their voices to quite a shrill note. A senior shot round the door.

"Shut up you fools, get into bed and shut up, Dragon is coming! Quickly, don't leave any crumbs."

There was panic. I shot into bed like a hunted rabbit. I could hear a lot of thumping and rustling as girls dived for cover and pretended to be asleep. Suddenly the light went on and the excitement and glee collapsed flat and fearful on the ground. There was a heavy silence. Then Dragon spoke. suspiciously and a voice laden with threat.

"What's going on here?"

I lay dead still, the top of my head just poking above the blankets. I was scared, but it was also somehow thrilling. I grinned to myself, because of the goodies I had tucked away under my pillow.

"I said, what's going on here?"

She must have shaken someone, because I heard a sleepy voice mumbling.

"Wha... what...?

As someone pretended to have been woken up. Risking a peep over the blankets I saw a tousled head struggling out from under the bedclothes followed by a pyjama-clad arm.

"Mrs Crawford? What is it?"

Her eyes screwed up convincingly against the light. The girl, I think it was Sheila, shoved the blankets away and stared up at her.

Dragon was not in the least taken in. She was an old hand at the play-acting of the girls. She could see through pretence and strip fibs and deception down to nothing but rickety bones. That is why I used to get so confused with her. I knew she could see through the lies and assumed innocence, then she would disorientate me by pretending to believe them and make like she was taken in. The punishment I expected to be meted out didn't come. Then at other times when I least expected it, her anger would explode and punishment would axe you like a guillotine blade.

She wasn't fooled this time either.

"Every girl out, strip your beds, stand in the middle of the aisle."

My heart dropped from my stomach to my feet. Uh, uh, here comes trouble - big trouble, I thought. Most of us lay there like logs, some frozen with fear of discovery. others pretending they were fast asleep.

A senior stumbled in, her eyes wide....

"Mrs Crawford!" she gasped, "come quickly, one of the little ones is thrashing around, I think she's having a fit."

Dragon grazed her with a very suspicious look, then seeing the expression on her face, started to follow her out. At the door she turned round.

"I want every girl out of bed when I come back. Beds stripped - and in a row in the middle of the dormitory."

She hardly left the room when we burst into action. There was such a flurry of blankets being pulled, goodies being hidden, crumbs brushed away, apple cores turfed out of the window, suffocated giggles and smothered laughs. I was full of admiration for the senior's quick intervention. They knew we wouldn't breathe a word about the raiders but they had come to our rescue anyway.

By the time the little one had "*recovered*" from the "*fit*" we were all standing solemnly in the middle of the dormitory, eyes heavy with sleep, bodies sagging with weariness and bewilderment. Dragon didn't bother to continue with her inspection, she knew she wouldn't find anything now.

"Get into bed, all of you, if anything like this happens again, you will all go to bed without supper for a week."

She stormed out to the accompaniment of huge mirth, winks and triumphant grins. It was quite a long time before they ventured on another raid, but we stored up the goodies to savour a bit every day.

Now we stood there, looking soberly at this soupy footprint. I wanted to laugh. I could picture the culprit picking her way so quietly and carefully over the dim objects in the darkness of the pantry, only to step right into the soup. I could imagine the dismay and annoyance on her face and see how she gingerly pulled her foot out of the bowl. She would have had the goodies down her front and been holding her arms round them so there was no way she would have been able to dry her foot or mop up the soup.

Dragon did not think it was a laughing matter. I stiffened the grin off my face and looked serious again, pulling my face into disapproving shock at the thought of such a wicked crime. Not that that was easy, because my stomach was delightfully full from the cookies and fruit the raid had scored.

Dragon was thoroughly annoyed.

"Own up! Who did it?"

There was no answer, no one moved, she sneered.

"I see, not only thieves, but dishonest too."

That rankled all of us, did she really think we could tell tales on one another? Couldn't she understand the loyalty and the mutual concern that suffused every one of these raids? Never did any girl keep extra goodies back for herself - we shared everything. How could she possibly expect anyone to expose the guilty one?

"No one knows anything then, isn't that right?"

Her voice dripped contempt.

"Very well, single file. Marilyn, bring a chair here please. Each and every one of you will get up on this chair and put your foot in this print. We'll soon see who the thief is."

There was a little shock wave of apprehension. We hadn't expected this and weren't quite sure how to handle it. One by one she marched us up to the table, and then stared intently as we placed our foot squarely on the proof of our guilt. I thought maybe I could wreck the evidence a bit if I accidentally slipped and smudged it, but the soup was beautifully dried and my attempt failed.

Two girls after me, the print found a foot that fitted to perfection. Mrs Crawford smirked triumphantly and moved up to grab the offender. Before she could put a hand on her, a voice spoke up from the rows behind her.

"Mrs Crawford, leave her alone. It wasn't her, it was me."

At that, several other voices spoke up too.

"No it wasn't, she's just trying to protect me, Mrs Crawford. It was really me."

"Don't fib, you know it was me."

"Come on you girls, what is this, you all know I did it."

"Mrs Crawford, they don't know what they're saying, I was the one."

I buried my face into Belinda's back and hugged her as tight as I could to try to drown the laughter. I should have known something like this would happen.

Dragon was a deep red and slowly blotches of white were appearing in her face too. The nerves in her cheeks were twitching and her lips were pulled so straight I thought they would split and fray any second.

"I suppose you think you are being funny?"

Her voice was as cold as an iceberg and just as cutting.

"Everyone of you, come here and line up."

She had them all fit the print - and of course they were all guilty. Dragon had forgotten that we wear regulation shoes that were all donated by the one company, so they were all identical.

When the raider had got back to the dormitory, she had explained the problem and the girls had realised that if everyone with the same size shoe spoke up, Dragon would never find the guilty party. Talk about frustrated fury. All she could do was make them go without supper, but we all contributed something and anyway they had quite a few goodies secreted away from the raid, so it didn't matter.

I was so used to going without food by now that I thought nothing of taking half my supper to them. Charlene was always complaining about how hungry she was, so I used to pretend I wasn't hungry and would give her my food. I also used food to pay other girls to do my washing duty. That was one task I simply couldn't handle. Washing for a hundred kids was no joke. The water was icy, the soap didn't make suds, it was slimy like it was made of fat. I cried more tears into those washtubs than there was water.

After washing about three of the little ones' sheets I would start vomiting. They smelled putrid because of the urine and that rotten stench mixed with awful soap twisted my insides into knots. The water or the soap or both affected my skin, so that after two or three sheets my hands would be split, chapped and bleeding. When I put them in the water they would sting and burn as though the water were boiling. The soap would rot my skin or something because where it split it went yellow white. The flesh inside would go sticky and the pain throbbed down to the bones.

At school I couldn't hold my pen properly so my writing was awful. Sometimes the cuts and sores would break open and ooze yellow, pinkish pus onto the pages. My geography teacher was the first to discover that it was a big mistake to query the stains on the pages. He had circled the yellow marks with a big red ring and punctuated it with a question mark and the words, "Kindly refrain from eating your lunch on your book."

He must have thought his sarcasm very clever, I was deeply hurt and livid with anger.

He handed the books out as usual at the beginning of the lesson, plonking mine down on the desk with a raised eyebrow and a little contemptuous curl of the lip. I had paid no attention, till I saw his remark. Trembling with anger I stood up, in the middle of what he was saying. I stalked up to his desk with my book and slammed it down in front of him.

"I suppose you thought that was a real smooth comment to make?"

He was startled and totally unprepared for my reaction. He didn't know what to say and just stared at me. I banged my hands down on his desk, one facing up, the other down - the cuts and sores were just starting to heal, but some of them still had pus around them.

"There's your lunch - *sir*!" I shouted angrily, "would you care to look."

He looked aghast as he surveyed my hands.

"The soap burns my skin, I'm sorry if I stained your stupid geography book. I will try so hard not to let the washing give me sores and cuts. In future maybe I'll learn to hold the pen with my mouth. Take your book and keep it for all I care."

Leaving him agape, I stormed to my desk, took my books and walked out the classroom. Tears of hurt and bitterness were scoring hot rivulets down my cheeks but I ignored them.

Stupid, stupid, stupid fools. How I hated their snotty ignorance, their *"upper class"* superiority, their snooty pride and scorn.

What did they know of the pain of being *"abnormal"*, unaccepted, always having to fight to be acknowledged as a person, an individual, someone who counted, someone who thought and felt and hurt?

The anguish and loneliness were shouldering painfully deep inside as I left the school grounds and headed for the outskirts of town. When the high barbed wire fence came into view I slowed down and circled the area cautiously till I came to our vantage point.

This was the Italian Prisoner of War camp. No one was allowed near it, but we orphanage girls had soon discovered that if you took a toothbrush with a bit of lead, they would make you a ring. In exchange, we gave them all kinds of articles they couldn't easily get. We had a secret place where we left things and one of the prisoners would saunter casually over and collect them, leaving the rings in their place.

I made friends with this guy, his name was Mario. I would crawl through the grass and lie hidden, close to the fence when they were wandering around the camp in the afternoon. The first time I spoke to Mario he froze. I suppose he must have thought it was a guard or somebody spying on him. But when I kept on whispering for him to come over, he made a conscious effort to relax and then nonchalantly wandered over, pretending to stop and tie his shoelaces while he peered in my direction. He couldn't see me at first, but I saw the strained, anxious expression on his face. It struck me as funny that he should be scared of someone like me, I lifted my head and said, *"Boo!"* he started - then saw me, a huge smile split his face.

Checking to see where the guards were, he straightened up and sauntered over, leaning against the fence as though he were soaking up the afternoon sun.

He was short and had pitch black hair that used to shine with an almost bluish sheen in the sunlight. His English wasn't too good though... we didn't always understand what he was trying to say, but I think he really enjoyed those stolen conversations. I didn't understand why they were kept behind barbed wire, but when I asked him, his explanation was so garbled that I was more confused when he had finished than I had been before he began. To me though, it seemed clear that they were being punished for something they didn't do, or had been forced to do against their will. I think that if I had ever been able to get my hands on some wire cutters, I would have set them all free.

I used to wonder whether my father was perhaps also behind barbed wire somewhere. Maybe that was why he never came to look for us. The thought plagued and *harried* me, so I tried desperately to think of other things to drive the picture of him behind barbed wire out of my head.

I lay in the grass and surveyed the camp; it was deserted. Being midmorning, the prisoners were probably still all out working. They were hired to neighbouring farmers who fetched them in lorries and brought them back in the afternoon.

Miserable and alone, I rolled over on to my back and stared up at the sky. The clouds were such an immense distance away and moving majestically, slowly changing shape as they drifted. One was a massive tree with spreading branches that dripped fruit, and gradually it became a horse with tapered legs and outstretched wings. Over there a formless blob blossomed into a gigantic rose with droopy petals. Little birds with spiky wings darted across the sky in amazing swoops, veering with breath-catching suddenness from west to east and sometimes dropping like stones before suddenly sweeping up into the sky again. Their beauty made something catch in my throat and I could feel the hot tears pricking my eyelids again.

Life could be so simple and so beautiful. I couldn't understand why people made it so complicated and so ugly. I started to talk to God about it. I didn't for one moment believe that you could only talk to Him in church. I've always spoken to him very freely and openly and I think He much prefers that sincerity to the fancy, hypocritical prayers couched in special voices and religious tones that people pray to impress others with. I don't believe he worries too much whether you're kneeling or standing or whatever you're doing. Nor do I think He cares whether you are wearing long robes and dangling incense around. I remember having to learn some Bible pages for punishment once, and the words there said that the sacrifices He wanted were a broken spirit and contrite heart. Well I certainly had that to give Him and He knew I wasn't pretending.

I trusted and loved Him in my own way. That doesn't mean I didn't give up on Him, because sometimes I did. When things were really black and miserable I started to believe that He didn't care about me at all, maybe He wasn't even listening, maybe He had forgotten me. That is when the darkness really closed in on me. Through all the heartache and suffering I had experienced, He had somehow always been there with me. I knew He was. I knew He was comforting me, so when I thought it was no good believing and no good praying, the whole world became totally meaningless. We had come back from church that one particular Sunday and I felt dead, grey and dried up inside. I could see my senior giving me funny looks, so I tried to act normal, but I simply couldn't find the energy. It was like life, light, hope - everything had drained away into the dust. I had sat in church trying to believe, they sang, I sang, but it meant nothing.

They prayed, I listened, but it was senseless and hollow. I went to the study room and tried to read, but the words were empty black blocks that jiggled in the light. I ended up staring sightlessly out the window and just letting thoughts mill about uselessly and disjointedly in my head. There was such an emptiness in me.

"Hello, Amber."

My senior was standing there holding out a glass of orange juice. I shook my head tiredly. Other girls were opening up parcels received from family or friends, reading letters, showing friends what they had been sent. No one sent me letters or parcels - not even my elder sisters and brothers. I obviously didn't exist in their lives any more either.

"Can I sit here with you?"

I shrugged non-committal.

"Don't give up Amber."

I looked at her dully.

"You know, when life gets particularly hard and unbearable it's because things are just about to change for the better."

That didn't make any sense to me at all. My life had always been hard and unbearable and the only changes there had ever been had brought even more misery. But it seemed just too much effort to talk and refute the statement. I sat there and stared blankly out the window.

"You think you're alone, Amber, but even when people aren't around you, God never deserts you."

Something lurched inside me - dear Lord, how much I wanted to believe that. But where was He now? I felt so bitterly and desperately alone and life was so utterly pointless.

"It's like walking with a friend, and when you look behind you see two sets of footprints," she smiled encouragingly, "and now you look behind yourself and you can only see one. Isn't that how you are feeling now, abandoned, lost, alone?"

Her words were like sharp sticks, I didn't want to look at her.

"Do you know what it means when you see only one set of footprints like that?"

Of course I knew... that's why I was in such unutterable darkness. Who cared about me? What difference would it make if I lived or died? There was just no purpose or meaning to life at all. But trying to put that understanding in words was so difficult.

"Amber, are you listening to me, are you hearing me? Look at me." She put her hand under my chin and turned my face towards hers. "When you see only one set of footprints behind you like that, it is because Jesus has picked you up. Those footprints are His, He's carrying your weight, Amber."

The tears welled up and brimmed over, could that really be true? Deep, deep inside myself I knew it was, but I was scared to really grasp hold of it and believe it.

As I lay there in the grass, I remembered those words and a quiet peace came flooding over me. I rolled over and resting my head on my hands let my gaze wander idly through the grass and over the ground. Tiny little flowers were scattered haphazardly between the stalks. They were so minute no one would ever see them unless they were lying down flat in the grass like me. So dainty and so fragile, they were exquisitely made and I was fascinated. Then a thought came from nowhere - what is the point of these flowers if no one can see them? Somehow I knew the answer, and I knew it applied to me too. They were there because they mattered. They were there because they had a unique beauty. They were there because God had made them and delighted in them. I felt overwhelmed.

A tiny movement caught my eye. The creature was flimsy and delicate that if I had breathed hard on it I'm sure I would have mashed it to nothing. Pale, pale green and almost transparent, it was carefully working its way up a stalk of grass. But the little hairs on that stalk must have looked like trees to it. Entranced, I let the dainty spectacle enthral me with its grace and fragility.

I had to learn the *"Beatitudes"* etcetera for punishment, so like most of things learnt that way, it was just a mindless chain of words strung together and rattled off by heart. But now some of those words came back, sonorous, golden, full of meaning.

"Consider the lilies of the field. How they grow... even Solomon in all his glory was not arrayed like one of these. Wherefore if God so clothe the grass of the field, which today is and tomorrow is cast into the oven, shall he not much more clothe you?....

Blessed are the poor in spirit, for theirs is the kingdom of heaven... Blessed are they that mourn, for they shall be comforted... Blessed are the pure in heart, for they shall see God..."

The little creature stretched its filigree wings and dipped between the stems of the grass. There was such a calm quietness in and around me. I sat up slowly and looped around. It felt like hours had passed but it wasn't midday yet. I could make it back to the orphanage and Dragon would never know that I had been gone.

CHAPTER THIRTEEN

The boys' orphanage was on the other side of the common that stretched between us. A huge rock stuck awkwardly out in the centre of the field that was patched with untidy, straggly clumps of yellowing grass and scrubby brown brushes. I was standing on the balcony one afternoon after study period when to my surprise I thought I saw a figure creeping cautiously toward the rock. It was making best use of all available bushes to hide - not very successfully I thought. Painstakingly, the figure picked its way to the rock. I leaned as far over the balcony as I dared, straining my eyes to make out what the figure was doing. I thought it was someone from the boy's orphanage, but I couldn't imagine what he was doing trafficking around the rock. It seemed to me he was scrabbling and digging in some hole on the other side of the rock, but the granite mass obscured him too effectively for me to be sure.

After a while he backed away from the rock. looked up at our building and with two fingers in his mouth gave a piercing whistle. For a while he stood motionless, scanning the windows, then he waved, pointed at the base of the rock and then quickly scuttled back to the boys' orphanage.

Intrigued, I craned my neck to see if there was anyone at the windows, but the angle was wrong and all I saw was the sun's reflection. I wanted to run down to the rock to see what the boy had been doing. While I was debating with myself whether it would be more prudent to stay where I was and see what happened next, a figure eased itself through our hedge and hurried down to the rock. While I watched in fascination, I saw the girl dig around the same area where the boy had been. As she turned to look towards our orphanage she was quickly cramming objects down her front. Then as swiftly and silently as she had came she slipped back through the hedge and disappeared out of sight.

"Ah ha!" I thought, "private postal system!"

So we were not as isolated as I had originally presumed. Separate boys and girls schools, separate orphanages and even separate blocks in church - it looked as though they were afraid that if we ever communicated with the boys we would organise a revolt and overthrow them. I often wonder today what they were scared of.

Scampering downstairs. I went looking for Belinda. She knew all the ropes - but I couldn't find her anywhere. Eventually, just before supper I tracked her down in a giggling huddle of girls near the storeroom. They were reading letters, occasionally repeating choice bits loud for the benefit of others, chewing sweets and other goodies and examining other objects I couldn't see.

"Hi Amber," Belinda waved joyously. "Come see what Henry sent!"

Her face was flushed and happy as she showed me a tiny little tin with about a dozen boiled sweets in it. She clutched a note in her hand and when I peered curiously at it, she stuck it jealously down her front. Just then one of the others shrieked, pressed her letter tightly to her chest and hunching up her shoulders in ecstasy said with a trembling but excited voice,

"It's Philip's turn for bugle tonight - he's playing for me!"

Her eyes were closed and there was a really soppy smile on her face. I gaped at her uncomprehendingly. Belinda laughed at my face.

"Oh come on Amber, can't you see she's in love?"

"What does she mean he is on bugle?" I asked.

"The boys have a bugle before lights out, like we have a bell. Philip's her boyfriend, he's on bugle tonight. So, when he plays, he will be playing for her and thinking of her. Isn't that fantastic?"

Belinda looked enviously over to where the girl was swooning and murmuring blissfully to herself.

This was a new scene to me and it took me a while to figure my way round it. I had never been interested in boys, mainly I suppose because I was too young, but also because I was more occupied with surviving, fighting my grandfather, fighting the bullies, fighting the teachers, fighting kids my age who tried to take advantage of my size, trying to assert my right to live, to be counted and to be respected. When this was no longer the primary and priority preoccupation of my life, I began to realise that I had time for other things too.

On closer examination of this new issue though, I grew to think it was a really nice perspective on our life. When the bugle's peal echoed across the common that night I thought of the lucky girl, lying in her bed dreaming of her boyfriend. I warmed inside, how tremendous to know somebody that had a special place in his heart for you, somebody to whom you really meant something. It was a new and almost awesome thought for me. It must be really wonderful to have someone play the bugle for you like that. What a precious thing to have somebody that belonged to you. I wondered sadly and a little hopelessly if anyone would ever care enough for me to send me letters and play tunes for me across the common.

Even at church they tried to keep us segregated from the boys, but that is where we discovered anew, what a magnificent book the Bible was. Passing it piously and reverently from one to another, we surreptitiously slipped in the letters that were being forwarded to the boyfriends in the next rows. Exchanging Bibles in the church ground was another favourite method of sending letters, so the good book was constantly put to good use.

But even though they kept us physically apart as much as possible, there was no way they could inhibit the oneness that came from a shared way of living, the unity and compassion that came from suffering and hurt, the understanding and longing for affection that were the fruit of rejection and loneliness. Those things brought us together like nothing else could. We sang alto and soprano spontaneously and instinctively to the boys' tenor and bass - no one had ever trained us. It simply flowed from a natural response to the music and the emotions within us.

They sat us in different galleries - the boys on one side and we girls on the other, but they couldn't stop our voices blending in the hymns, nor the reaching out and touching that took place through the songs as our souls and spirits yearned and soared on the notes. We gave ourselves completely to that singing. We didn't even notice the congregation, we sang to one another with such intensity and longing that often the congregation would fall silent, and just listen. It was our hurt and pain that we sang, our longings, the hopes and joys. Our hearts flooded into those melodies with an intimacy that made people weep. As we sang, our beings touched, we were holding one another's hands, talking to one another, crying with one another and longing for the happiness and freedom that no one could give.

The beauty of our singing filled that church with probably the only real love and compassion that it has ever known. Lost lives. trampled souls, emotions battered and mocked, even bodies that were marked with pain and suffering rose up whole, believing full of hope and faith as the notes echoed like bells, like ringing crystal or muted mountain springs around the cold stone walls. Glory came to us for a few moments of golden joy.

I'll never forget the day the old lady in the right hand aisle forgot herself. The climax of the song had trembled in the tense atmosphere as the congregation held its breath in awe, then had quietly faded away to a poignant silence. Overwhelmed, the old biddy had gasped, cheered and started clapping enthusiastically, her hat bobbing and jerking to the energy of her applause. The solitary clapping had echoed loudly and then increasingly self-consciously in the gathering disapproval of the very traditional congregation, slowly it had faltered and then lamely it had stopped as the lady realised where she was. With a face glowing almost purple with embarrassment she had cleared her throat, shuffled her books, dug in her handbag, looked distractedly to the right, left and in front, while people made a discreet space around her. We started nudging one another and tittering about the old lady's discomfort. The preacher was delightfully disconcerted. He had to stare at the raised eyebrows, sidelong looks, remonstrative glares and even indignant faces of the stuffy congregation, and cope with our obvious hilarity as we enjoyed the scene. And he couldn't exactly shout: "Order, sit down and shut up!" like the teachers or Dragon did either.

The unease and restlessness presented a perfect opportunity for the bombing raid. Little balls of peanut butter, raided from the big tins in the storeroom, spheres of paper and other objects were shot with unerring aim at the more unpopular targets down below. I use to love getting the peanut butter in the "fruit and vegetable" hats that were such a source of irritation to me. Women came to church all dolled up to the nines, feathers nodding as they inclined their heads to one another. I found it such a hypocritical farce that I took great delight in poking holes through the masks with blobs of peanut butter. Because that is about how flimsy those social masks were, one little peanut butter ball would tear the whole structure apart.

It was impossible to see who the culprits were. The ammunition appeared in the air from nowhere, splattered on the target from directions impossible to determine. Of course we all sat there in cherubic innocence, appalled at the very hint of accusation and censure which could be raised against us. Neither were we the only ones to use the church congregation for target practice. The "normal" kids would often sit together in their Sunday school classes and they were certainly not adverse to joining in the fun.

"It's not fair! Why are we always blamed for this?"

I argued once when the preacher had kept all us orphanage kids behind after church to give us what he called "a good Christian talking-to." He blanched at such disrespect, he was not used to children answering his holy remonstrances with denial and aggression.

"Who said that?" his eyebrows were arched in horror and his fingers pressed tightly against each other.

I stood up indignantly.

"I did, but it doesn't make any difference who says it, we all think it and we all know it's true. If anything goes wrong, it's always us orphanage kids who are blamed. Why do you all automatically think we are guilty? Do you think the other kids are all innocent little angels? It's like you're trying to make criminals out of us."

There was a chorus of assent and comment from the rest of the children, boys and girls.

"Who said that? Stand up!" the preacher demanded insistently. I sighed and started moving out of the row towards the aisle.

"I'm standing up." I explained in disgust. "You're just not tall enough to see me."

No way was I going to say I was too small... inside I was taller than him anyway.

Somewhat abashed, he cleared his throat and scratched around for something to say.

"Well... ah... well, yes, but you must admit in all fairness and honesty, that in ninety-nine cases out of a hundred, you are the ones to blame..."

And he glared defensively at us. The protest, cries of denial and shouts of scorn drowned out any further comment. The preacher was out of his depth now. He was accustomed only to respectful *yes sir, no sir, three bags full sir,* replies from the po-faced kids who didn't dare say what they thought or felt. He fluttered his hands at us helplessly, looking desperate as he tried to calm us down.

Nobody could hear what he was saying, we were all protesting and complaining too loudly, thoroughly enjoying it as we edged one another on. Then in the midst of the fun, Dragon's icy voice cut through the racket like a pick-axe.

"What on earth is going on here? Keep quiet!"

The silence was so sudden the preacher was totally disoriented. Now I started to feel sorry for him, because Dragon was frizzling him up with a contemptuous glare that said: "Incompetent old nincompoop..." among even less complimentary expression. Without even thinking, I piped up.

"Mrs Crawford, we were all just agreeing with the preacher's wonderful idea of having a choir of boys and girls to sing for the church. We got excited about it and maybe we got carried away and made too much noise."

The preacher stared at me in utter disbelief and was about to start waving his hands in denial when a thought apparently struck him. He hesitated, stroked the side of his chin reflectively and then a funny crooked little grin twisted his mouth up his cheeks. He looked almost shyly up at Dragon and queried.

"Well, it is quite a promising suggestion, don't you think?"

I turned round to look at the other kids. Faces were lit up, some gaping in amazement and nudging one another, everyone realised the potential in such a magnificent idea. Freedom! Opportunities to bunk out during choir practice, hours away form the orphanage, a chance to meet with our boyfriends, the opportunity to learn new songs and maybe even more than that - to be admired, respected and acknowledged by others.

There was an outburst of comment as everyone tried to shout out their opinions. The preacher smiled a huge smile and Dragon was taken aback - it was obviously not what she had been expecting and she wasn't quite sure whether she had been wound up or not. She gave me a long suspicious look, shook her head ever so slightly to herself in doubt and then reluctantly agreed with the preacher.

"Well, I'm sure that something could be arranged, Mr Pigott and I could discuss it with our staff and see what times could be suitable.

When we got outside the girls flocked around me, thumping my back with glee, hugging me in delight and telling me what a brilliant idea it had been. The approval and congratulations for the boys were even more satisfying! I went back to the orphanage thoroughly pleased with myself. More than one of the boys had noticed me for the first time and I was thrilled when there were two letters for me from the rock postal system a few days later.

I was transferred to the senior dormitory when the school moved me from standard five to standard six. The lights from the hotel shone in through the windows, so the dark wasn't so bad. Just as well, because Charlene had left the orphanage, so I could no longer run to her for comfort when the fear of darkness started to press in on me. Like my other sister and brothers she didn't once bother to visit or contact me after she had left. She simply disappeared out of my life.

It hurt I suppose, but it was another of those pains I could do nothing with except push it down as deep as it would go and just refuse to think about it anymore. Fortunately I had a lot of friends at school, both from the orphanage as well as from "outside", yet I could always feel that invisible barrier in me. I could make friends just up to a point, beyond that line, no one could come. From time to time I would let my thoughts drift back to the friends I had at primary school and wonder what had become of them. Then with a typical cynicism I would shrug my shoulders to myself and sigh, they probably wouldn't want anything to do with me any more. So it was all the more wonderful when one of them suddenly and unexpectedly appeared from the past and was as close to me as she had been before.

When I heard my name called, at first I didn't want to believe it could be true...

"Amber! Amber!"

I spun around; I knew that voice! Rita was running towards me, waving excitedly. I couldn't believe it, what on earth was she doing at our school? I grabbed her arm.

"Rita? Rita! Are you staying here now? Where's Rebecca, is she also here?"

"We've moved! We've come to live here. My Mom's bought a cafe so we've all come to stay here."

We babbled on almost incoherently getting up to date with each other's news, both talking at the same time. She had been out in my class and being a new girl, had to sit in the front, right next to me.

I was so happy, but strangely, seeing her again made a lot of ugly shadows loom up heavily out of somewhere deep inside me. She had been there when my grandfather had massacred the cat. She knew about my aunt's death, about the typhoid epidemic. In a way it was very strange to see her again, it was like another life suddenly reappearing in all its ugly hatred and pain.

It was then I began to realise how much I had changed in the orphanage, but also how very deeply all those memories and hurts had been pushed down. They hadn't just been forgotten. Time hadn't "healed" them either. They had just laid low awaiting the opportunity to surface with their torment and despair.

Rita's Mom came to see Dragon to get permission for me to go and help out at the cafe. I was one of the few in the orphanage who received no parcels from "outside". Dragon kept envelopes for each one of us. This is where she kept money that was sent to us or any money that we made, working part time. She actually favoured those who had no family by allowing them to go to work at the sports stadium or on the berry farms so that they could earn some pocket money. When we needed something personal, she would let us take money from those envelopes. The rest of the money was kept for holidays.

My envelope had always been empty. At first it used to hurt me that others would get letters and parcels from family and friends while I had nothing. With time I got over the hurt. My first boyfriend soon found out that I had no one "outside" who cared for me, so he often used to send me money by "rock post".

Dragon called me to the office. I spent the minutes from the dormitory to her office frenziedly running over all the latest escapades, letter deliveries, raids and school revolts, wondering which had been discovered or reported and frantically finding excuses and justifications for all of them.

She smiled as I stood in front of her desk and at first I looked over my shoulder in surprise to see who she was smiling at. The reaction dented her expression a bit and put some testiness in her voice, but she was obviously trying to be nice. I think what really amazed me was the fact that underneath, she seemed genuinely pleased that someone had invited me.

"Amber, Mrs Joubert apparently knows you from the time you were staying with your grandfather."

I glowered at the mention of that monster. After lifting her eyebrows slightly at my reaction. Dragon continued.

"She says you and her daughter are good friends and has asked whether you can go and help her work at the shop this weekend."

I had hoped desperately that this was coming, because Rita and I had planned it and then asked her Mom to go and see Dragon. It was exciting, and I could feel my heart thumping quicker. Dragon leaned back a little in her chair and smiled again. For a second time, the flutter of surprise whispered in my chest, because I picked up genuine pleasure in her for this opportunity. When would I ever be able to

figure this female out? Clasping her hands on the desk in front of her,
Dragon asked.

"Well, what do you say to that? Would you like to go?"

I was afraid to look too eager in case Dragon then perversely
refused permission, but there was no way I could mask the desire in
my eyes and in my voice.

"Oh yes, Mrs Crawford, please. I would like so much to go!"

There was a strange softening in that big-boned face and she
nodded.

"Very well then, I'll tell Mrs Joubert that she can come and pick
you up on Friday evening and deliver you back on Sunday evening in
time for church. You do realise of course, that this is a working
weekend? You are not going there to play and fool around, I will
expect you to hand your wages over when you return, and of course
you will be scrupulously honest about it, since I do have to agree with
Mrs Joubert on the amount you will work for. Can't have our girls
being exploited now, can we?"

This was a typical two-edged Dragon kind of statement, it tended
to make you uncertain whether she was really concerned about your
well being or whether she was just poking warnings at you with her
sarcastic jibes.

Mrs Joubert came to fetch me before supper on Friday. It was
weird to walk into a normal house again, to sit at such a small table,
to sleep in such a small bedroom. I half waited for the bell to go to
signal "lights out" and was awake automatically a few seconds before
the "wake up" bell was due to ring. I lay quietly for a while, lost in
the unfamiliar surroundings, then as the memory seeped in I turned
over and drifted blissfully off to sleep until Mrs Joubert woke Rita and
me with a steaming cup of hot chocolate.

The "work" at the cafe had only been an excuse, we played at the
back of the cafe and had a glorious time. We would of course help
out where and when we could, but I think we were probably more of a
hindrance than a help on those occasions.

On the way back to the orphanage on Sunday, Mrs Joubert gave
me an envelope.

"There we are Amber, that's your pay!" she laughed, "Make sure
you give it to Mrs Crawford."

I was upset...

"But I haven't worked. I haven't earned this money, I can't take this from you!" I cried in dismay.

"Don't be silly!" she teased. "Do you want Mrs Crawford to say you can't come next time I ask?"

I was torn between feeling bad at taking money in addition to the wonderful time I had and the fear of not being able to come again. Rita added her pleas.

"Oh, come on, Amber. If you don't give her your pay, then she'll know that you didn't do any work and you'll get into trouble and so will we."

The thought of Mrs Joubert getting into hot water with Dragon settled it. I gave Mrs Joubert a big, tight hug when I got out of the car and told her that someday I would find a way to earn it all. I noticed she had tears in her eyes when she waved good-bye, but wasn't quite sure what I had done, I just hoped fervently that I hadn't upset her so much she wouldn't ask me out again.

The weekends and sometimes Saturday afternoons I spent with that family were wonderful splashes of freedom and light in the monotony of orphanage life, work, tasks, duties, shifts and study. If only it could have lasted, but a year or so later, they sold the cafe and moved away. We lost touch and I never saw them again.

It was during the early weeks of the first term that the first social was held. The girls were all very excited and worked up about it. Dragon had announced the date one evening before supper and there had been such a sudden buzz and noise in response that she had to wait a while before she could give details.

"As usual," she had intoned in the special voice she kept for official announcements, "you will be escorted there and chaperoned. The social will last until ten-thirty and you will be escorted back. Any misdemeanour will be severely punished."

She swept a warning gaze over our heads like a scythe mowing grass.

"You all know perfectly well what I am referring to and I stress that I will not tolerate any wanton behaviour."

Her icy voice severed the titters like a scalpel.

"You will at all times remain within the hall, and if you need to answer a call of nature, you will approach the chaperon and inform her where you are going. You will report back to her upon your return, is that understood?"

"Yes Mrs Crawford!"

The obedient chorus rose from angelic looking girls, trying to appear submissive, sweet and willing, not with too much success.

There was wild activity during the intervening period, Debbie and Grace were subjected to all kinds of manipulations and pleas, sweet-talk and promises. Those who could sew, begged them for needle, thread, material or patterns. Those who couldn't tried to weedle alterations or new clothes. Some of the girls took money from their envelopes to buy odds and bits, everything from make-up to ribbons and scent.

I was just a spectator for this first social, since I was considered still too young, having only just turned thirteen, but I remember it all so vividly. The atmosphere was electric, the girls were light-hearted and full of enthusiasm and anticipation. The social started at seven, but they all started getting ready, primping and preening themselves early in the afternoon. I was swept up in the general fun, helping here, giving a hand there. When the chaperon finally summoned them to the door they had undergone a phenomenal transformation. I was really impressed.

They all looked so much older than in their school uniforms, and some of them were already behaving differently, giving themselves such airs and graces that I burst out laughing, much to their annoyance.

They trooped out in the usual files, wafting perfume and powder scents in their train, looking like a flock of multi-coloured butterflies.

We all sat up and waited for them to come back, just as excited as they were and not a little envious. They buzzed in just before eleven, sparkling - effervescing even with happiness, with the lilt of the music, the joy of the dancing and intimacy of chatting with boyfriends, the warm ecstasy of holding hands and the thrill of the stolen kisses.

I became increasingly tense as midnight approached, expecting Dragon to burst in through the door with gown flapping, dishing out punishment and ruining the starry evening. To my surprise there was no sign of her, not even when the girls were laughing at the tops of their voices as they re-hashed the evening's events, bouncing on one another's beds as they cradled themselves in delight over some incident or another.

It was late, or rather early morning before exhaustion finally took its toll and the girls finally fell asleep. I lay awake a little while longer, imagining what it must have been like and wondering whether anyone would ask me to dance when I went to my first social.

CHAPTER FOURTEEN

The storeroom was in the garden and was always kept carefully locked and bolted. The bulky tins and sacks were kept there because there was no room for them in the kitchen pantry, oats, mielie meal, brown sugar and on occasions fruit.

I was doing some extra time in the study room when Belinda came shooting in at the door. Her eyes darted all over the room looking for me, then she came hurtling down the aisle, hair frizzed out and eyes sparkling.

"There's a lorry downstairs and they're off loading all kinds of stuff into the storeroom, come look, *quickly* She was tugging at my sleeve urgently, so I shot out with her to go and survey the operation.

We joined a couple of other girls who were already crouched down at the corner of the building, talking to one another in whispers.

"What are they bringing?" I queried peering over someone's shoulders.

"Looks like peanut butter, maybe jam. Bags of stuff, that could be walking sugar. There's oats too by the looks of things."

Some big concern often donated big bags of thick, molasses - heavy brown sugar that "walked". When you ladled it out from the big bags into bottles and tins for the pantry, it seemed alive, the way the grains heaved and settled. We considered a raid hugely successful if we could procure oats and walking sugar. The treacly sugar mixed with the raw oats was a taste sensation we considered scrumptious. Peanut butter was another favourite. Rolled into little balls it served as ammunition as well as appetiser.

Watching the tins and bags being off loaded, we let our digestive juices decide then and there that evening was the ideal occasion for a raid.

Word spread quickly, everyone loved a raid. The adventure of getting out of the dormitory and the orphanage unseen and unheard, the challenge of getting past the locks and bolts and then returning without detection were temptations far too strong to resist, not that we ever tried!

I was in on this one and loved every second, as frightening as it was from start to finish. The shadows all seemed alive to me and I kept startling and bumping into whoever was closest. My heart was thudding so fast and loud I could feel it in my throat and ears. I had to suck my breath past this thick pounding to get air into my lungs so I was gasping as though I had been running for miles. My knees were shaky and my hands were trembling, but as the action really started, I forgot about the fear, and the exhilaration of the escapade took over.

One of the seniors was an expert lock-picker. She was included on almost every raid because of her expertise. We crouched tensely in the darkness behind her as she patiently probed into the lock and then the keyhole. At last she pushed the door open and we slipped in like shadows. Knotting our pyjamas at the bottom, we started to stock up - oats, sugar, peanut butter, rusks, dried milk - it was a tremendous haul. We couldn't see what all the stuff was because it was pitch black in there, but going by feel, we managed to identify most of the goods.

I pried a tin open to find the oats. Almost yodelling with delight I began filling up the pillow slip I had brought. Someone whispered my name urgently.

"Give me the bottles, Amber, I've found the peanut butter."

I carefully pulled the bottles out and handed them over to the groping hands.

There was a stuffy, half-sweet smell in the storeroom. The shuffling and whispering was muffled in the bank room and the air was thick with tension tinged with sparks of fear. I couldn't see much, but I could feel the movements of the other girls and I was very much aware of the girl standing at the door keeping watch. Her silhouette was outlined against the opening and I kept shooting glances in her direction to make sure she was still there.

When we had as much as we could carry, we closed everything up, hopefully as we had found it, and one by one eased ourselves out into the blackness outside. My pillow slip was cumbersome and awkward. I had made it a bit too full and it was difficult to get a proper grip on the thing, but I gamely lugged it as far as the stairs. There milling hands from inside took over and we all tiptoed silently upstairs. Look-outs had been posted at the top of the stairs and at the door of the dormitory and they passed the word as they saw us coming.

It was always so difficult to keep our voices down after a successful raid. The relief and thrill of achievement were so great we wanted to scream and shout and sing at the top of our voices. Instead we had to laugh and talk in hushed whispers.

Everyone got a share of the goodies - even the littlest ones. It was so funny waking them up at night for our midnight feasts, because they were so confused and disorientated being woken up in the dark. Some of them would drop back off to sleep with their mouths still full and we would have to shake them awake and make them eat and swallow before their eyes shut again.

The bounty was especially precious to me, I secreted a lot of my share away to use as barter. It would pay some girls to do washing duty for me. A portion would be used as exchange for toiletries or other items that some girls received in parcels from outside.

However, the greatest enjoyment from the raid would come only days and sometimes weeks later. That is when supplies would be fetched from the storeroom and a bemused Grace or Debbie would report to Dragon that although the door had been locked and bolted, some of the tins and sacks had been tampered with and goods were obviously missing. Then there would be a crackdown, with Dragon supervising searches of our beds, lockers and other private property. But by then of course it was far too late, the food had long since been eaten.

We would stand by looking indignant or hurt and innocent while the search was being conducted. All of us were highly adept at assuming all kinds of expressions to fit the circumstances. Then when she came up with nothing, Dragon would get very strict about the observance of rules and regulations until she had worked out her anger and frustration. We were expecting that and walked round on tippy toes for a few days, smiling at her discomfort while being perfectly obedient.

It was round about this time that I discovered that knitting was a door to privilege and greater freedom. Lots of the girls would sew and knit on Saturdays while others wrote letters, read books or just sat and chatted. Soon after I arrived at the orphanage, I would sit with one of the seniors and wind her wool for her, because I had no one to write letters to and by Saturday had generally finished all the books I had. I watched her knit and thought,

"Well, that looks quite easy, I'm sure I can do it."

I borrowed some needles and a bit of wool from her and by imitating, taught myself to knit. At first it was very simple things, like making doll dresses and booties, but I quickly learnt how to read patterns and it wasn't long before I was one of the fastest and best knitters in the orphanage.

As with all things in our little community, my fame as a knitter spread quickly and among the first to hear of it was Dragon. She would wander around from one girl to another on Saturdays, looking to see what they were doing sometimes just clouting someone across the ear. I suppose because her adrenaline level was low and it gave her a boost. This one Saturday she stood behind me for a while before I became aware of her. I only noticed something was odd because I caught a few of the girls shooting cautionary glances at me and indicating with their eyes. When I turned round she was peering down from her bony height, watching every stitch with her gimlet eyes.

"Why Amber, you are very dextrous, let me see what you are doing."

She held the knitting at a distance and then brought it close up and inspected it like she was looking for fleas. Then she took a deep breath full of satisfaction.

"Well! I see you are all very even, how long have you been knitting?"

She looked surprised when I told her and then beckoned me to follow her. A bit warily I trotted behind her to the sewing room where she rummaged about in one of the drawers and came up holding a dress pattern. Adjusting her glasses, she looked carefully at the size and knitting instructions, drawing her finger down the schedule of sizes on the back of the pattern till she found what she was looking for. Then going to the cupboard, she pulled out the correct needles and handed them to me with the pattern.

"Here, do you think you would be able to knit this dress? It's not a complicated pattern and you can come and fetch the wool from my office tomorrow afternoon."

I glanced briefly at the pattern and knew that I could do it without any hassle, but wasn't going to let Dragon know that. I assumed a doubtful, hesitant expression.

"I don't know, Mrs Crawford," pursing my mouth. I frowned and shifted from one foot to another. It wasn't as if she had exactly given me much option. I thought to myself. "Well, make up your mind, take it with you tonight and have a good look and then come and fetch the wool tomorrow."

I wasn't quite sure about this knitting business, what if it didn't come up to her standard? I didn't fancy the thought of an irate Dragon taking her disappointment out on me. She had a very inventive mind and I didn't relish some of the solutions she had already come up with on the rebellious and recalcitrant. And when would I find the time to knit?

That is when I started to see the shimmering of a whole host of new opportunities. If she wanted me to knit her a dress, she was going to have to make time for me somehow, because even Dragon couldn't expect me to fit it in to the busy orphanage schedule. Which meant that she would have to dispense me of some duties.

And if I didn't let on how quickly I could knit then maybe I could even wangle a lot of extra free time... This was beginning to look more promising, so the following afternoon I duly presented myself at her office door.

As usual, it was ajar. I saw myself in the mirror, still tiny, but rather petite than just small now, a neat, trim little figure in perfect proportions and as usual impeccably dressed and groomed. I was very particular about my personal cleanliness and neatness. At night I would carefully spread my school tunic under the mattress so that it would look perfectly ironed next morning. I was invariably the best turned out girl in the orphanage and took pride in the fact too. My hair had grown longer now and framed a little pixie face with big eyes that could look very appealing when I chose, or become huge and baleful when I chose not. Few people could sustain that glare for long and I didn't hesitate to make use of it when the need arose.

I had hardly raised my hand to knock when her voice called. "Come in!"

To my surprise I found her in the lounge with my chemistry teacher. Both of them were wearing tennis togs, so I assumed they had been playing earlier. He had obviously been invited for tea. "Ah, here you are."

She moved to the table to fetch a parcel which she had obviously prepared beforehand. Old bag, I thought, she had no doubt what so ever that I would knit her dress for her. For a moment I was torn between a desire to get at her and refuse to do the thing and the wish to show her just how good I really was. But the need to be admired and appreciated won the upperhand, not however, before I had taken great pains to make Dragon believe that it was really going to be a struggle for me.

"Mrs Crawford, are you in a hurry for this dress, because I'm not a fast knitter."

She surveyed me coolly and then said in a flat, calm voice. "No hurry, take your time, learn while you are doing it and do it properly."

"But Mrs Crawford," I insisted as she started trying to dismiss me. "When will I find time to knit? We are getting so much homework and I have all my house duties to do here too. I'm small you know, and I can't work as quickly as the bigger girls."

Dragon was no fool, I believe she saw exactly what I was aiming at. A funny little quirk pulled the corners of her mouth and I thought I saw a flash of amusement in her eyes.

"Well then, we'll have to see about relieving you of some of your less urgent duties then won't we?"

My heart lurched in exultation, it was working!

"Which ones Mrs Crawford?" I persisted. I was determined to have a firm commitment before I took a stem towards the door.

"Some of them take much longer than others. And you know, because of my size it is harder for me to do them. So when they're finished I'm too tired to do anything, even read."

I watched her carefully for signs that I might be overstepping the mark. Her face was void of expression and she just looked at me with her little black eyes.

"Well, leave it with me. I'll look into it and you will be informed accordingly."

"When Mrs Crawford?"

I had dug my heels in now. I wasn't going until she had made definite promises.

"Young lady, as soon as I have studied the situation and made my decision. Be patient. You may go now."

"But Mrs Crawford, I have to organise my schedule and see how to fit my homework in, so that I can start on your dress."

I stood my ground stubbornly.

The chemistry teacher was amused, I could feel his reaction without even looking at him and that provided me with added stimulus. I appealed to him with innocent eyes.

"Mr Phillips knows, don't you sir," I smiled ingratiatingly, "how much work we are getting at school now, and I work slowly and carefully."

Maybe Dragon didn't want to be shown up in front of Philips, or maybe she realised I wasn't going to go without rock-solid arrangements. She sighed.

"Amber, you are one of the most difficult girls in the orphanage, trust me, I will make all the necessary arrangements."

"When Mrs Crawford?"

"Good heavens girl! Tomorrow! Now leave me in peace and go and prepare for church!"

I smiled triumphantly.

"Thank you Mrs Crawford."

I replied sweetly and turning to Phillips grinned at him too, "Good afternoon sir."

Hugging myself with satisfaction I considered the motions that evening. It looked promising, and indeed so it was.

Knitting became a doorway to all kinds of privileges and my status changed almost overnight. I was already popular among the girls and that rating improved even more. The privilege of knitting meant that I was often sent to the stores, and thus I became the secret bearer of letters for the others. Had I ever been caught my ears would have sung for a week, not to mention other more delicate portions of my anatomy.

I was an excellent knitter and Dragon's satisfaction with my work brought me other privileges. Best of all, the heavier, more demanding duties fell by the wayside. Good-bye wood-sawing and washing to my unutterable relief and pleasure. It was actually quite easy to knit for Dragon's flat, bony figure. She was basically just straight up and down, she had angles more than curves. She also commandeered my services for others, so I ended up knitting socks and a scarf for my chemistry teacher too, since he was one of Dragon's regular tennis partners. I often used to wonder whether there was anything going on between those two.

I think it was to prove to myself that I could do anything as well as her that I ended up becoming such a good tennis player myself. I used to watch the bigger girls play and fetched the balls for them, then one day I took a racquet and started hitting the balls around. I enjoyed it and was soon practising against the wall and then joining in the games.

I loved the competition. I had a stubborn determined streak in me that would drive me on until I had won. I was constantly competing with others, especially people I didn't particularly like. I suppose it was an attempt to show them that I was just as good as, and better than they were. Maybe I was trying to be accepted, maybe I was trying to earn their admiration. I just knew I couldn't rest until I had achieved the goals I set for myself. and they were generally higher than those of others.

Knitting gave me access to the more pleasant tasks and the nicer areas. Most of the time, Dragon would have me knitting in one of the staff rooms, where she could keep an eye on the progress. One day while I was sitting there trying to concentrate on the pattern to get my mind off my sore bottom and tired arms, Grace came in with an armful of flowers. She was flustered and upset and obviously in a hurry.

"What's the matter. Grace?"

We all loved the two gentle sisters, they never had an unkind word for anyone and had infinite patience.

She whisked the hair out of her face with a harassed gesture, "Oh hello Amber, I didn't see you in the corner there. Mind you, you're so little I suppose you could just disappear among the furnishings. Oh it's just that I've got so much to do today, and now Mrs Crawford wants me to arrange these flowers in here and I really just don't have time."

I leapt up. "I'll do them!" I offered.

She looked doubtful, pulled hesitantly at her chin and then casting a look over her shoulder at the door, where work obviously beckoned, nodded briefly.

"Very well, but you must be quick, and make sure you clean up the mess."

I'd never actually arranged flowers before, but I had an artistic flair and loved bringing out the beauty and grace I could feel lying hidden in things. I began to set the flowers in the vase, pulling them gently this way and that till they leaned or curved like I wanted.

"And what," said the threatening voice, "do you think you're doing?"

I had been so absorbed in the flowers I had heard nothing. Dragon had come breezing in to examine my knitting progress and was not amused to find me otherwise occupied. I nearly knocked the vase over.

"Grace is so busy." I explained. "I offered to help with the flowers."

Somewhat mollified, she came over to inspect my handiwork.

"Hmm, not bad, but try putting the gladioli more over like this," and with a few deft jerks, she leaned them over at a near perfect angle. I was impressed. This woman was a store of ceaseless surprises to me. She always came out with such unexpected actions and talents I never dreamed she was capable of. Then she pulled out all the other flowers and made me start all over again, under her supervision. At first I was indignant, but quickly realised that she knew what she was doing, so I swallowed my pride and watched carefully.

So I graduated to become official flower arranger, Dragon didn't always appreciate my inventions and there were days when frustration would drive angry tears into my eyes, because she would tear one creation after another apart and make me start again. But she did teach me to arrange flowers. She even let me pick the flowers from the garden and that was really a special privilege.

While I was in the staff room knitting one day, she brought visitors in there. Catching sight of me she called me over.

"This is Amber. She is our prize knitter and flower arranger. She did the flowers in the vase over there."

She waved proudly at my arrangement in the staffroom. I was amused to see that Dragon received the compliments as though they were being made to her. Gratified, she turned a very pleased face in my direction.

"Amber, please go and make us some tea, and tell Grace to send the cakes from the big round tin."

And thus yet another privilege was accorded to me. I could hardly get over this. I still couldn't figure Dragon. Sometimes it seemed that she hated me from the depths of her being, and then she would do unexpected things like this and look as if she really had a soft spot for me.

Eventually, I stopped trying so hard to figure her out and decided just to enjoy the situation and take advantage of the privileges as much as possible.

Serving tea in the staffroom was a boon to all of us, because I could eavesdrop on the conversations and very often we got forewarning of impending events and changes this way.

I was very good at serving tea. I could be very polite and sweet when I wanted to and people seemed attracted to me. Somehow, when you are a servant, people also seem to talk as though you were just part of the furniture. They forget that you can see and hear. Dragon would discuss things with her guests that normally she would never dream of mentioning within our earshot. Of course I spread the news immediately, and knowing all kinds of things like this benefited us tremendously.

From serving tea, Dragon promoted me to their dining room. I enjoyed cooking and took great delight in making the meals look good with all types of little decorations made out of carrots, radishes, tomatoes and other vegetables. I found books in the library that were a mine of ideas for decorating and trimming dishes and loved experimenting with them. My diet improved dramatically too, because it stands to reason that I had to taste everything I prepared to make sure it conformed to standard!

Dragon and her adopted daughter ate in the staff dining room with Grace and Debbie. She often asked me to prepare the meals or serve tea there. I think it was her way of saying "thank you" for all the dresses I knitted for her. Perhaps she realised that knitting was not the cushy job some seemed to think it was.

Sitting for hours on end made your back tired and sore. My bottom sometimes felt worn through and I became painfully conscious of all the bones involved in my structure. My shoulders and arms would ache and after a long session I couldn't even see straight, but, it was worth it.

Especially when I began to perceive that Dragon seemed more lenient with punishments when I had transgressed somewhere, a rather common occurrence! I think she was afraid that if she was too severe I would stop knitting her dresses, or would foul the pattern up somehow. Perhaps I'm speculating now, but I think it might have had something to do with the way she reacted over the fruit raid.

It must have been about December, January because the evenings were balmy and long. We used to sit in the garden or on the front stairs and watch the sunlight stain the trees a bronze red colour, then deepen through angry crimson to purple, while the tree trunks became solid black chunks of night. There was a lethargic kind of calm in the air and we used to sit and drink in the quietness. One such evening I was leaning with my arms on the step behind me and my head thrown back, watching pink wisps of cloud that had been stretched and whipped across the paling sky.

A lazy voice drifted from the clump of girls a short distance away.

"The apricots on Botha's farm are all ripening..."

A pregnant silence followed. Then another voice added with a tinge of interest.

"So are the peaches..."

"Botha doesn't keep dogs in the fields."

Then unspoken suggestions was finding fertile ground and the seeds were germinating rapidly! I could feel sudden excitement rising up from my stomach. I sat up and caught a few huge grins from the equally aroused girls on the lawn. Getting up quickly I darted over to them. Others were sitting up, moving closer, the fun of the adventure already taking hold as we shifted into comfortable positions to plan.

"Tonight would be ideal, there hasn't been any time for the plan to leak."

Pamela's eyes were sparkling with glee. It didn't take long to work out the details. I hadn't been on a fruit raid before and the pent-up anticipation was almost too much. During dinner I felt as though I was going to crack from excitement and tension. Old Dragon even glared over at me at one stage and asked sarcastically whether I had "ants in my pants" and if not, would I please sit still.

Old Bag!!!

To me it seemed that the evening would never end. Dragon's light stayed on for ever. Then just as we were getting ready to sneak down the stairs, Grace's light went on. We shuffled back up the stairs, shoving and smothering giggles when we heard the toilet flush. Another ten minutes of agonised waiting. At last none of us could stand it any more and as one we rose to our feet and drifted like shadows down the stairs.

The farm was less than a quarter of an hour's stroll away. There was so much adrenaline thundering down our veins that we reached it in just over five minutes. Being the smallest I went ahead to reconnoitre. I crawled unseen through the long grass, insinuating my small frame between the bushes till I arrived at the fence. Holding my breath I eased out of the cover and inched forwards till I was pressed close against the mesh. Grit and sand were grinding painfully into my knees, but I clenched my teeth and ignored it, scanning left, right and beyond into the orchard as far as I could. There was nothing, not a movement, not a sound.

Cautiously I signalled to the girls behind me to come.

One by one we crept right up to the fence. Angela was the biggest, she knelt down and we stood on her back to climb over. This was the trickiest part because the fence swayed and rattled and we landed on the other side with a thump that seemed to echo boomingly into the night.

It was very black and the shadows were thick and inky, so it was relatively easy to melt into the darkness, stand dead still and become invisible. We waited for as long as we could bear it, then went on again. I suppose it must have taken us just over half an hour, darting from shadow to shadow, waiting, listening and then creeping silently on again. We were so absorbed in our noiseless advances that none of us noticed the oncoming source of our downfall, a full moon.

We had arranged to split up into two groups, one would head for the peach trees while we would concentrate on the apricots.

Picking fruit at night is not as easy as it sounds. Branches and twigs come at you from all angles and poke your eyes and jab your cheeks. You have to feel around for the fruit and my vivid imagination kept picturing huge hairy spiders or slimy twisting snakes that were waiting just under my fingers to leap up and grab me. Shivers of horror and panic kept cramping my leg and arm muscles and I was as jittery as a frightened bird. Finding the fruit is only half the task, because then you have to squeeze gently to see if it's ripe and worth picking. Fumbling on in the dark like that and half stumbling around under the branches and leaves that grabbed at your clothes and hair you become oblivious to everything else. I know I was so intent on the mission that it was only after ferreting through two trees and then turning towards the third that I saw my shadow on the ground, a ground that was now eerily lit up with a startling brightness. Eh, eh, this was trouble. The moon was up and there wasn't a cloud in the sky to obscure the silver luminescence souring all over the orchard.

I *froze*. Every movement among the trees was brightly illuminated. I saw branches shaking, thicker shadows moving among them and then to my horror clearly distinguished even features and expressions. I hissed loudly to warn the others. They had been as lost in their hunting as myself. I saw the startled whites of eyes and the sudden fright on pale, moonlit faces. Out of earshot of my hiss some girls were still picking and the branches were shaking and quivering far too noticeably for comfort, especially since all the other trees were starkly motionless. I groaned inside. I didn't dare cross over the expanse of grass to warn them, my movement would have been completely exposed and would instantly have revealed our presence. I groped in agony of indecision for a solution, but it was too late. Loud voices suddenly rang angry challenges through the trees.

"Who's there? What's going on? Hey stop!"

Then the loud thudding of feet towards us. As one we turned and ran, caution thrown to the winds, scattering peaches and apricots with each frantic step. Botha might not have had dogs, but he had some very fleet-footed guards. They had patrolled so professionally that we hadn't even known they were there. Cursing under my breath I headed for the fence, with a sinking feeling I knew we were trapped. In fact, they overhauled us while we were still a distance from the fence, and that wretched moon made sure there was very little blackness for us to disappear into.

The guards frog-marched us up to the house where all the lights made a harsh yellow hole of accusation in the night. I felt like I was under interrogation lamps and made good use of my size to hide behind the bigger girls. Botha was furious. He shouted names at us till he almost choked, calling us filth, thieves, corrupt, immoral and a host of other epithets that were somewhat less mild. His wife appeared momentarily in the background to see what all the commotion was. She looked shocked to see a bunch of girls there, shook her head in disgust and disappeared into the house again. When Botha had finished his harangue, more out of breathlessness and loss of words than anything else, he shouted an order at the guards and stalked thunderously into the house.

We stood there and looked at one another and then burst out laughing. We all just looked so funny, twigs and leaves in our hair, faces smeared with fruit and dirt, apricots and peaches stuffed down our fronts. Only Angela hadn't been caught, she had been waiting on the other side of the fence and by now would have shot back so fast she was probably trembling under the sheets. Botha came back with a nasty satisfied little smirk plastered all over his fat cheeks.

"Now we'll see if you horrible thieves will ever take to stealing again."

He marched up and down the veranda, slapping the side of his pyjama-clad legs with a big sjambok. For a moment I had thought he was going to lay into us with it. I had tensed up in readiness to let fly at him. If he raised that thing to me he would discover what a hideous mistake he had made. But it was just for effect - stupid, red-faced piece of insignificance that he was, he wanted to intimidate us I suppose. He failed dismally, because we were still choking back our laughter. In fact when he saw our faces congested with mirth, he almost had apoplexy.

"It's not bloody funny. Don't you know that stealing is a sin?" He shouted with pulsating neck veins.

"It's a crime! You can go to jail, and I'm going to make damn sure that's where you're going."

He blustered and swore, making us all the more hysterical with laughter as he grew angrier and angrier.

I think the arrival of the police van saved us from a massacre. He was so infuriated with our totally unprincipled lack of repentance that he was ready to slaughter us when the van headlights bounced over the farm road. Two young policemen climbed out, one of them very tall strode purposefully over to where we stood at the bottom of the steps, hanging on to each other as we giggled and laughed.

"Bloody lot of thieves. It's those damn orphanage kids, caught them stealing my fruit. Next time I'll get dogs and set them loose!"

Botha was waving his sjambok menacingly, emphasising his words by slapping it heavily down on the low veranda wall.

The policemen looked at each other and then motioned to us. Our guilt was obvious. Trailing apricots and peaches, we climbed into the back of the van. still giggling and chortling, but feeling trepidation now seep in as the van started to bump and jolt over the farm tracks. Soon there was a bleak silence in the back.

"Dragon is going to be livid," someone said in a frightened whisper.

"Oh, shut up. So what?" replied another voice in annoyance. "She's been livid before, she'll survive this too."

"Yes, sure," someone else replied with a gurgled laugh. "But will we?" and the comment caused more hysterical giggles.

"At least let's try to get as much of the fruit in as we can." Came the reasonable suggestion, and from then on we were too busy hiding fruit in pockets, down fronts and in sleeves to have time to let the panic rise.

The van lurched to a halt in front of the orphanage. Dragon had already been alerted, by the furious Botha I suppose, and was waiting imperiously on the steps. It didn't look good. We tumbled out the back of the van.

"Line up!" the command slashed out.

With eyes downcast, all looking repentant and ashamed, we shuffled into line. I peeked to the side and wished I hadn't. Laughter rose in great waves and bubbles from my stomach and I almost choked trying to keep it down. Every girl looked deformed, bumps and lumps all over her body from the hidden fruit, twigs and leaves sticking in tousled hair, lips pressed tight to keep grins away and then Dragon towering on the stairs in her gown like a Roman Emperor about to send the gladiators to their deaths. I coughed and spluttered to disguise the shrieks of laughter I could feel billowing up inside. Dragon was talking to the policemen.

"Where did you say they were caught?"

Respectfully, the policeman had removed his cap and was clutching it self-consciously as he replied.

"Mr Attie Botha's place ma'am."

Dragon gave a little sniff and turned again to survey us.

"You should be ashamed of yourselves for such disgraceful behaviour," she said.

To my surprise, it rang without any conviction at all. I risked a look at her. I was astounded, her eyes were amused, she was trying to look angry, for whose benefit I wasn't sure, ours or the policemen's, but she was acting. She caught my eyes, frowned and pursed her lips.

"Upstairs you wicked girls, march! Get yourselves cleaned up and get into bed without delay."

I couldn't believe she was going to let us off this easy. We shot upstairs without losing a second. The fruit was quickly salvaged and passed hands with such speed it was little more than a blur as we stripped and dashed to the bathroom.

In hushed surprised voices we speculated about Dragon's strange reaction.

"Oh she's just building up the suspense, you watch, she'll either let us have it when we come out the bathroom, or she'll summon us all tomorrow and then we'll really be in for it."

I tended to agree. Dragon would never let a golden opportunity like this for beating up on us just pass by unheeded.

Next morning we were tensed up like violin strings. Dragon didn't appear for breakfast. I did not like this temporary reprieve, I would rather have had it over and done with before school. All of us sat like condemned criminals through the lessons, I didn't think any of us concentrated much. We trudged back to the orphanage like prisoners going to the guillotine. Dragon sat at the top of the table for lunch. Her condemning stare stabbed glacier-cold rapiers into our hearts and dripped icy disapproval into our souls, but she said not a word.

Thoroughly stymied by now I couldn't help examining her expression, but I could make nothing of it. During the afternoon the tension waxed and waned like waves roaring up a beach and then draining back through the sand. We couldn't figure her out at all. Then we decided that she was going to do the big disciplinary bit at dinner, make examples of us, line us up in front of the whole orphanage and humiliate us as much as possible. With gritted teeth we walked into the dining room that night, geared up for the worse.

My stomach had closed down into a tight little knot of anguish and I could eat nothing. I was shoving the food around my plate, the nerves in my throat and chest tight and jumpy when her voice cut over my head.

"Amber, eat your food and stop playing around with it!"

I nearly fell off the chair I was so startled. I put a forkful of something in my mouth and chewed. Tasted like mud. With supreme effort I swallowed. It got stuck somewhere on the way down and I just about choked. Someone gave me some water. By the time I had drowned the morsel and the coughs and recovered, most girls had finished eating. Dragon was ignoring me. I glanced over at some of the other culprits. They were as bewildered as I. Ah, I thought, I know what the old bag is going to do, she will wait till after dinner and then summon us to her office.

Dinner ended. Nothing. We sat around uncomfortably and uneasily, waiting. Nothing happened. Bed time came, no sign from Dragon. The bell sounded for lights out. I was exhausted by the tension and dropped off almost immediately. When I opened my eyes next day, the suspense flooded back. Today she would do something, she was probably organising some tremendous punishment that would put everyone off raiding orchards for good.

That day passed and the next. Gradually, we started to relax. To our utter amazement, Dragon never said or did anything about that fruit raid. I dug around in my mind for every possible explanation and never did really come up with anything satisfactory. Perhaps she didn't like Botha and thought that he had got what he deserved, perhaps she felt sorry for us, perhaps she was as amused by our appearance as I had been, perhaps she didn't want to punish us because of the knitting business. Or maybe she was just not in the mood for beating up on us, though that seemed highly unlikely, she was always in the mood, so much so that she would walk past us as we stood in line to go somewhere and just let random slaps fly for no reason whatsoever except for her own personal satisfaction. Maybe she reasoned that leaving us in suspense was a more effective punishment than a physical hiding.

Whatever the reason, the whole affair died just there. I must admit the way she dealt with it was quite effective. Somehow it took some of the adventure out of raiding fruit. I know that next time a group of girls went, I wasn't as enthusiastic as I might otherwise have been. The fruit didn't seem to taste as sweet when the danger was watered down!

CHAPTER FIFTEEN

"Amber you make sure you've got the flowers, we need little ones for her place as well as a bunch of nice big ones for the arrangement."

I nodded impatiently, had already planned to pick them in the early evening. It would look as though I was collecting blooms for Dragon's staffroom. I was elated at the prospect of the surprise. It was Belinda's birthday the next day and preparations were in full swing. It was normal procedure for other girls to take over the birthday girl's duties. We wouldn't let her do any work that day and it really meant a lot to be able to have a day of glorious freedom like that, a special day that made you feel special and wanted. That year we had put our heads together and devised a whole lot of additions to make the day extra meaningful.

We experienced so little affection, so little genuine love and concern from others. We were misfits and were made to feel it. We were outcast from the "normal" kids and they let us know it. A lot of the time they treated us like criminals, made us feel it was our fault that we were orphans. So we turned to each other for the love and understanding we were denied by "normal" people. It was in the orphanage that I first really experienced genuine concern. It was there that the first authentic salve of love was gently applied to the deep jagged hurt in me. Orphanage girls were the first to spend time with me because they sincerely cared for and wanted to help me. Their words of honest truth helped me to learn to receive affection and give it without expecting anything in return. It was the comforting arm of a senior who had herself been through the anguish of rejection and despair that held and helped me to let out the flood of bitterness and hatred that was damming up in my soul. We took special pains for one another. We looked for ways to help and support, to encourage and comfort. So we were highly pleased with ourselves in devising the new birthday surprises.

Belinda was the first guinea pig to try them out on. She had not the faintest inkling of what lay in store. We were experts in the art of dissimulation and she never even suspected what we had prepared.

The previous evening, I spent much longer than usual in the garden selecting small dainty blossoms to arrange around her place at the dinner table. Cheeky, pert little scented flowers and coloured leaves for a small arrangement above her plate and then longer stemmed blooms for the vase that would be placed at her bedside while she was in the dining room. I was very excited about our arrangements, if it worked we would have instituted a whole new tradition that I really believed would bring so much happiness to the birthday girl and make the day rich and meaningful.

Every single one of us had a little gift for her. We knew that it wasn't the size or cost of the present that meant anything, it was the love that went into it. Some of the littler ones really made us laugh, because they would put certain sweets aside for use as birthday presents, but like little kids are, they would have to keep examining and checking up on them. The constant handling, unwrapping and wrapping eventually reduced the poor sweetie to a mangled mass of melted gunge. Yet the birthday girl would invariably receive that treasured sweetie with a pang of affection and appreciation.

One little girl came to me with tears in her eyes the evening before.

"Amber." She lisped, tugging at my skirt.

"Amber, Pleath help me..."

The hot tears brimmed over and trickled miserably down her little cheeks. I crouched down next to her.

"Sandy, what's up?"

In between sniffs and snivels, she confessed that she had eaten the sweetie she had been saving for Belinda, the temptation had just been too much for the sugar-starved mite. I was most amused but hid my grin because she was so concerned and upset about it.

"I feel *tho* greedy and *tho* awful, now I haven't got anything to give her and *it'th* her *biiiirthday* tomorrow." She wailed the words out, unable to contain the bitter remorse any more.

I sat down with her and let her weep on my shoulder. When the storm had subsided a bit, I stroked her hair and whispered in her little shell-like ear.

"I tell you what Sandy, you come with me to the garden and we'll go and choose her a special flower. Then I'll give you a bit of ribbon and wool and you can make a lovely bow for it to give Belinda. Hey? What do you think?"

She perked up immediately, tears quickly drying as the hope glimmered over her tiny horizon. All was not lost! She pulled at my hand...

"Amber can we go now?"

I smiled at her and ruffled her hair.

"No sweetheart, it's too early yet. The flower will wilt and die if we pick it now. Wait till later."

The kid followed me around like a puppy for the rest of the afternoon. Every half hour or so she would run up and yank at my dress or arm.

"Amber, *ithn't* time yet?"

At last the sun started sinking. Sandy came bounding up to me just as the senior in charge sounded the bell for the little one's bath time. The look of dismay on Sandy's face was so comical I yelled with laughter. Shame, she had been waiting all day and now that the longing was almost in her hand, she was being summoned elsewhere. Tears of panic sprang to her eyes and she looked around desperately to see if the senior was coming for her.

"Sandy you wait for me right here. Sit down and don't move. I'll come right back."

I ran up the stairs to get a few minutes reprieve for the frantic little Sandy. She was almost hysterical when I came back. When I told her she had time to choose her flower, she looked as though she was scared to believe it. Then with a whoop of joy she ran to the flower beds. She had been nosing around there on and off all afternoon in between her shifts of tracking me around so she knew exactly where to go. Almost hidden by a huge straggling jasmine creeper that was engulfing everything within reach, Sandy had discovered a stunted rosebush with miniature roses poking cheekily out between the jasmine tendrils. The buds were fully open, others just unfurling their petals.

Sandy knew exactly which one she wanted and I heartily approved her choice. Pinkish white, it was half open, the petals crisp and pearly. Despite its minuteness, it was perfectly formed. I picked it carefully and entrusted it into the grubby fingers.

"Gently now, don't crush the poor thing," I admonished, but Sandy was cradling it like it was so fragile it would disintegrate.

"Go and bath now. After supper I'll bring you some ribbon and we'll make a pretty bow for it."

I watched her scamper off. It was so easy to fill a child's day with happiness. That's another reason I found it so difficult to understand Dragon. It would cost her so little effort to have the kids hanging on her lips, worshipping every step she took, yet she seemed to go out of

her way to intimidate them and make their lives a misery. I just
couldn't comprehend it. Maybe she hated looking after other
women's kids and took her resentment out on them by slapping them
and beating them up. Maybe she hadn't been able to have her own
and couldn't stand the thought that women who could, either just
abandoned them or died and left them alone. I shrugged. I didn't
think I would ever be able to figure her out.

Very early next morning four or five of us sneaked out of bed and
crept silently into the dining room. I decorated Belinda's place at the
table, loving the delicate blossoms in an intricate pattern around the
plate. The scented flowers I arranged daintily in a tiny Chinese vase
Grace had lent me. Then I dashed into the kitchen with the bigger
blossoms. Grace would take the vase up to Belinda's place in the
dorm while we were at breakfast.

Other girls were decorating her chair with paper decorations
intertwined with flowers. Some of the cards that girls were giving her
we opened up and balanced on the table above her plate. The bell
sounded for breakfast, and with delighted grins, we quickly piled a
small cluster of little presents on her chair: sweeties, tiny gift-wrapped
objects, a hanky tied up with blue wool, a square, silver-paper
enveloped matchbox with something inside that rattled...

Debbie had been drawn into the plot. It was her role to waylay
Belinda with the excuse that she had to fetch something from the
sewing room. Debbie apparently made as if she were totally unaware
that it was Belinda's birthday and just pointed her out "randomly"
when she was looking for someone to help her. By the time Belinda
had been to the sewing room with Debbie, everyone was in the hall,
eyes expectantly fixed on the door. Dragon said her usual grace while
everyone fidgeted with rapidly increasing suspense.

"Sit!" came the command, but Dragon's chair was the only one
that scraped. She was just looking up in surprise at all of us still
standing in taut excitement, faces lit up with grins when Belinda came
in at the door. There was a huge, spontaneous chorus.

"Happy birthday Belinda!"

Then the girls all started singing, waving their hands and smiling
massive, cheek-splitting smiles.

"Happy birthday to you... uuuuu, happy birthday to you!!!"

Belinda stood transfixed at the door. She was as pale as a sheet,
then she went red, then tears started down her face and she took a few

hesitant steps into the dining room. Everyone was talking, laughing and shouting greetings, she was trying to smile through the tears.

The orphanage senior shouted above the noise...

"Okay! everyone, Quiet! Quiet! The rest of you sit down, come Belinda, come and sit."

She moved towards Belinda to lead her to her chair. She stood there and just stared at the flowers. With shaking hands, she reached out touching the gifts, letting her hand move gently over the paper. When she looked up the tears were sliding softly down her face. She tried to speak but just closed her eyes and shook her head slightly. There was silence in the room, Belinda looked up and let her gaze wander over the faces turned expectantly and full of delight towards her.

Dragon hadn't moved through the commotion. Her eyes flicked from one to the other as she took in every detail. The senior gave a little signal and we stood and made a little half circle around Belinda. I gave the note and we burst into song. It was Belinda's special tune, the melody she was always humming. Unrestrained, the tears dripped onto her dress as she touched the flowers, then turned and impulsively hugged us. The little kids were wildly excited and started cheering and banging on the table with spoons.

When the noise reached cacophony level, Dragon decided it was time to intervene.

"Silence! Silence!"

It still took a while before the buzzing and clattering subsided. We scraped chairs and sat down, thrilled with the obvious success of our innovations and also moved by Belinda's reaction. She was a daredevil type of person, very tomboyish and I don't think many people realised the gentleness and softness that her hard exterior masked.

By now she had regained her composure and was laughing through the tears, examining the gifts and cards and admiring the flowers. At the end of the meal, Dragon rose to her feet and signalled again for silence.

She smiled a taut little smile and instinctively I thought: "Careful you old Dragon, you might crack your face if you over do it..."

I half repented when I heard what she had to say.

"In all my years as principal of this home, it is the first time I have encountered such gestures as you have demonstrated here this

172

morning. I would like to congratulate those girls who initiated the
procedures. You are to be highly commended for your thoughtfulness
and for the trouble you have taken to prepare the event. Well done. I
hope to see this continued for future such occurrences."

We looked at one another with pleased surprise. It wasn't often
Dragon praised us. Maybe the old bag had human feelings after all.
Or perhaps she was suffering a lapse... I couldn't help feeling cynical
about her apparent humanity, she was so inconsistent in her moods
and reactions. When I was feeling particularly malicious about her, I
would picture her goose-stepping down the hall, with all of us lined up
in stiff uniforms and outstretched arms shouting "*Heil Hitler*" as she
high-stepped past.

It would be a while though before we could institute these new
birthday proceedings again, because a totally unforeseen drama struck
the orphanage. The massive upheaval tangled even normal routine
into impossible knots and many girls were emotionally as well as
physically affected.

Those of us on bath routine discovered it first. The little kids had
been scratching and complaining all day, rubbing their heads almost
hysterically. When we got them into the bath, we saw why. *LICE*.
Thousands of the things, infesting the kids' hair. Appalled we called
on Debbie and Grace, within minutes Dragon came striding over to
see for herself .

It was action stations within seconds. Three girls were despatched
to the infirmary to find "*blue butter*". Five were sent over to the
boys' orphanage to ask for tins of paraffin. Dragon herself arrived
with the shears and before we realised what she intended, she had
snipped every last lock off the little ones' heads.

Shame, they looked ludicrous! I'd never realised how lumpy a
bald head was and was highly amused at the different shapes of their
poor shorn heads. When the paraffin arrived, it was smeared over it.
The smell was nauseating, but it was the only remedy available. The
kids were crying and sobbing, the itch had abated only slightly and
seeing themselves in the mirror had made them doubly miserable.

We were sent off to inspect their bedding, but didn't really know
what to look for. The lice we did find, we crushed and then shook all
the bedding out and aired it. But it was too late, the epidemic had
already gut down roots and it spread like a bush fire. Every day more
girls discovered the loathsome creatures crawling through their hair.

Screams and agonised shrieks would report the event. Tears, panic, rage and anger filled with a virulent hatred of the hideous insects drove many girls almost to the point of hysteria. The damn things were everywhere. We all saturated our hair with paraffin and assiduously rubbed blue butter behind our ears because it was said that no lice could move where you had smeared the stuff.

The entire orphanage was permeated by a permanent paraffin stench. I think if anyone had struck a match in there the place would have exploded with a spectacular bang. All of us were issued with white cloths and fine combs. To our horror we discovered that some of the lice were so plump, you could hear them drop when you combed your hair. You had to mash them quickly before they crawled on to someone else.

The girls whose heads were shaven were all allowed to stay at home from school to avoid the mockery of the as yet unaffected. The numbers remaining at the orphanage grew almost daily. Those of us who hadn't been infected yet applied paraffin in generous doses, smearing blue butter behind our ears until we looked like creatures from outer space.

Every day we had to line up for inspection. Grace and Debbie, aided by a few uncontaminated seniors carefully picked through our hair to look for the tell-tale nits or the lice themselves. I remember seeing pictures of baboons plucking the vile things off each others' bodies too and in the midst of the loathsome plague had to grin because it was just what we looked like. If the lice were in your hair, you were given a few days grace to try to get rid of them, and your name entered in the book. If you were unsuccessful, the next stop was Dragon with her shears. Wretched woman, she seemed to take a great delight in shaving our heads. Some of the children were so badly infested that they began to run temperatures. The itch was so bad that their scalps were bleeding from their anguished scratching. Others had so many nits they almost looked grey-haired. It was revolting. The disgustingly repugnant insects drove us to a paroxysm of frenzied hatred. Some girls would mash them so viciously when they found them that they practically dented the floor.

It went on for months. The reek of paraffin had so saturated us that it seemed to swirl up from our pores and leak out of our ears and noses. It was a torment from the pits of hell. Dragon just made it worse. She had no compassion whatsoever, she seemed to take a

perverse pleasure in shearing our hair away. Her very approach with
those shears oozed sadistic satisfaction. How I hated her during those
few weeks. I wished so fervently that the lice would not just get into
her hair, but infest her whole body. I so wanted them to crawl under
her skin, bore into her flesh like maggots and heave in and out of her
eyes and ears so that she could feel what we were feeling and show
some mercy and some sympathy. But she was like a machine, no
emotions, no feeling, just a dead face and the relentless shears.

Eventually there were only a few of us left with long hair and
somehow it didn't feel right. We decided that all the hair must go.
So one Saturday morning we lined up all the girls and cut everyone's
hair off. Then we washed with a powerful disinfectant that made
everyone smell like a public bathroom. After that we rubbed in
paraffin and applied the blue butter to every ear on the premises. We
looked beautiful! From being a tragedy, it become a joke, now we all
looked the same, we were in this together and we were going to whip
it. The enthusiasm was as infectious as the lice had been, we threw
the hair on to a huge bonfire and then getting totally carried away,
hurled anything else we thought might be infested with the horrible
crawling creatures onto the fire as well. We felt the repercussions of
that hasty act later. Physically and painfully, but it didn't matter.
Clothes, bedclothes, towels, face cloths, anything that could have been
contaminated was recklessly lobbed into the flames. You could smell
the stench of burning hair for miles. A pall of smoke hung over the
orphanage and drifted like a fat oily slug towards town.

Whether it was that assault that did the trick or whether the
epidemic was already dying down, the infestation disappeared. As the
days went by without any lice or nits appearing we realised that we
had rid ourselves of the nightmare. The rejoicing was great, there
was such an atmosphere of relief, of lightness. There was a renewed
spate of raids as excess energy and inventiveness came bubbling up
again after the long repression.

As with all things, we pooled the ointments and creams we had and
cleaned and treated one another's sores. I was giggling like a lunatic
one day while helping Belinda and when she demanded to know the
joke, I told her about the baboons picking the lice out of each other's
bodies and even popping the filthy things into their mouths and
crushing them between their teeth. The image spread rapidly and
before long girls were pretending to be baboons, walking up and down

the corridors and aisles with bandy legs and curved arms, hooting and scratching under their armpits, then suddenly diving on others to pick through the newly sprouting hair in search of lice and nits.

We all went back to school to face the barrage of teasing and derision but we soon grouped up and launched vicious attacks on the mockers. The teasing came to an abrupt halt.

Even the boys were scared of us. Many of us wore scarves, I must admit I quite enjoyed it, I looked good in one and knew it! As the hair started growing back, a number of girls were delighted to see that it was thick and lustrous. For a few brief, sad, moments, the sight of Jimmy, sick with typhoid flashed in front of my eyes. I remember how his locks became black and curly after his sickness. Then I pushed the memory away, it was so useless thinking about things that were gone.

The months slipped by and became years. The orphanage was home and the children my sisters. They were certainly a lot more like sisters to me than my real sisters. Year after year, I saw the girls pass through matric and then leave. There was a lot of crying at that time, from the girls leaving as well as the girls left behind. I remember crying when a close friend of mine left, crying for myself more than for her, for the emptiness her departure would leave, for the loneliness that stayed behind. I really couldn't understand why those who were leaving cried, I often wondered whether they were crying for joy or for those they were leaving behind. I was generally thrilled for them when their time came to step out into the outside world. To me it was a dawn of liberty, an escape from a hellhole and it was a source of constant encouragement and hope, because it meant that one day, my turn would also come.

CHAPTER SIXTEEN

The years at the orphanage had brought a certain amount of change in me. The rebellion and defensiveness were still there, but muted. They no longer surged out with violence and destructive aggression. Instead there was a hint of humour about them, of mischievousness rather than bitter resentment. The fear and hatred that my grandfather had inculcated in me had been pushed down somewhere into hidden depths. I actually thought they had gone. Only occasionally would mists of hatred seep into my awareness, released by some incident or memory. But it was seldom, and some instinctive reaction would dispel them almost instantaneously.

The nightmares still came. Yet despite the terror they brought choking to my throat, they had become a part of my life and I think I accepted them as such. They were hideously vivid, agonisingly real, but it was not so desperately traumatic to recover. Previously I would wander around for days in a trance-like stupor, expecting the apparitions from those nightmares to materialise in every shadow and corner. Now it was a matter of perhaps hours and I would have a firm hold on reality again, easily able to distinguish between the concrete and the dream world.

By the time I was in my matric year, a number of factors had made life considerably more bearable. As Dragon's semi-official "*knitter*", I enjoyed several privileges that eliminated the worst of the drudgery and gave me a measure of freedom and trust that benefited both me and the other girls.

Yet strangely there was such a deep-seated sadness in me. Even in the midst of mischief and laughter, I was always aware of this shadow inside, more insistent and prevalent on some occasions than others, but always, always there. It put a subtle distance between me and others. I don't quite know how to define it properly, a kind of loneliness, an awareness of being different, a realisation of not belonging, not participating. At times it almost seemed as though I was looking at people and things around me through a veil, but a veil so tenuous and delicate that if I had put my hand out towards it, just the air moved by the gesture would have torn it, except I could never bring myself to do that.

In some inexplicable way, that veil was protection. It separated me, it held things off. But it brought that profound weariness, the deep sadness with it.

Dragon hadn't changed. She still beat and slapped the girls for no reason except her own sadistic satisfaction. By this time I had given up trying to understand and analyse her. Now I just accepted what came from her, whether it was the unexplained and unexpected favours or the sudden harshness and intimidation. I don't know, maybe she was just a very insecure person, maybe she was afraid that if she showed humanity people would take advantage of her. Perhaps it was just her way of always keeping everyone unhinged so that she could have better control.

I had become the regular baby-sitter for my bookkeeping teacher and his wife. He was an adorable man and I used to go out of my way to produce excellent work for him. I know it used to frustrate some of the other teachers, because they all knew I wasn't stupid and could achieve high marks if I tried. It was just that so much of the time it didn't seem worth it, or some stubborn streak in me refused to give good work to a teacher I disliked or disrespected.

I remember one incident of my second last year very clearly, where the shorthand and typing teacher came very short. I worked hard for him and knew that my typing was far above average, but for some reason, I just couldn't enjoy the shorthand and eventually simply gave up on it. One particular day, the shorthand exercise contained some stupid mistakes in it, more than my usual quota. It was probably an off day for him too, because it seemed to irritate him immensely. I was actually sorry when I saw his initial reaction, because I liked that man and didn't enjoy disappointing him. Particularly in view of the fact that my typing was so much better than everyone else's.

He heaved an exaggerated sigh and picked up my exercise book between thumb and finger and dangled it in the air with arm outstretched and a disgusted look on his face, as though the thing was emitting some evil smell.

"Amber Waverley. Stand up please."

I could sense that something ugly was approaching and instinctively, the dark forces inside started to condense and rise. At the same time I was almost crying out, dear God please don't let this man attack me. I didn't want to be hurt by someone I liked. I didn't want to hit back, but I knew that if he did hurt me, there would be instant retaliation.

"What, may I ask, is this?"

He flapped the book irritably in the air. I stared at him innocently.

"It looks like my book, sir." I replied, feeling the anger starting to seethe. Don't humiliate me in front of everyone. I thought desperately, please don't.

But by this stage he was being about as sensitive as an ox and blundered on, to the growing amusement of the class.

"Aah," he sneered sarcastically. "Your book, so you have at least the courage to admit it. I know I would greatly hesitate before so doing."

He dropped it disgustedly on the desk, flapping his fingers as though to dislodge dirt and then wiping them to remove imaginary slime.

He should have stopped there, that was enough, he had conveyed his irritation quite sufficiently. But he kept on, I think the titters of amusement coming from the class egged him on.

"So what, may I be so bold as to enquire, is your excuse for this appalling offering? Did we sleep poorly perhaps? Or is it that we were so overburdened with other tasks that we had no time to dedicate to our shorthand? Or perhaps in our great intellectual superiority we deemed shorthand too lowly a task for our genius?"

I just looked at him. Irked by my silence, he leaned aggressively over his desk.

"How now, little Amber, silence from you who are always so loquacious? No suggestions?"

I still said nothing. He leaned back in his chair and tilting his head slightly backwards, he sneered.

"Well, I have a suggestion for you. I suggest you rather take up cookery. Then at least one day you will be able to do something useful, like cooking for your husband, though if your cooking is anything like your shorthand, then I pity the poor man."

The class was in fits by this time. So was I, but of a completely different kind. I still said nothing, but I could feel the hardness in my face. The anger was burning red-hot and molten. I clenched my teeth and could feel all the muscles in my arms and shoulders tighten as though they were going into a cramp.

Very quietly, I gathered my books together and started packing them into my suitcase. The teacher was not expecting this. He looked a bit puzzled, then bewildered. The sarcastic smirk had disappeared.

"And what do you think you are doing?" he asked a bit defensively.

I said nothing. When my books were in the case I stood up and without a backward glance, walked out. The class was silent for a while and then ripples of laughter, surprise and delight echoed behind me.

I marched straight to the cookery class. The teacher happened to be the current girlfriend of the luckless shorthand teacher. They had often been seen out together in town and he frequently gave her lifts to her home after school.

Finding an empty seat, I plonked myself down, took out my books and started paying attention to an extremely taken aback teacher. The class sat in stunned amazement. They didn't know what was going on. Neither did the teacher.

She stared at me blankly, her mouth opening and closing as she looked for words. Eventually, she pointed at me.

"You, what on earth are you doing here? What do you want? You don't belong in this class."

I returned her stare with the utmost calm.

"Well Miss," I explained patiently, "your boyfriend Mr Webb appears to think that I would benefit more from your instructions than his. And since he has the experience, I submit to his superior knowledge."

She was so angry she lost her breath. The class roared with laughter. She was puffing up like a toad in a rainstorm and I thought at any minute her bra would pop loose. I watched it with interest, but just as I thought it wouldn't be able to take the strain anymore she exhaled...

"I beg your pardon! How dare you..."

Then she lost her breath and words again. The girls in the class were practically off their chairs with enjoyment.

"You come with me right this minute young lady."

Grabbing me by the arm she stormed to the principal's office with me in tow. I was relishing the revenge, but at the same time weeping inside with hurt and anger. She didn't even knock at the principal's door. Barging in, she half shoved, half threw me in front of her while she ranted at her about the despicable rudeness and effrontery I had shown. She went on and on. I lost my temper.

"Oh shut up!" I shouted, eyes flashing.

"She heard you the first time. Do you think she's deaf or something?"

At this the Principal rose to her feet in a fury. She had to speak because the teacher was swallowing her tongue with rage, frustration, astonishment and impotence. Her cheeks were red and puffed out. She looked more like a toad now than ever.

"That is quite enough from you!" she thundered.

"Miss Alcock, you may return to your class now, thank you."

She sat down and fixed me with glittering, livid eyes.

"I have had just about enough of you and your disobedience, rebellion and trouble-making."

My own eyes must have been boring searing holes in her. She shifted a bit uncomfortably. I was seething inside. She was being most unfair, making out that I had stirred up others and was a constant problem and that was not true. I was a hard worker and one of the brightest kids in school and for her to accuse me so generally and so unjustly burnt acid into my gut.

"It appears that you have caused quite enough upset for today. So take your things and go home, now!"

That was the last straw. Home? When had I ever known what that was? I refused to let the tears come to my eyes, but I could feel them. The crying inside became a howl of anguish and pain.

"Home? What home?"

When I started talking my voice was quiet and controlled, but to my dismay, it grew louder and angrier until eventually I was almost screaming. I walked up to her desk while I spoke and ended up leaning over it, shouting in her face as she grew paler and moved backwards from the vicious fury lashing out at her.

"What the hell do you think home means to me? I haven't got a home. You want me to go home. I'll go, and with pleasure. You people seem to think that girls like me have no emotions, that we don't think, that we don't hurt, don't feel. Do you know what it's like to be constantly mocked and humiliated for who you are, for what you do? Do you think it's fun to be ridiculed and scorned? Is that what a teacher is supposed to do? Well if you think I'm just going to sit down and shut up and take that kind of treatment you can forget it, because I'm not! I'm not just nobody that you can shout at and mistreat and mock when you feel like it. I'll go, yes, gladly, but I haven't got a home to go to. You're the principal, you should know that! unless you are so damn blind and unfeeling that you just don't care. Yes, I'll go. I'll go back to the orphanage where I come from. And I hope that one day you'll pay for this."

I stalked out. Picked up the suitcase that had been left at her door and walked back to the orphanage. The tears were burning and my cheeks were so hot they felt swollen. I could almost feel the sparks shooting out of my eyes. I was infuriated, hurting and desperately miserable. The further I drew from the school, the slower my steps became. The anger started to sink down as the wave of bitter unhappiness swelled over it.

At the orphanage I went and sat on my bed and hugged my knees, gazing unseeing through the window. There was an almost whispered voice at the door.

"Amber? Amber?" it was Grace, timidly approaching the bed. I smiled weakly.

"Deary, are you all right?"

She eased her dumpy weight on to the bed next to me. I nodded off-handedly.

"Yes, I'm okay now, thanks Grace."

She patted my hand, and then kindly stroked my head as she stood up.

"Well dear," she peered at me queryingly, "I don't know what it is about, but Mrs Crawford would like to see you in her office. You are home a bit early aren't you?"

Poor Grace, she was a very inquisitive type, and she was obviously longing to know what was happening, but was too polite or too cautious to ask outright.

"Yes. Well I suppose I'd best go now and get it over with, hey?"

I knocked at Dragon's door and there was no answer. I knocked again, louder, still nothing. Carefully, I opened the door and peered round it, no one was in. Annoyed, I shut the door again and leaned huffily up against the wall with arms crossed.

"Stupid bag, why isn't she in if she wants me to come and see her?"

I waited another five or ten minutes, still no Dragon. The apprehension gave way to anger and I was just about to turn round and go back to the dorm when she appeared round the corner, in tennis clothes. Stupid cow - she had gone to play tennis purposely made me wait!

She strode past me with a mere sidelong glance, opened the door and then slammed it behind her, in my face. I stared at the panels in front of my nose and boiled with rage. Well, she was not going to rile me. I swallowed the fury and waited and waited.

About twenty minutes later I heard her voice, as though she had only just become aware of my presence.

"Amber, come in."

I was in two minds whether to stand there and ignore her for a while and give her a taste of her own medicine, but then realised that it would achieve nothing and gritting my teeth, clumped in. She looked up at me with resignation, elbows on her desk and hands clasped together.

"Fireworks again, Amber?" she shook her head tiredly. "I don't know what on earth to do with you. What have you got to say for yourself this time?"

I looked at her with as much antagonism as I could muster and then just shrugged my shoulders and looked away.

"Well? Look at me please, when I talk to you."

I returned her gaze impassively.

"Have you nothing to say?"

"There's no point in talking."

I caught a strange expression in her face, and cocking one eyebrow, she half smiled.

"Try."

Well you asked for it. I thought, and let fly.

"Mrs Crawford, I'm not a little girl anymore. I don't appreciate being mocked and derided in front of others and I especially don't appreciate injustice and unfairness. I am not the type to take that kind of treatment sitting down. I do not believe that just because someone happens to be a few years older than myself that he has the right to use hurtful sarcasm to break me down and insult me for something I don't believe I'm guilty of.

"As far as I'm concerned he got what was coming to him. He thought he was very clever setting me up as a laughing stock, so all I did was let him see what it felt like. I don't believe I did anything wrong. He made a class laugh at me. I made two classes laugh at him. Now just because he is supposedly adult, he's right and I'm wrong. It's not fair and I don't see that I have done anything to deserve this kind of treatment."

I was trembling with anger by now. Dragon kept her eyes on me unblinkingly throughout my tirade. She motioned for me to sit I supposed that meant that I was in for a long sermon.

"Amber." Her voice was as soft as the hard old bitch could make it. "You are often too harsh on others because of what you perceive is to be slights that aren't."

She raised her hand to hush the protest that leapt to my lips.

"Let me finish please."

I subsided.

"Because you have been hurt and rejected in the past, you automatically presume that every action you perceive to be aimed against you is intended to hurt and reject."

She raised her hand again as I opened my mouth to interrupt.

"Please accord me the same courtesy of allowing me to finish what I have to say as I granted you."

She waited with a query on her face until I nodded.

"Very well. When you first came to this home you were a frightened, hurting little animal that lashed out at anyone and everyone. You were full of distrust, bitterness and hatred and quite frankly I did not hold high hopes for you.

"Over the years however, I have seen you change. You have been learning to cope with life and its challenges in an admirable fashion and you have in turn been able to reach out to help others who have been struggling.

"I have watched you acquire skills and knowledge and been satisfied with the way you have responded to privileges and added responsibility granted to you. You are in fact one of the girls of whom I have been growing increasingly proud, and I foresee a promising future for you. You have great qualities of determination and strength of character. You are diligent and kind. However..."

Here she stopped and let her eyes burn holes into me.

"There are still many things you have to learn and many areas where you still need to mature and control yourself!"

Her voice rose towards the end till her words echoed in the room. We were used to her sermons, so I had started off feeling blasé about the thing. However I was startled by her unexpected praise. It was like confirmation of that suspicion that in some weird way I was a kind of pet to her. Being taken aback like that made her words stick. She went on.

"You have so many positive aspects to your character that it would be a tragedy if you allowed those few negative elements to dominate and destroy the good. You must learn to rein in your aggression and antagonism. Not everyone who rebukes or admonishes you does so with the intent of hurting or rejecting you. It is time you realised that much rebuke is administered with the specific intention of bettering a person, turning them from a path of destruction, helping them to change."

She continued in the same vein for a while, then I suppose seeing that I had switched off, concluded with a verbal rap over the knuckles.

"I do not expect to have similar behaviour from you in future. I expect you to be setting a better example for the little ones, because I notice that they tend to look up to you. Give them more to look up to."

She waved her hand in dismissal.

As I reached the door. she called out. "And you........ !"

As I turned I distinctly saw the amusement in her eyes and around her lips.

"I suggest you apologise to the teachers... even if they were one hundred percent at fault. You know it shows great strength of character to say you are sorry when you know the fault is not entirely yours."

Old bag! I was amazed, she thought I was right! She thought the whole thing was funny too!

Feeling much better and considerably lighter. I waltzed out to the garden to wait for the others to come back from school.

CHAPTER SEVENTEEN

"...so I have obtained permission from Mrs Crawford for you to spend the Christmas holidays with us and enclose the money for the train fare and for purchases along the way. We look forward to seeing you again".

Love Denise.

I stared at the words till they danced. *Denise*?

What on earth had suddenly made my eldest sister remember me? After nine or ten years? What had gotten into her? Suspicion writhed inside me. My family had never exactly manifested any tender concern about me before, so what was this all about?

Of course there was no money in the envelope. Our mail was censored and Dragon removed anything of value to keep it in our personal envelope until she gave permission for its use. I turned the letter over and over and read it again from start to finish. So Denise was married, with a baby. I tormented myself with questions. Why had she suddenly remembered me now? Why had she invited me for the holidays. She had never written a single letter since the day she left my grandfather's place, when I was little more than eight or nine. I was seventeen years old now, almost eighteen, what did she want from me?

I tried to picture her, married with babies... and failed. I could still see the cowed girl obeying my grandfather's every command with a submissive and obedient little smile. I still felt her angry slaps when I stood up to him. I still heard the fury in her voice when she turned on me for provoking his wrath. Did I have any reason to think she had changed her attitude towards me? Why in all this time had she not even bothered to even contact me, much less send me anything? Distrust mushroomed until I felt inclined to ignore the letter altogether.

Belinda thought I was crazy.

"Amber she's your sister. So what if she hasn't written to you? Maybe she was also going through such a difficult time that she didn't want to. Maybe now that she's on her feet and has her own family, she really understands how sad it is to be in an orphanage and she

186

wants to make it up to you. Don't be so stubborn and proud. I would go. Even if it's just an excuse to get out of the orphanage."

She kept on until she convinced me. Anyway, curiosity really was getting the better of me. And deep down, though I didn't admit it to myself then, I longed to have a family. I longed to love my sisters and be loved by them. I know now that what I subconsciously smothered with uncomfortable ripples of fear was a faint stirring of hope, hope that I could be accepted, hope that I could be wanted.

So as the holidays dawned. I found myself on the train heading to Denise's home. The moment she greeted me, I knew I had made a mistake. She was painfully effusive, and as false as a piece of scenery in a pantomime.

"Oh Amber! How lovely to see you again!"

The hug was as hypocritical as the smile.

"My how you've grown! The last time I saw you, you were hardly two bricks and a tickey high, and just look at you now!"

She babbled on while I closed up inside and felt the hurt jab needles into me. The question nagged, so if she was lying, then why did she ask me to come? Guilt? Curiosity?

When we arrived at her house she took me to my bedroom. There was a box of sweets for me and a cake of perfumed soap. I was very guarded and said little, keeping my answers down to yes, no and non-committal responses, because I saw immediately that she wasn't in the least interested anyway, I doubt if she even heard what I said to her questions.

The reason for my presence became very clear quickly. She needed a baby-sitter. I was actually little more than a general maid of all work. She very quickly switched off the bubbly sweetness and became acid and demanding. It was a dreadful period. I don't even want to think about it anymore.

It was worsened by the problems Charlene caused with her lying. And she wasn't even there, she was in a small town not far away, but close enough to wreak emotional havoc.

I had only been with Denise for a day when there was a knock at the door and lo and behold, a Probation Officer from the Social Welfare was standing on the doorstep with the obligatory expression of righteousness and piety. I disappeared immediately because that sense of foreboding was leaking out from somewhere deep inside me and I knew trouble was coming.

The Officer stayed for quite a while and at one stage I heard very angry voices raised and what was obviously an indignant denial at a high-pitched tone from Denise. My stomach turned in anguish, what was it now? The door had hardly clicked shut behind the Social worker than Denise came storming into my room in a towering fury. Grabbing me by the arms, she swore and cursed at me, shaking and rattling me till I felt my teeth cracking. I hadn't the faintest idea what she was on about. Her accusations went completely over my head. For a while I even thought she had gone insane. She was shouting at the top of her voice about social workers and what an ungrateful little bitch I was, how dare I and that I should pack my things and leave immediately.

"Dead am I? Died during the week? What a filthy liar you are! How can you say such a wicked thing? What on earth did you cook up such a monstrous lie for? How dare you say I've died?"

She was so angry the tears were flicking out of her eyes and her face was congested.

I was completely disorientated. I didn't know what was happening. I started shouting back at her till we were both yelling at the top of our voices. I jerked myself loose and as she raised her hand to slap me I grabbed the lamp by the bedside and warned her in a hiss.

"You touch me Denise and I'll break this thing over your head."

She glared at me with glittering hatred, then with tight lips and her arms stiff at her side took a step towards me.

"You put that down now you little monster, and I demand that you tell me why on earth you told them that I had died?"

The unbelief whirled up from inside me. Did Denise really know me so little that she could think me capable of something like that? I was stunned and hurt.

"I don't know what you are talking about. I haven't spoken to anyone about you. Why should I say you've died? And to whom was I supposed to have told?"

I was angry, but the hurt and bewilderment must have registered on Denise because it seemed to dawn on her that I was genuinely in the dark.

"Didn't you tell Social Welfare I was dead?"

She stuck her head forwards, half accusingly, half doubtfully.

I just looked at her blankly. What would I want to do such a senseless thing for? But Denise wanted to believe that I was guilty, I could see that clearly.

Bitterness and resentment oozed up from inside and again I felt the dark shadows of rejection and loneliness creep in. This was suppose to be my sister. Yet she treated me worse than a stranger, hurling accusations without the slightest proof and more than willing to believe the worst.

The atmosphere was thick and tense. I was sullen and spoke only when addressed. I helped with the baby who was quite a sweet little thing, just very demanding, and for the rest just tried to keep out of the way as much as possible.

Then on Saturday who should arrive but Charlene, effervescent, full of herself and as self-centred as ever. Denise was most surprised to see her.

"Why didn't you let us know you were coming?

"Oh Denise," Charlene lied, "I wanted it to be a surprise for little Amber. It's such a long time since I've seen her!"

Surprise... I thought bitterly. Unwanted surprise. Charlene had never thought twice about accepting the food I had always given her at the orphanage because she kept complaining of hunger. It had never once appeared to enter her mind that I went without meals to do that. She just took it for granted. And once she left the orphanage it was like I had never existed. Yet now, all of a sudden, she had wanted so desperately to see me.

So desperately in fact that for the whole weekend I caught three glimpses of her, once at dinner on Friday night, once on Saturday afternoon as she arrived from an outing to change before going out again, and then once as she was leaving. It was at dinner that the truth of the Social Worker business slipped out.

Denise's husband was not the kind of person to be satisfied with vague answers. He wanted the details and he wanted them all.

"So how did you manage to get a weekend pass? I thought the Nurses' Home was particularly strict about student nurses?"

He queried suspiciously.

"Oh they are!" nodded Charlene, and then smiled.

"They allow compassionate leave," and dedicated herself to her meat with great vigour.

"Did you see what's showing at the cinema this weekend?"

She asked to change the subject, but Arthur was not going to be shaken.

"So how did you manage it?" he insisted.

"Manage what?" asked Charlene with wide, innocent eyes.

"Oh there will still be lots of tickets, I'm sure, we won't have problems getting a seat."

Arthur looked grimmer, he would not be put off.

"No Charlene, not the cinema, the weekend leave. How did you manage to get it?"

Looking miffed, Charlene mumbled something incoherent while she stuffed food into her mouth. Then she pointed at the baby who was happily whacking his baby food with his spoon and splattering the tablecloth with gay abandon.

The diversion didn't work either. Arthur put his knife and fork down and drummed impatiently on the table.

"Charlene," he said in a threatening tone. "I asked you a question. How did you manage to get leave? You didn't just walk out without permission, did you?"

Charlene looked indignant.

"For goodness sake Arthur, I'm not that stupid. I got leave. I was lucky, that's all."

"How?"

Arthur's voice was getting louder and more insistent. I looked from one to another, feeling like a spectator at a tennis game. I realised that Charlene was hedging because she feared his reaction, that meant she had done something she knew was wrong. I cringed, I did not want to get involved in these "*family quarrels*" because I really did not feel part of this family.

"Oh I asked for compassionate leave."

And she fixed him with a challenging stare.

For a moment Arthur was nonplussed.

"Compassionate Leave? What do you mean?"

"I said I had to look after my little sister this weekend. I explained that she was from the orphanage and that she was alone. When they knew she was under age, they didn't hesitate."

This is when Denise's eyes narrowed into ugly little slits.

"You told them she was alone?"

Defensively, Charlene returned to stabbing the food in her plate.

"Well what did you expect me to do? Sit there cooped up in that damn Nurses' Home for months and months on end? This was the ideal opportunity to get out for a little freedom and fun. And of course it is just so lovely to see you all again, you know how much I miss you."

She smiled such a sweet, charming smile that I felt nauseous.

Denise saw straight through it.

"Charlene, how could Amber have been alone if she was coming here? How did you explain that she had even got out of the orphanage if there was no one to go to?"

Trapped, Charlene had no option but to tell the truth. She hesitated and it was obvious now that she was afraid of Denise's reaction, rightly so.

"Oh Denise, don't be so stuffy," she blustered. "It doesn't matter what I said. The fact is they let me out and here I am and no harm's done."

Denise leapt to her feet and her plate almost upturned as she thumped against the table.

"Charlene you bitch, you told them I had died, didn't you?"

The words soared over the table and lashed into Charlene's sulky face.

"Oh Denise so what? It worked didn't it?"

Denise was so overcome with fury and indignation she could hardly breathe. Arthur's face was black, it looked as though he was exerting all his self-control not to get up and mangle Charlene into shreds.

I sat motionless. I didn't want any of this wrath and hatred suddenly turned in my direction.

"You stupid idiot!" Denise was trembling with rage. "Do you have any idea of the trouble and damage you have caused?"

Charlene's mouth began to drop. Her selfishness wouldn't have even tried to contemplate possible repercussions of the lie she had so glibly proffered.

"Surely you would have the sense to realise that they would have sent someone immediately to check out on Amber? What a moron you are!"

Her disgust dripped vitriol and Charlene began to go pale.

"They... sent someone?" she breathed in dismay.

"Of course you fool, what did you think they would do? They couldn't have left a minor on her own, without supervision, in an unknown town, without known family or acquaintances. For all they know she might have absconded or something."

Charlene's thick brain finally began to assimilate something of what she had done and she was appalled.

"Oh dear..." was all she could stutter. Her hand going to her mouth and her eyes darting rapidly from Denise to Arthur and once, as an afterthought in my direction.

In seething disgust, Denise stomped out of the room, not even wanting to breathe the same air as Charlene. At the door she turned back and pointed a warning finger at her.

"Don't think that I will ever let you back in this house Charlene. This is the last time you ever come here. Do you understand?"

Arthur glowered confirmation of the threat. Charlene sat numbly and then lowered her gaze to her plate. As unobtrusive as possible, I slipped out of my chair and sidled out. I hated and loathed quarrels and arguments. Perhaps because so many of them had hurtled around my ears and churned up my heart and emotions as a little child. I couldn't stand it when people started raising voices and talking ugly. It was as though the intensity of anger or hatred or resentment sent barbs of burning pain and anguish into me. I knew it meant that the nightmares would be back that night. How bitterly I regretted coming. But at least I knew that it would be the last time. I would never let myself be enticed back into this kind of atmosphere again.

Rather the orphanage and Dragon.

Of sisterly tenderness and concern there was little sign during those holidays. Of family affection even less. I was counting the days. I still remember with vivid intensity the relief feeling of lightness and freedom that flooded me when the train began to pull out of the station back towards the orphanage.

Never again, I swore never again...

When I got back to the home, Dragon sent for me. I suppose she wanted to make sure I was really back. I was half surprised when I realised that she was actually genuinely interested in what the holidays had been like. I was very evasive.

"It's a long time since I've seen my family, Mrs Crawford. We've all changed."

I did not think I needed to add that the change in them had been for the worse as far as I was concerned. She looked at me enquiringly.

"And Charlene? How is she getting on now?"

"Oh like she always has." I replied non-committal.

"Did you enjoy the holiday?"

I shrugged my shoulders. "It was all right."

Her eyes bored right through the facade I was so firmly holding on to.

"I see," she said with pursed lips.

I really believe she did. When Denise sent a letter again for me to go to her over the next holiday, Dragon didn't answer her until she had asked me how I felt.

I had no hesitation.

"No thank you, Mrs Crawford. I think I'd rather stay here."

At her attempted persuasion, I become adamant, half fearing she would force me to go. But she didn't, she just gave me a penetrating look, then turned on her heel and left. I never heard from Denise again.

It often happened that during the holiday one of the girls who had gone out to family would suddenly reappear among us. We never asked questions. We knew that something had gone wrong. For some reason people seemed to have difficulty accepting us orphanage kids among them, maybe it was also because we couldn't always adapt. I preferred not to go in the first place, rather than to go through the torment and distress of feeling like an outsider and then knowing that there was no alternative but to pack and go back to the orphanage.

Dragon was also no fool. She had been principal for many years and had experienced many dramas with girls whose relatives ill-treated or misunderstood them and sent them packing in high dudgeon. She was also familiar with the other types, girls who would go out of their way to be as difficult as possible so that family had no option but to send them back. I have no doubt that she realised that I was not to be blame, she had known Charlene and her sulky sullenness and she was well aware of the fact that my "*family*" had never demonstrated the least bit of interest in me since I had been in the orphanage.

So I spent the next holiday as usual with the handful of girls who remained behind while others were farmed out to family or friends. Those holidays were memorable in many ways. The bungalows at the old vacated POW and intern camps had been donated to the orphanage. Dragon announced the fact one morning at breakfast, about half way through the term.

"Of course if we are to make proper use of these buildings, we will have to dismantle them ourselves. And I thought it might be a profitable idea if they were then erected at a seaside resort for orphanage outings."

She had that funny half-smile on her face while we erupted with excitement. What a tremendous suggestion. We began planning shifts immediately for groups of girls to go over to the camps and start tearing the buildings down.

It was awful work. We didn't just tear buildings down, we tore clothes, nails, fingers, stockings and scratched and lacerated limbs till we felt as though we were doing convict labour. But it was really worth it. We had also long since development the attitude that you would receive for what you gave. We had discovered that with the choir, we gave time and effort to rehearsals, to singing, to entertaining and in return we received so much, tangible, for our spirits and souls as well as the material advantages of liberty and meetings with boyfriends.

The first holiday there was especially exciting, but it was also fraught with drama and tragedy. I loved the sea and was a very good swimmer so I was more in the water than out. It was glorious! There was a lagoon there, with the waves washing over the rocks and while there was a bit of current, I had no difficulty with it and my prowess as a swimmer.

The chaperons, mostly teachers, more or less allowed us to do as we pleased. We were mostly older girls, with just a few little ones that we took great care of. They were golden days. I remember them wrapped in sparkling waves and constant sunshine, crunchy sand and an infinity of shells to marvel at, some of them broken, but some still perfectly whole and miraculous in shape and colour.

I delighted in diving into the lagoon. I would open my eyes just a slit and watch the white bubbles swirl upwards from my fingers. I loved the thrust and surge of the waves pulling at my body and I cavorted around like a dolphin, pushing off the sand bottom and bursting out of the water to plunge in again with a shower of spray and splashes.

As I shot through the water and broke out on the surface, I noticed a crowd of people running furiously towards us in the lagoon. They were waving arms and as I shook the water out my ears I heard loud, frantic cries and hysterical screaming. I turned around wildly, trying to see why they were all rushing to the lagoon. About twenty yards from me there was a flurry of splashing, limbs thrashing about and panic-stricken chilling screams being suddenly cut off to a gurgle by slopping waves.

It was just as well that I was close to shore, because I froze. Fear ate into me like spilt acid. Someone close to me grabbed my arm and started dragging me towards the shore. When we got there, we stood riveted, watching the scene unfold.

Pamela and Jenny were sisters, not twins, but very, very close.

They had been laughing and chasing one another when Jenny had slipped and banged her head on a rock. Her body had disappeared under water and a hysterical Pamela had been unable to find her in time. When they pulled the two girls out, Pamela was clutching Jenny as though she could pour life back into her again. Jenny's body was limp, her head hung back at a frightening angle, Pamela was shouting at her, pulling at her head, trying to make her sit up.

I was crying in panic and hysteria by this time.

Stop it! Stop it! Stop it! The words churned through my head. Make her stop it! Make her stop it!

Pamela was screaming and crying, calling Jenny, pulling at her arm. One of the teachers knelt down by her and put her arms around her to comfort her but she went totally berserk. Girls were milling around, crying, sobbing, lost in fear and panic.

People were running towards us from all over the beach. Someone threw a towel over my shoulders and started to lead me away. I couldn't tear my eyes from the scene as I stumbled up the beach. Eventually the ambulance arrived. The teachers accompanied the ambulance, holiday makers on the beach stayed and comforted us and tried to revive our spirits. I wondered if any of my sisters would ever cry like that for me. I wanted to run away, but was cold and stiff with fright and horror. They made us some warm tea and cautioned us not to go back to the water today. There was no need for such a warning, none of us wanted to go near the sea again, least of all me.

Pamela was devastated. I use to find her alone in some remote corner of the orphanage garden, sitting huddled up, crying her eyes out. I knew how she felt. I remember the pain and suffering when my Mom died. I would sit next to Pamela, I never knew what to say to her, so I would just hold her and soon the tears would be streaming down my face. I felt so helpless. I wanted to comfort and strengthen her, but the words wouldn't come. At times I would go looking for her, knowing I would find her in a tight ball of desperate grief. I would hold her, then we would sit and cry until we both felt empty and exhausted, inside there were no more, tears, just an aching hollow.

With time the immediate agony became dulled and she stopped crying, but the deep hurt remained in her eyes. She became quiet and introverted. I don't think she ever got over the loss of her beloved sister. I felt terribly sorry for her, but at the same time in a strange way. I envied her that love. My sisters would never have grieved for me like that. I had never experienced such an encompassing love.

It was that intense, crying-need for love that led me to make so many mistakes after I left the orphanage. The desire to be loved and accepted can be so strong and so overwhelming that it blinds you, deafens you to truth, colours reality and makes you see and believe things that aren't there. Yet you are convinced they are, because you want so desperately to believe in them.

I often wonder how many orphanage girls fell into the same miserable pits and traps that I did. I would assume that there were many of us. We were so eager and exuberant in facing our freedom on leaving the orphanage, so full of hope and expectancy. But we were also very naive, inexperienced and so unprepared for the problems that would confront us.

I remember how scared I started to become in my final year. Scared that I wouldn't make it. Scared that I would fail matric. Scared that as I reached my hand out to grasp the opportunities seemingly ahead, they would be snatched mockingly away. I was convinced that anything I loved or considered precious would somehow be cursed or harmed. So I was afraid to love. At times when someone was particularly important to me, I would push them away from me, put massive barriers up against them so that they would not be hurt by the evil forces I was convinced would harm what was dear to me.

I had discovered what an immense risk it was to love something. One stood to suffer far too much in loving another being, be that an animal or a person. I felt that if I had nothing and no one, then I had nothing or no one to lose and so I wouldn't be hurt. So I isolated myself ever more from others. The invisible veil that always separated me from them grew thick and increasingly impenetrable and in a twisted way, while I felt so lonely at times, yet I felt safe. In there, where searching eyes and minds could not find me. I huddled away in my own personal aloneness.

CHAPTER EIGHTEEN

By the time we reached our final year in the orphanage. Dragon's attitude had undergone many changes. With all the wisdom of my seventeen years, I assumed that she treated us with greater circumspection and even respect because she knew she could no longer dominate and intimidate us. Thinking about it now, I realise that that wasn't the whole truth. As much as I dislike admitting it, she did contribute to making my life a lot easier. The privileges and favours she granted me relieved me of a great deal of the more unpleasant and demanding work. Without my being aware of it at the time, she was actually imposing a greater trust in me by allowing me relatively more freedom and according me more responsibility in certain areas.

Unlike most of the girls there, I was already used to having to fight for my rights and stand on my own two feet, but the confidence Dragon placed in me reinforced that attitude and removed it from the solid foundation of rebellion and stubborn independence that it had been built on. She rather encouraged an attitude of awareness of our potential and our personal abilities. I know I became increasingly confident and self-assured. At the time it never crossed my mind that Dragon could have had anything to do with that, but on reflection now I see how very subtly and imperceptibly she influenced me.

I enjoyed being a senior. The added responsibilities were not a burden to me. I felt genuine affection for a lot of the littler ones that I could feel looked up to me. Dragon didn't beat us up anymore, and though I was still very determinedly independent and prone to disregarding regulations I considered unnecessary or stupid, she tended to cast a blind eye over much of that. She did however come up with some weird propositions that made me look at her very suspiciously out of the corner of my eye.

She had called me to her office, and as usual my first reaction was to wonder what I had done wrong this time. There was a box on her desk and with her funny half secret crooked smile she told me to take it to see... 'Whether they fitted.'

Intrigued I opened the box to find a really lovely pair of shoes with a bit of heel. Of course they were a perfect fit. I was surprised and thrilled. Dragon looked pleased at my expression and then told me in a cautionary tone of voice.

"Mind they are only for Sundays, so don't spoil them by wearing them during the week."

I almost liked her. Those shoes made me feel grown-up and special. It was when she saw me wearing them for the first time that she came out with her strange remark.

"You look very nice Amber. You are becoming quite a mature young lady now. I think it would be a wonderful thing for you to marry a minister, that would be just what you need."

I was speechless.

Me? Marry a man of God? Had she gone out of her mind? I gaped at her in disbelief and she began to look somewhat offended.

"You should think about it. I think you would make some minister an excellent wife."

Turning on her heel she walked off, while I stood there staring at her retreating back. From that time, she would often make that remark and I would wonder in amazement how someone with her experience could know so little about the thoughts and reactions of people in her charge.

During the years I had been there, several of the girls had run away. They were all inevitably caught. Some of them were given another opportunity. Others were sent to reform school. What happened to them there I don't know, I still thought it senseless to run away, it achieved nothing. I wondered sometimes why Dragon had never threatened me with a reform school. I was no less brash and rebellious than many of those who had been sent away for stepping over the line too often. Somehow there always seemed to be a bit more grace, another opportunity, a second chance for me. I believe that my *Special Friend* was watching over me.

I might not be a good Christian in the more traditional "*accepted*" way, but to me the Lord Jesus has always held a special place of intimacy. I know that He is aware of every thought and that I can hide nothing from Him, so I have no qualms about talking to Him very openly and frankly. You see, if He created me and knows me so well, then He understands me and can accept me as I am. I don't have to pretend to be someone I'm not to try and impress Him or persuade Him about something, that is just foolishness. I believe that He has always pulled me through. Even the worst times, when it really looked as though life itself was a blasphemy, that I was worse than nothing, I know He heard my heart agonise, even when I didn't have words to express what I felt. So I knew that He was picking me up and helping me over that awful stretch of the way.

So that's why I believe that somehow He intervened for me, without my even being aware of it. He influenced Dragon to give me another chance. He must have either shortened her vision or blanked out her memory or done some incredible miracle to soften her concrete heart. Whatever, the thing is it worked. She seemed to consider me her special project. Maybe she thought she could reform me or something! So there I was, in my last year at the orphanage, the recipient of several very unmerited favours and privileges, at the watershed of a new beginning.

I was still knitting for her and for her friends too, and though my bottom, arms and back suffered, I seemed to be able to endure the cramps, pains and stiffness a little better. Perhaps my rear end had developed calluses.

Matric loomed on the horizon. In some ways it was almost hard to believe that it was my last year at school. I think I was lucky to have made it that far, not because I couldn't handle the work, but because I came so close to being expelled so many times. I wanted so much to be a sweet, nice girl that everyone like, and at times I was. But then something would happen, or someone would say something that hurt or antagonised me and before I could think, the words would be out of my mouth. As I grew older I learned to control this spontaneous lashing out with a bit more success, and sometimes I would have to sit and consciously clench my teeth to keep my jaw closed, or bite my tongue to stop myself from blurting out my thoughts and feelings.

For some reason I still don't fully understand, the teachers always seemed prepared to give me another chance, and yet another. Perhaps they felt sorry for me, perhaps they knew something about my early childhood and made allowances for it. I must say though that I was never rude in an ugly and insulting way. I was cheeky and wouldn't stand for being humiliated or embarrassed in front of others.

The teachers impressed the importance of matric on us. I was perhaps even more aware of its significance than most, because I knew that my future depended on me alone. I had no family or friends to help me. I had no outside contacts who could wangle a secure job in some nice comfortable office. This knowledge brooded in my consciousness like a cancer. Then I would try to shake it off and encourage myself.

"Oh, come on Amber, your sisters have already gone through all this and left and made themselves a life, and they have been through much the same sort of hell as you, so there is no reason why you can't do it too."

I was stupid enough to cherish the illusion that they would help me. I studied particularly hard during this year but simply didn't have as much time as most girls, because of the orphanage chores, the knitting, the Saturdays earning money at the stadium selling cold drinks and sweets. As the months slipped inexorably by I felt increasingly drained. A perpetual tiredness settled in my limbs. I felt heavy and listless. And all the time there was the shadow of the future lurking ominously in the background.

They gave us two weeks study leave before matric and one afternoon, the tiredness seemed to press more heavily on me than usual. Fear would keep trying to ooze out of the depths I had pushed it in. There was an oppressive feeling around my forehead, pushing down on my head. It was useless trying to drive myself to study through the murk and pessimism crowding in. I went to find Dragon and asked whether I could go and lie down. She gave me a quick, sharp stare.

"Why, what's the matter?"

"I'm just feeling so tired Mrs Crawford and I've got an awful headache."

I felt pale. I must have been looking off colour because she told me abruptly to get some aspirin from Grace and then go to bed.

It was a relief to lie down in the silence of the empty dorm.

Shadows from the trees outside lay heavy on the walls, because there was no wind to ease the afternoon heat. I must have dropped off because I was suddenly plunged into nightmare fear and horror. Invisible forces were trying to crush me. I was trapped, I couldn't breathe. I opened my mouth to scream and no sound came. Gasping and gagging in terror I tried to run and couldn't lift my legs. With agonising slowness I managed to drag one foot up and lurch forward on it. Then the other wouldn't move and I started tilting towards the ground. Behind me I could feel the menacing presence press closer.

My heart pounded so fast and loudly it woke me. I lay paralysed, sweat on my forehead and my mouth dry like ash and dust. An icy cold laid a clammy film over me. Shivering with fear and cold I stood up to fetch a jersey. I felt so strange, I turned to get back on to the bed and stood transfixed in horror. I was looking down at myself lying stiff and motionless on the bed.

Where was I? I looked at my arms and body where I stood next to the bed. Yet there outstretched before me, was another me, seemingly unaware of my presence. Who was the real me? Then suddenly a door slammed. I jerked up straight, and was once more on the bed, staring in total confusion at the dormitory door. For a while I just sat there, rigid and uncomprehending. Then that infinite weariness enfolded me again and I lay down, passive and uncaring.

I must have drifted off again, because I opened my eyes to find myself shivering. Oh yes, I thought, I was going to get a jersey. I went to the locker for my jersey, turning around holding the garment, I saw my body lying on the bed. With trembling hands, I dropped the jersey on the bed. As it hit the legs of my body on the bed, I snapped awake again. I was lying in bed, staring at the ceiling, and there was a jersey draped over my legs.

My whole being started to shake, slowly and continuously, it became uncontrollable as the panic and confusion grew like some evil fungus.

What was happening to me? Was I going mad?

My thoughts became incoherent. I found myself stumbling and falling down the stairs, tears pouring down my cheeks. Someone was sobbing and crying out loudly, distractedly. I wondered who could be so distraught. Then a person grabbed my shoulders and shook me. I realised that the voice crying and sobbing was mine.

Slowly the shouts registered and I heard Dragon commanding me to control myself, to stop crying and to tell her what was wrong.

I was dazed, completely confused. I didn't know where I was or what was happening. The next thing I remember is waking up to find Grace sitting next to me with a book. She leaned over carefully, tilting her head back a bit to look out of the bottom of her bifocals.

"Are you awake now dear? How do you feel?"

I felt weird. *Woozy*, like my head didn't belong to my body. I tried to talk, but my tongue slurred and felt awfully thick. I just shook my head tiredly and closed my eyes again. I suppose they must have given me a sedative or something. It was morning when I woke up again and I felt fine. I couldn't shake the memory of standing next to my own body. Dragon knew I had nightmares, but I honestly didn't think she would believe or understand what had happened. I myself didn't understand it, so I didn't even bother to try to explain. I just let them all put it down to a particularly bad nightmare.

"It's the strain of all the study and the worry about the exams," Grace said soothingly. And that became the general consensus of opinion.

The exams came and went. Then there was the agonising wait before the results. When they were eventually published I was too nervous to go and see whether I had passed or not, so when the others shot off to the school, I stayed in the orphanage and busied myself with a whole lot of totally unnecessary work.

Every time I found my thoughts sneaking over to the girls at the school I would forcibly compel them into another course.

"Amber!!"

I could hear Belinda screaming from the front door. My heart sank, it was though I retreated to a tiny little dark blot deep inside me. Feet running down the corridor and my heart beating faster and louder till it was thudding so loudly it was like a drum in my ears. Belinda burst through the kitchen door. She was jubilant, eyes shining and mouth wide in triumph.

"Amber, I've passed, I've passed!"

She grabbed me around the waist and started swinging me around the kitchen floor. I had such a sick feeling in my stomach. And me? I thought, what about me? At the back of my mind a sad thought floated its brief longing through my awareness. Didn't she think to come and tell me whether I had passed? Doesn't she care enough?

Breathless and grabbing at the stitch in her side, Belinda cocked her head and peered mischievously at me.

"Don't you want to know whether you've passed or not?" and her mouth stretched into a wicked smile.

In a flash I tumbled to her teasing. I snatched at her hair, but she jerked away, laughing wildly. Just out of reach she danced tantalisingly.

"I know your results! I know your results!"

She chanted in a grinning sing-song voice. I leapt at her and there was a savage chase through the kitchen. Pots and saucepans were flying as we careened into tables and grabbed desperately at things for support. Hurtling round a corner of the table, Belinda clutched out to steady herself and the tray of cutlery was swept with an impressive crash to the floor. Eventually the two of us collapsed in a heap on the floor, yelling and writhing and kicking. I was tickling and poking her, shouting blood-curdling threats at the top of my voice. She couldn't break away because though I was so tiny, I was very strong and I had a firm grip on her.

Eventually, panting and laughing she gave up and lay flat on the floor, her chest heaving and her face red.

"What is going on here?"

Debbie stood imperiously in the doorway, hands on hips and an astonished expression on her face. Grace peeped from over her shoulder. I folded with giggles because I could imagine the scene through her eyes. Pots and saucepans scattered all over the place, knives, forks and spoons littering the floor, chaos and pandemonium. And of course my diminutive figure kneeling menacingly on a supine and wildly cackling Belinda.

I struggled to my feet and dusted my knees.

"Oh hello Debbie, hello Grace."

I smiled as though they had sat down for afternoon tea.

"Come in, I was just congratulating Belinda on passing matric."

I shoved my toe into her side so that she shouted and doubled up from the unexpected tickle-prod.

The sisters didn't know whether to be amused or to get cross about the trashing of the kitchen. But Belinda and I immediately started clearing up, so they unruffled their bushy feathers again. While we worked I hissed a warning in her ear.

"You had better tell me, and fast, otherwise you're going to regret it."

She giggled again, moved out of reach and carried on busily with wide innocent eyes.

I made sure I finished up before her, then stood waiting threateningly at the door. She tried a dodge, but then gave up. Putting her arms around me, she started to whisper, her voice growing louder with each word.

"Amber... you... have... passed!"

The last word was shouted and it half deafened me as it echoed inside my head. I felt the word and what it meant with a overwhelming flood of relief through my whole being.

Passed! To me it seemed like a dream. That meant my future was assured. I would be able to get a job soon. Then I would leave the orphanage and I would be free. Free to live my life. Free to do what I want. Free to pass the hours and days without bells, without rules without regulations, without someone shouting at me, telling me what to do, when to do it, how to do it and for how long!

I stood transfixed and then shrieked and together with Belinda dashed out into the garden. All the pent-up tension and fear exploded, like mad things we ran around, chasing one another, shouting and laughing with exhilaration, joy, relief and excitement. Similar noises were echoing from within the orphanage, as other girls reacted in much the same way, charging up stairs, leaping on to the beds and pillow fighting.

A chapter had ended, a new one was about to be opened. It was like I was living in a kind of interlude between the two. The orphanage had to let you go when you reached your eighteenth birthday. Probably because they received no more money for your keep. The girls who were waiting for a job placement had to work for the orphanage.

I believe Dragon herself organised the job I went to. She had this fixation about me marrying a minister and I am firmly convinced that that influenced her choice. To put it down to coincidence would be just too much.

She sent for me just before lunch one morning and with a very satisfied expression informed me that a position had been found for me and that I would be speaking to the superintendent of the organisation that afternoon at three. My heart lurched. I was so excited I could actually feel the blood running faster through my veins. It was marvellous, and it was really happening to me.

All kinds of tremendous things took place now, and it was like Christmas, Easter and birthday all rolled into one. I lived in a state of perpetual excited anticipation. It seemed that wonderful things waited around every corner. Grace had me called and to my enormous pleasure it was for fitting the new "*going away*" clothes. The orphanage provided us with spanking new items to help us start our lives out in the world. I suppose that in today's terms it would be pitifully little, but to me it was a treasure of lovely things. Grace had chosen patterns that suited me beautifully. I had a neat, trim little figure and knew that I was attractive and sought after, so the clothes were a delight. They gave me two gorgeous pairs of high heel shoes as well as some "*flatties*" for work.

It seemed that everyone wanted to give me something. There were toiletries, little personal items, cards, make-up and all kinds of pretty and useful odds and ends. The orphanage also ensured that I had quite a bit of pocket money to get started with. I began to realise that despite barriers and walls I had so carefully constructed, many girls felt genuine affection for me. I could never understand how those on the point of leaving could be sad and spend so much time weeping. Me, I was almost hysterical with joy! I always seemed to be laughing. I had the most ecstatic visions of how happy I was going to be.

I saw myself doing all kinds of things, working myself to heights unknown and then going to my grandfather... and at that point I faltered. I never quite knew why I wanted to go there. I don't know what I would have done or said. Something really bad, it must have been. I hated him with such an indescribable hatred that it couldn't have been anything good. To show him perhaps that all his efforts to break and destroy me had failed. To lord it over him? I don't know, perhaps to flaunt the success in front of his bitter face?

I was outside Dragon's office at ten to three already and those ten minutes must have been the longest I had ever known. At last she called me in and to my astonishment I saw I still had to wait another three minutes. It felt as though I had been waiting at least half-an-hour already. The phone rang. I was so tensed up I felt it resounding through my bones and blood. Dragon answered, chatted briefly and then handed me the receiver with a warning glower.

"Be polite now Amber," she hissed, "Listen carefully."

With clumsy hands that felt like big legs of lamb, I took the receiver from her and held it self-consciously to my ear. The tinny voice ricocheted into my ear.

"Hello Amber, this is the Superintendent of the House speaking. How are you?"

I gulped, my breath was coming quick and shallow and I stumbled over my words.

"I'm fine thank you madam, how are you?"

"Well, so you are about to make a big step! We look forward to having you here and are sure you will settle down quickly and be a credit to Mrs Crawford and the Home."

I was nodding agreement and then realised how silly that was, because she couldn't see me, but before I could get a word in, she carried on.

"Well, let me just give you an idea of your duties here so that you can start preparing yourself for what will be required of you."

She spoke for quite a while, but not much seemed to make a very permanent impression. Perhaps I wasn't concentrating but her voice was like continuing rain or a long wave of water pouring over me. It was the sudden silence that made me come to. She was obviously waiting for some response.

I thrashed around for something to say and then mumbled.

"Sorry? I'm afraid I didn't catch that last sentence, would you mind repeating please?"

There was a slight impatient catch to her reply.

"I asked whether you had any questions or whether it was all clear enough."

"Oh no ma'am," I hurried to assure her. "I understood everything. I'm sure I will manage and will learn quickly."

"That's fine then. I shall see you at the station. Please pass the phone back to your Principal, and good-bye."

I was so nervous I didn't even say good-bye, just solemnly returned the phone to Dragon. She motioned for me to stay and turning her back, concluded the conversations, making final arrangements I suppose.

I stood there feeling awkward, but aware of the bubbling anticipation effervescing inside. It was exciting, but scary too. Dragon hung up and turned to look at me with an appraising glance.

"I believe that you will do well at the Home, Amber. You will find it is situated in a most privileged spot of the town, on huge grounds and with magnificent views. You are a most fortunate young lady. You are about to embark on a new venture which will, I trust, prove to be a most auspicious start to your life in the outside world."

She smiled, almost wistfully and pointed to a chair.

"Sit down please."

I was a bit taken aback at this unexpected invitation but sat down as she also settled herself, crossing her legs and folding her hands in her lap.

"The time has almost come for you to leave us Amber and there will be many who will be sorry to see you go."

I thought momentarily of my little boyfriend, but somehow didn't think she had him in mind.

"You have made a great deal of progress during your stay and I trust that you have learnt some valuable lessons."

She was obviously expecting an answer, so I obliged politely.

"Yes, Mrs Crawford."

I suppose I'm in for another of her sermons, I sighed to myself. Oh well, I might as well submit with good grace, the poor old bag is not going to have another opportunity to shoot one off at me. But again, to my surprise, it was not a sermon. She sat silently for a while, with a strange, almost distant expression in her eyes. Then, as though she were shrugging off some uncomfortable thought, she continued.

"I have watched you grow and mature and have been gratified to note how you have coped with the problems and responsibilities. I have also been pleased to see that in many ways you have changed remarkably, for the better."

Then as though she were afraid I might get a swollen head, she quickly qualified her statement.

"Not, of course that I have always agreed with your methods. In fact I disapprove in the strongest possible terms of the ugly streak of rebellion that you allow to surface from time to time. It is with your best interest in mind that I advise you to make a determined effort to rid yourself of it. While I concede that there might well have been reason in your early childhood for you to have developed such an unfortunate trait, I urge you to take a long, honest look at yourself and your current circumstances, and admit that there is no longer any purpose in maintaining such a destructive and negative approach."

As usual Dragon was waxing lyrical. Sometimes in the dormitory, we would imitate her, with her long words and endless phrases, till everyone was rolling on their beds with laughter. This time however, there was so much sincerity in her voice, that though I tried to distance myself from it with the usual cynicism. I didn't really succeed. I listened, and despite myself I was touched. It was as if Dragon really cared.

"I would like you to remain in touch with the orphanage, particularly during the first, probationary months."

She stopped, hesitated as though debating whether to say anything more and then, with a strange abruptness, added the final words.

"You are one of the few Amber, who have managed to contribute something to the orphanage and the girls here. Despite, as I repeat, your very stubborn and independent lapses, your support and encouragement of many of the girls have been noted and appreciated. It is always rewarding to see someone not only cope with difficult circumstances, but overcome and give back, instead of just sitting on the receiving end all the time, making demands and holding expectations that are impossible to fulfil."

I could feel my mouth dropping, certainly my eyes must have been big enough to fall into by then. Was this really Dragon talking? I wanted to stick my fingers in my ears and jiggle it around to clear them, was I hearing properly?

Dragon was standing up, obviously a move of dismissal. I jumped hurriedly to my feet. Perhaps now she was going to laugh cruelly and tell me she had just been teasing me, that I was really a good-for-nothing that had no hope in life and that had caused nothing but trouble. Instead she stood there gazing down at me from her angular height, with that funny smile twisting her lips.

"I wish you all the very best good fortune for your new life. I shall see you before you go, but in the meantime, I trust that you will be preparing yourself in every way to face the challenge that lies ahead... You may go now."

I walked out of the office like I was floating, I could still hardly believe that Dragon had given me so many compliments. Things certainly were changing around here! I thought in amazement.

The few days that remained before my departure were gone in a whirl of activity. The happiness bubbled and sparkled up higher every day. I was going to be free! I was going out into the world, as an adult, a person able to make her own decisions, with no one lowering over my shoulder to control, dominate and criticise. The exuberance and enthusiasm buoyed me up on waves of excitement and anticipation. My life was about to begin!

CHAPTER NINETEEN

I had never felt so free! The train wheels clattered a constant drum roll to life and liberty. My whole being was dancing, leaping and glorying with joy and exhilaration. I have waved so wildly at Grace and Debbie and the girls who came to see me off that I nearly fell out of the window. I think I willed the train to pull off and then hurtle at top speed through the countryside. Faster and faster, go, go, go! I was loosed. I was free, I was on my own at last and life lay open and inviting before me!

It never crossed my mind that maybe failure and heartache were waiting out there too. None of the girls who had left the orphanage ever came back there. It never occurred to me to wonder if any of them had failed, and what happened to them if they did. I had determined that this was the first day of my life.

Everything that had happened up to that day was now dead. It was finished. It was a new start and I was grimly determined to keep it that way. I never wrote to any of the girls who also left or who stayed behind.

Briefly and nostalgically I wondered whether my little boyfriend had received my last letter. He still had three years to go. He was younger than me, but I had a very gentle, soft affection for him. He would carry my books for me and very timidly hold my hand. But I left him behind too. What was the point of keeping in touch, I thought. We are all going to go our different ways. It is better to lose and forget the past.

My job was a live-in position, so I didn't have the additional worry of having to find accommodation. Little did I realise that it was not so much to help me as it was to keep check on me. It meant that the much vaunted freedom I was so exhilarated about was actually very limited, I would still be under the iron fist of the matron or superintendent there. I suppose I can understand now how they must have seen the set-up. Here I was, one of the worst rebels from the orphanage suddenly given a huge dollop of liberty. I imagine they thought I wouldn't have been able to handle it and would have gone completely wild. That actually hurts, because it is just more proof of how little they understood me, how pathetically little they grasped who and what I was and how I felt.

But that all lay in the future, I loved every minute of the train journey. It was like a bridge between the old and new and each clickety clack of the wheels was taking me further from the old hurts and horrors. I had been loaded with gifts and had spent a good half hour opening them all and thrilling over them.

Wonderful, unheard of snacks and sweets to eat and to my delight piles of books! I had a reputation for being an avid reader and the girls had not stinted in providing lots of reading material.

The train stopped often along the way. At each stop I wanted to get down and have a look, but several times the conductor came running up to tell me to hurry and get back on, the train was stopping only briefly and was about to leave. Eventually I just poked my head out and soaked up the sights and sounds as much as possible from the compartment.

The excitement of the departure began to abate as the day wore on and mingled with a growing tension about the future. Would I make it? What if I couldn't stand the job? What if the people didn't like me? That steely antagonism shot up like the blade of a flick-knife. They'd soon find they couldn't push me around. I decided I had had enough of being manipulated and dominated. I was not going to put up with more of that.

The speculation introduced a more sober note into my reflections and doubt began to slide disquieting shadows in amongst the thoughts. The journey rumbled on. Uncertainty and apprehension began to insinuate troubling ripples into my mind and tiredness crept in their wake. I felt increasingly nervous and agitated. the train was due to arrive at four and it was already quarter past. I saw the conductor walk down the corridor and rushed to call after him.

"Excuse me, excuse me!"

He turned with a smile.

"Yes Miss?"

"What time do we arrive? I thought the train was supposed to pull in at four."

He shook his head, looked at his watch and then shrugged his shoulders.

"Any time now Miss, we're running a bit late, but that's normal. Maybe another five or ten minutes."

But fifteen minutes later there was still no sign of the station. I was tired, I felt dirty. The grime and grit of the train had managed to slide a film of discomfort over my whole body.

Stupidly, I felt close to tears.

"Oh don't be so silly." I told myself impatiently, but couldn't find encouragement anywhere.

The train shrieked a steamy whistle and there was a nerve tearing grind of metal screeching on metal. The wheels began to slow to the high-pitched squeal of the brakes. I could feel my heartbeat thick and uncomfortable in my throat. There was a tight pain in my chest and my hands were sweaty. With mounting excitement, I peered out of the window, eyes straining to scan the platform.

I don't know what I was expecting.

Banners with "Welcome Amber!" on them? A delegation waving flags? A red carpet? I saw nothing. The train chuffed slower and slower into the station and with each clack of the wheels, my heart sank lower. Dumbly I gathered my things together and struggled out into the corridor. With a final jerk, the train came to a halt. Doors opened. Someone helped me with the luggage, and there I stood on the platform.

Absolute desolation took hold of me. I felt lost, unwanted. No one announced my arrival. No one seemed to be waiting for me, suddenly I was no-one again. I meant nothing, I didn't count. An overwhelming forlornness swamped me. I stood looking around helplessly and then a voice behind me said.

"You must be Amber. Hello, I'm Mrs St Clare. Welcome to Sunningdale."

And with no more ado, she took my suitcase and started walking away.

"Come along, the car is this way."

Drenched with disappointment, I gathered the bits and pieces and followed her. I wanted to cry and laugh at the same time. She looked so awkward, squat and round, short like me, but round as a toffee apple, trotting along on her skinny stick legs. She was trussed up in a very tight corset that made her breasts bulge. She turned round to check if I was following her and her face looked congested from the effort of walking and breathing at the same time.

She heaved and wheezed as she spoke.

"Come along now dear, we haven't got all day."

Her head shook continuously. I stared, fascinated. She didn't look all that old. What on earth made her head sway like that? There had been a very old woman in my grandfather's town that used to sit on her veranda in the afternoons, shaking her head like that. I thought it was age. Now I realise it must be some kind of nervous disorder.

I was closing up inside and disillusion clogged thick and heavy in my stomach. I did not take to this apparently unfeeling woman. Well lady, I determined, you don't know what you have ordered by mail. But if you are going to push me around and treat me like dirt, believe me you will find out very quickly.

She scurried along at a surprising speed, considering her clumsy build and I had to rush to keep sight of her. At last we arrived at the car. She dropped the suitcase, took a deep breath, brushed her hair out of her face and then with a broad smile gave me her hand.

"Well now, now that we are out of the crush and rush, let's see what we have here... I am Mrs St Clare, Amber, and I'm very pleased to meet you. You must have had a tiring journey. Shame, never mind, it's not too far to the Home then you can have a nice hot bath and something to eat."

Her grip was firm and seeing her warm smile I started to feel much better. All the defensive hackles that had risen in preparation for a showdown sank down again and I slowly changed my attitude. I had long ago learned the art of insinuating myself into people's hearts. Even as a little girl I had been aware of this strange ability to draw people to me. It was an instinctive reaction but with time I learned to rely and draw on it. Perhaps it was the nice, good Amber trying to come out. I don't pretend to understand or be able to explain it. But it enabled me to take over in situations, in a gentle, unassuming way. Mrs St Clare, or Toffee Apple as I had by now labelled her, was making an effort to be friendly. I smiled and responded and before long I could feel that she was starting to warm towards me.

"I'm sure you will enjoy the work my dear. There are always people coming and going and you will find none of the jealousies and spites that are normal in today's office situations. You will be our youngest staff member and no doubt you will bring a bit of needed zest and sparkle to the surroundings."

She turned and smiled encouragingly.

"The House is on very large grounds and you will of course be at liberty to wander around as you please, once you have completed your duties. Of course there are rules and regulations governing the House, as there must be to ensure that everything is conducted decently and in order, but I am sure you will have no problem with them."

Her smile was more a warning than a welcome this time.

"I am the Superintendent and you will be receiving the greater part of your instructions from me. I know that we will get on very well."

There was no doubt that she was letting me know who was the boss here. I began to wonder what Dragon had told her about me. She probably had visions of an unreformed and unrepentant delinquent rebelling at every opportunity. The tiredness welled up heavily inside. It was the first time I was to realise that the past cannot be as easily shaken off as one would wish.

"Ah! We're almost there. Now just watch up ahead, as we come round the next corner you will catch your first glimpse of the House."

It really was lovely, far more than I had expected. The grounds rolled gently through gardens and lawn and tall trees were scattered indiscriminately between beds and alongside the drive. The buildings stretched way beyond the gardens, but I caught only brief flashes as the road wound on and upwards. We arrived at the door and Toffee Apple was smiling broadly.

"Well Amber, here we are, your new home. Meisie will take you up to your room and you can have a nice hot bath, and then when you've changed and rested a bit, you can come down again and have some tea and cake."

Meisie was a coloured girl dressed in a pretty light blue uniform with a white apron and cap. She stretched a rubbery mouth in a toothless smile and made a funny curtsy-like bob.

"Welcome Ma'am," she echoed, took the suitcase and walked into the building.

"Just follow her my dear, while I park the car, she'll help you to settle in."

I trotted obediently behind Meisie, my head swivelling right and left to take in as much as possible of this new place. It looked very homely, but I had to hurry because Meisie was disappearing around a corner at the end of the corridor, so I stopped trying to absorb everything at first sight and went rushing after her. I caught up with her at the bottom of the stairs. There were several doors along the short corridor upstairs and Meisie led me into one.

"Here we are ma'am," she said with her gap tooth grin, putting the suitcase down and drawing the curtains. It was an enchanting, "little-girl" room in pink and blue, small but very pretty. I walked to the window and looked out over the gardens. There was an air of such peace. The soft, blurred cooing of doves smudged the atmosphere with quiet contentment. It smelled fresh and full of life. Meisie stood with her back to the other window that gave on to the street where the occasional car or bus growled past down the hill. She looked at me expectantly.

"Is this all right ma'am?"

I nodded happily, not quite knowing what I was suppose to do now. Unpack? Go downstairs?

Then I remembered Toffee had said something about bathing.

"Meisie, where's the bathroom?"

Again the rubber lips stretched over her gums.

"The bathroom ma'am, is here, so come.

And she led the way again.

I realised how considerate Toffee Apple had been in letting me relax from the journey in a hot bath. It restored me. The disillusion and disappointment gurgled down the plug hole and I felt the excitement cautiously curl up into my stomach again. She must have given me about an hour on so to get a bit settled when there was a knock at the door.

"Amber? Would you like to come downstairs now? It's tea time and you can also meet some of the residents."

I felt a nervousness writhing in the pit of my stomach. I gave my hair a few last swift brush strokes and very apprehensively walked down to the lounge.

All I saw when I walked through the door was a crowd of people, and they all cheered and shouted greetings and welcome. I stopped, stunned and overwhelmed. All these people had come here to say hello to *me*? My heart sounded. I couldn't distinguish any features, just a mass of people. Some came and shook my hand and others patted my shoulder or gave me a hug. They were all talking and asking questions and I couldn't make one word out from another, it was a wave and splash of noise and voices and I was totally overcome. A surge of emotions closed my throat up and tears were pushing insistently to be released. I swallowed and tried to focus. There was just a confused blur of faces and forms. I found myself smiling and shaking hands and answering incoherently to questions I didn't hear. Toffee Apple must have seen my disorientation and bewilderment because she immediately took control. With an arm firmly around my shoulders, she steered me confidently to the table, gave me a cup of tea and stood guard while I drank it. The warm sweetness helped me to regain my composure. I was so moved and touched by the reception that I kept wanting to cry. The people were so kind and it seemed so sincere. Their faces were all smiling and relaxed.

After I had had a piece of cake, the Toffee Apple started taking me through the crowd introducing me. I didn't remember half the names but I could feel that I loved them all. There and then I made up my mind that I would never hurt or be nasty to any of them.

"And this is my husband, Mr St Claire," she was saying. I liked him the moment I set eyes on him. Tall, with a gentle, almost timid smile, he had a slight stoop and quiet grey eyes. He gave a small, sidelong glance at Toffee Apple as she introduced him and I realised immediately who wore the pants. My heart warmed to him even more.

The surprise tea party helped to take away the strangeness and unease of the new place. They made me feel so welcome and so wanted. Lying in bed that night I tried to absorb the fullness of the day's events, but within seconds I was asleep, and for once spent a dreamless night.

My job was receptionist and general office assistant at this Mission House. It served as a kind of halfway house between Europe and Africa, with missionaries stopping for a short or long visit on their way either to Europe, Northern Africa or the UK. There was a constant turnover of new faces as missionaries came and went, arriving from far-flung places that sounded mystical and exotic. I was fascinated by their stories and intrigued by the thought that people would give up their lives, their comfort, their personal desires to endure the most incredible hardships in foreign countries just so that they could preach and teach the Bible.

There were a whole lot of luxuries which took me a while to get used to: like turning on the tap for hot water, that I or the girls had not had to saw wood for in order to stoke the boilers, and like not having to do kitchen duty! And bliss and wonder of wonders, not having to do everything to the sound of a bell. I woke up automatically at an early hour, the years of training at the orphanage had conditioned that into me, then waited with increasingly tension for the bell to ring.

There was no bell.

It was strange to get up and get dressed in my own private room, without the buzzing, talking and clatter of dozens of others, but it was also the most wonderful thing to have a room of my own.

Even before I arrived at the orphanage I had been a very private person. I had learned to live inside myself where no one could see the real me or hear the words I really spoke. The privilege of physical privacy was something I never tired of savouring. I could go into my own little room and be there, on my own. Nobody invaded it with their thoughts or their presence. It was filled with my own being. It became a haven, a refuge, a secret and private place where I cherished my dreams and feelings and cried out my hurts and doubts. There were always flowers somewhere in the room. Small dried arrangements that I tied in attractive bunches and hung here and there, bunches of multicoloured blossoms on the dresser, or posies of tiny flowers with delicate petals, veined in rose and pearl.

For a long time I derived an acute pleasure from being able to hang my clothes up in my own wardrobe, pull the drawers out and pack my things in there and push them in again, knowing that mine were the only clothes in there. I could arrange them as I pleased, take them out when I wanted. I felt almost guilty at first, not having to share things. It seemed selfish to have everything for myself.

My first day at work wasn't difficult. There were a lot of things to learn, but I have always had a very quick mind and I grasped the routine very quickly. I revelled in the attention and fuss that centred on me. It was wonderful to be singled out as an individual, spoken to and appreciated for my own thoughts and feelings. It was strange at first, being almost isolated instead of being addressed as one of a group. For a while I pondered on the unaccustomed attitude of people towards me and the unfamiliar response I evoked. I couldn't understand what it was I was feeling and experiencing. Then one night as I lay trying to figure out what was happening to me; it dawned on me out of nowhere that what I was absorbing so hungrily was the affection and love these people were showering on me.

A spasm of trembling shook my body. Could I be right? Could these strangers really feel that way about me? Did they really care?

I wanted to believe with such intensity, that it hurt. At the same time I shoved the thought away almost angrily.

Oh, don't be so stupid! Who on earth do you think you are? Why should they feel anything for you? What have you done to deserve it? They are just feeling sorry for you, that's all.

And the evil seed of doubt insinuated its slimy roots deep, down into my mind. It wasn't affection and love I felt, it was pity. They must have been told the whole sordid tale of this delinquent orphan and the horrible things she had done. They probably felt revulsion but, because they were Christian people, tried to overcome it with pity. Anger began to foam poisonously in me. Distrust spawned the aggression and defensiveness that had always hedged me in. All my good feelings about the residents melted like powdery ice in the heat of my disappointment and rage, rage at having believed for a moment that I could be liked, at having been taken in again because of my eagerness to trust and be accepted. I turned my face into my pillow and choked out the burning disillusionment in tears of fury and bitterness.

Confusion flooded me now and all I wanted to do was run away.

Would there ever be any place for me? Would I ever be at home somewhere, among people who accepted me as one of them? Would I be an outsider all my life? Where were my sisters? I had told them I was leaving and where I was going to work. Why hadn't they made any attempt to contact me, encourage me, see if they could help me?

Resentment and hurt welled up overpoweringly from the pit of rejection I had thought closed forever.

Trust! I thought with cynical scorn. I will never ever trust anyone ever again. The only person I can ever trust is myself. My dreams crumbled, like burnt limestone. I could feel that domineering, self-centred brash female I had been taking the upperhand again. I felt miserable and defeated.

Dear God was there really nowhere I belonged? Wasn't there anyone who was prepared to accept me and like me as I am? Why did everything I touch, powder into dust and bitter ash?

I curled up into a little ball and burying my face in the pillow let the hot tears soak into it, till weariness and despair gradually dragged the darkness of sleep into my mind.

When I woke up next morning I felt drained. A sickly light was seeping into the bedroom as the sky reluctantly loosed the black-purple of night. My limbs felt heavy as I dressed. The house was still cottoned in the sleep of early morning when I tiptoed down the stairs. Feeling almost like a thief, I slipped into the kitchen to make some tea. The kitchen was bigger than the one at the orphanage yet funny enough it felt cosier and more homely. I put the water on to boil and started easing cupboard doors open to look for a cup.

Standing on the very tips of my toes, I stretched up as far as I could strain, yet my fingers barely touched the handle.

Waggling my fingers desperately, I tried to coax the thing to open when a voice behind me said.

"Yes Missie, can I help?"

I yelped with fright, slipped and would have fallen flat on my bottom if strong arms hadn't grabbed me. I looked up petrified into a pitch black face that was a mirror of concern.

"Hey *Nopsie*, you all right?"

I started to laugh, his eyes were huge and white in his black face, and when he talked his teeth flashed spotless and shiny in the darkness. Then I felt ashamed for laughing in case he thought I was mocking him.

"Oh I'm sorry. I just wanted to make some tea. I didn't know where the cups were. Have I done something wrong? I'm terribly sorry."

He put me securely on my feet and then from his impressive height loomed over to examine me more closely. I felt very tiny and very insignificant.

"You the new lady come to work here," he stated, obviously for his own benefit.

"Want some tea? I make it now. You sit there Nopsie, tea won't be long."

He had a really weird accent and he didn't look much like the other Africans I had seen. I watched him curiously as he prepared himself for work, tying the apron conscientiously and carefully arranging tea things, putting water on to boil in huge kettles.

"What's your name?" I asked.

He turned to beam at me.

"Patrick," his voice was proud.

"Reverend O'Riley, he baptised me Patrick!"

I discovered later that he had learnt his English from this Reverend O'Riley, which accounted for the unusual intonation and the sing-song way he had of speaking.

Patrick was originally from Blantyre. He had been brought to South Africa as a young man, but when I came to the Mission House he must have been well past his fifties.

"I'm Amber."

I contributed unasked and he smiled and nodded. Then he brought the tea over, together with hot buttered toast and marmalade.

"Here's some tea then Nopsie," he said. And you eat some toast too. You need some fattening, hey?"

He bared his teeth in a huge grin.

"You watch, you eat my cooking you grow quickly," with his hands on his hips he leaned over me with a throaty chuckle.

I didn't quite know what to make of him. I wasn't used to such familiar kind of attitude from a black person and wasn't sure how to handle it. But his smile was so spontaneous that I relaxed and smiled back.

"Do you do all the cooking Patrick?" I queried with a mouth full of delicious toast and marmalade.

"Yes Nopsie. Me I'm qualified chef and I cook now thirty-five, maybe forty years."

"I can help you sometimes you know," I offered

He roared with laughter. I was a little offended.

"Well I used to do kitchen duty in the orphanage you know, and often cooked for the principal and her guests."

He must have picked up the hefty tone in my voice, because he was immediately contrite.

"Sure Nopsie, you can help sometimes. I was just laughing because I think you too small to reach things!"

His teeth shone out in that face-splitting grin of his. I was about to get hurt when I suddenly realised how funny it would look: this long slab of Patrick and the little full-stop that was me working together in the kitchen. I started to giggle and then choked on some crumbs. Concerned, Patrick leapt to my side with an amazing agility and gave me such a thump on my back I went flying. Fortunately he grabbed me as I shot by him. The crumbs had been dislodged, out of pure self-defence I think.

It was the start of a solid friendship. Often I used to perch on a high chair and chat to him in my free time, and give him a hand with tea and snacks. I would do odd jobs for him and I could see he really appreciated it, though he would never say anything directly to me. Frequently I would find a plate of delicious snacks in my room, sweet or salty titbits that I could nibble in the evenings or the long weekends.

Patrick did much to lift my spirits that morning. By the time the official breakfast time come round I was feeling far more confident and assures, though I still felt closed and wary when people addressed me. Little by little though, the natural suspicion and distrust began to wear off, because the attitude of the residents towards me didn't change like I expected it to.

They remained friendly and open. Perhaps what I had interpreted as pity was really compassion, but I still wasn't prepared to accept and receive it as such. I felt the diffidence in me and though I smiled and was friendly, I knew the barriers were firmly in place.

CHAPTER TWENTY

"I see you also like Sweetpeas."

I whirled around, guilty. Mr St Clare was standing there with a benign expression on his long face.

"Oh dear," I sighed, and tried awkwardly to hide the plucked flowers behind my back. "I suppose I'm not allowed to pick the flowers..."

He looked surprised.

"Oh no, not at all," he protested, flapping his hands in embarrassment.

"I mean, yes of course you can pick the flowers. Goodness no, I wasn't accusing you!"

His timid smile crept shyly over his features.

"Flowers should be enjoyed to the uttermost you know, both in the garden and wherever else they give pleasure. I love Sweetpeas too, and Jasmine."

It was a Saturday morning and he didn't work weekends.

"Do you mind if I stroll along with you a bit?"

I was a bit taken aback, but also flattered. We wandered slowly through the garden and he told me the names of some of the flowers and trees. He was such a gentle person. He always used such consideration towards others, as though he were afraid of hurting or offending them. I think it was because he himself was so sensitive that he was often hurt by people's remarks and attitudes, and he didn't want others to suffer the same way as a result of his lack of perception.

At first I thought he was just feeling sorry for this poor rebel orphan and was doing his Christian duty in speaking to me, but with time I had to acknowledge his sincerity. He didn't have a wrong motive anywhere in his being. I felt his gentleness went too far. Toffee Apple dominated him totally. I sensed the hurt and loneliness in him and it became yet another bond of understanding between us. I went out of my way to serve him and make him feel good. I could see that Toffee Apple had robbed him of his manliness, drained him of authority and in some subconscious way, I tried to restore it to him.

As the months passed, I began to confide in him and turn to him for advice. It was a tragedy to see what could have been a strong, wise and independent man stripped of his own real person and made to conform to a pattern that someone else had imposed on him. I couldn't understand how he could have accepted something like that.

I would never ever have submitted to that kind of subjection. Heaven knows, my grandfather had tried hard enough to bend and break me to conform to his idea of what I should be. I had stubbornly refused to be anything but the *me* I felt myself to be. As far as I was concerned, God had made me the way I was and that was the way I was going to stay, be that mixed up and crazy or not. The road I had travelled had been a rough and difficult one, but I was the only one who could sort the mess out, and I would certainly not allow anyone else to come along and tell me how and when to do it.

I opened up more with the residents. There were seldom more than thirty at a time and mostly there were far fewer. They accepted me as I was, treating me like an equal and I mixed freely with them. It wasn't as if I was a lowly receptionist while they considered themselves up on some holy pedestal above me. Many of them had children and being little more than a child myself, I got on very well with them, playing games and going for walks with them when I was off duty.

I had come to the realisation that these were genuine people of God. There was no hypocrisy or religious playacting with them, theirs was a sincere and true relationship with God. It was the first time I had come across people who I considered knew God almost like I knew Him, as a special Friend who was there, even when it didn't feel or look like it. These people lived what they preached and I respected them. Never did they try to reform me or preach condemnation on me. At all times they showed me only affection and even love though it was terribly difficult for me to accept and receive it. Those carefully erected inner barriers were solid, rigid structures and did not dent easily.

I made sure that I fixed the hours of work without any chance of equivocation. I worked religiously to those hours, never less and very, very seldom more. I was not about to allow Toffee Apple to expect longer hours as her natural due. If she was a stickler for rules then I would play those same rules against her, the rules said just so many hours of work and no more. I derived satisfaction from my work, as long as she wasn't around too much, but I found it relatively easy to avoid her. She governed with an iron hand and there was no doubt about who ran the place. I believe that she always nurtured her doubts and suspicions about me. It was as though she was always expecting me to suddenly break out and do something ugly or rebellious.

There were tennis courts and croquet fields and I spent quite a bit of my free time playing. I was good at tennis, thanks to Dragon's example and really enjoyed the game. Croquet I tended to find a bit slow, but soon discovered that it didn't have to be the genteel game it appeared to be.

It was Roy who taught me to play croquet. He was at the Mission House when I arrived, busy recuperating from some African sickness, malaria or yellow fever or something like that. His wife had died somewhere in North Africa and he and his three girls had been there alone in the bush until he contracted this illness. They were lovely kids, soft-spoken and polite, but could be really cheeky when they wanted. It was a lot of fun being with them, they would tell so many fascinating stories and knew all kinds of games. Some they had invented themselves and others they had learnt from various tribes. They had learnt to look after themselves as little kids, as I suppose most of the missionary kids had to. The missions were mostly far away from towns and more civilised areas so the people who went there had to be really dedicated and strong in faith.

I had been sitting on the verge, watching a group of men at croquet. They were teasing one another, swinging the mallets around and making the most ludicrous bets. There were times, watching and listening to them that I felt such a longing in myself. They all seemed to know who they were, where they were going, what they were doing. A quiet self-assurance emanated from them. There was such a deep confident peace about them. I wished I had that. It was obvious that they loved being at the Mission House. You could sense they felt they belonged.

I hugged my knees and rested my chin on top of them. I wanted so much to belong, like they did. They had that sense of belonging all the time. It wasn't just that they belonged there... I thrashed around in my mind trying to pinpoint it... they belonged.

I sighed in frustration, then jumped as a hand touched my shoulder. Roy was crouching behind me with an inquisitive smile.

"Want to learn how to play?"

224

I didn't really, not then, but I didn't want to hurt or offend him. He was one of the quiet ones and didn't seem to associate all that much with the others. So I nodded and jumped up while he ambled towards the now abandoned mallets.

Roy had infinite patience, he had to with me. Eventually though I got the hang of the game, but not before I had become aware of the attraction he felt for me. It made me feel really good, but also very wary. It was when he was trying to show me how to hold the mallet that the realisation of his affection hit me for the first time. He was standing to the side and behind me, then reached over to fix my grip on the mallet.

When he put his hands over mine I could feel it. There was like a warmth, a magnetism, almost a deep trembling that I sensed in him. At first it made me very uneasy. I didn't know how to relate or handle it. I turned the tense moment into a laugh and tease. skipping away with feigned enthusiasm and laughing determination "*to get it right this time*". Without making it obvious though, I was carefully sure that I was never alone with him anywhere. I knew that there was nothing I could offer him, just a hurt, confused, lost bundle of trouble and woe. I felt his eyes on me when I was in the lounge or dining room, and he never failed to saunter over to chat when I was doing reception work.

After a while, he and the girls left for the UK and it was several weeks before I saw him again. I was in reception when they returned. He walked in with a huge grin on his face, gave me a long hard hug and tousled my hair, obviously overjoyed to see me again. A sad weariness began to filter through me. I could sense that he spent weeks weighing up alternatives and making decisions and I knew that I was involved in his tentative plans. He was more affectionate than ever and I caught a few knowing looks from other residents too, which annoyed me. I carried on as usual, not showing him any special favours and in fact trying to avoid him without being rude or cruel. It was useless, I could feel what was happening and wanted desperately to avoid it. He was a kind person and I liked him, but I didn't love him and I didn't want him to get any false impressions. He was not to be put off. The day came... out in the garden when he sidle up to me and said quietly.

"Amber, I need to talk to you, do you mind if I walk with you a bit?"

My heart sank, I knew what was coming. He walked in silence for a bit, then took my hand and put it in the crook of his arm, covering it with his other hand.

"I've known you for quite a while now Amber. I've been watching you and doing a lot of thinking. You get on very well with my daughters and they think the world of you. I know that I am quite a bit older than you, but I have grown to love you and I ask you to consider very seriously whether you would marry me."

I had known what he was going to say, but it still stunned me. Dear God what on earth could I do or say without hurting this man? I didn't love him. I don't know, perhaps I saw him as a father figure, but I could not in all honesty and sincerity tell him I loved him and would marry him. Deep down I was also afraid of bringing the wrath of God down on me. These were His people, I didn't think that He would take at all kindly to my marrying Roy if I didn't really love him.

Seldom in my life have I ever been at a loss for words, but now I was dumb. I felt awful, I didn't know what to say. My heart ached for Roy, but surely he could have seen that I didn't love him? He squeezed my hand encouragingly.

"Perhaps it's come too much as a surprise, Amber. Don't be in a hurry to answer, I'll wait."

But I shook my head, it would be horribly unjust to give him cause to hope.

"Roy, I'm sorry. I like and respect you very much, but like a father."

I felt him wince.

"You are such a good friend, but I don't love you, not enough to be able to marry you. It wouldn't be fair. It would be dishonest."

I looked up at him and wished I hadn't. Hurt was so stark in his face, he looked as though I had slapped him. I felt dreadful. He patted my hand again, walked another few steps and then sucked in a deep breath.

"Are you sure Amber? You wouldn't like some time to think it over?"

I shook my head miserably, he said nothing more. We walked up to the House in silence. All I wanted to do was run away. I couldn't face him and didn't want to see or hear anyone else either.

"Well, it's tea time," he said in an attempt at brightness. "Let's go and have a cup."

He headed for the lounge and I made some lame excuse about having things to do. I went upstairs and closed the door. If only it was as easy to close the door on hurts and problems.

I couldn't bear the thought of having to face him and the others at supper, but there was no avoiding it. I sat very quietly, not participating in the usual chatter and steadfastly avoiding anyone's look. It was needless concern, Roy behaved as he always did, and no one appeared to notice anything different. Relief cautiously rose up within me. Roy's attitude towards me remained constant. Never was there any sign of bitterness. He remained as affectionate and friendly as he had always been. I was taken aback, but so pleased. After an initial awkwardness I began to relax in his presence again, the heavy feeling of guilt lifted. A week or so later he and the girls left for the mission fields of North Africa and it was many months before they passed through the Mission House again. By then the incident had become history, but the pain and discomfort were all but forgotten.

One afternoon shortly after Roy's departure I was engrossed in the books when I became aware of a figure waiting impatiently at the counter. I stood up hurriedly and began making apologies for keeping the person waiting when I stopped dead in my tracks, eyes fixed on the face before me. I gaped at him, astonished.

"Charles!" I gasped, "what are you doing here?"

He smiled awkwardly.

"Well, aren't you even going to give your brother a hug?"

I stood transfixed and just stared. He was grown up - tall, I couldn't take my eyes off him. The last time I had seen him was after Denise and my eldest brother Deryck had left my grandfather's house. He had followed shortly afterwards. How many years was it now? nine? ten? I began to laugh and cry at the same time as I flew into his arms. All the hurt and grief of the rejection was gone. The questions about why they had all abandoned me, the crying out for their love and care just disappeared.

Toffee Apple came bustling in from the lounge. She had obviously heard the commotion. She stood there with eyebrows raised in disapproval, what a sight it must have been, little Amber buried in the arms of a stranger!

"Mrs St Clare!" I could feel my face glowing with happiness. "This is my brother, Charles."

I giggled inside, I could see she didn't believe me, but after he corroborated the statement she invited him in to the lounge for tea, I was still on duty and couldn't leave the desk for a while yet. He told me afterwards that she had given him a real third-degree interrogation until she was satisfied that he was who he said he was.

He spent the rest of the afternoon there. I was in seventh heaven, so excited, so intrigued at seeing him and hearing about the others again. Charles was married with a family of his own now, but as he talked I recognised again the timid Charles I had known as a child. I began to mock and tease him for the way he had always given in to my grandfather. He looked embarrassed and then began to remind me of the daredevil cheek I had defending myself with, against the monster's hatred and bitterness.

"Where on earth did you find the guts to do it?" He asked in wonderment. "You hardly came up to the man's knees, he could have squashed you like a bug if he tried."

For some reason it made me laugh, and that infected Charles. Before long the two of us were shouting with laughter, remembering incidents that hadn't been at all funny at the time, but that now seemed so ridiculous.

We played tennis and I tried, unsuccessfully, to teach him croquet too. The hours flew, when the time came for him to leave I didn't want him to go. I could feel crying inside me although I was smiling at him. He had still given no reason for his decision to come and visit me, and I was afraid to ask. I wanted to ask when he would come again, but I was scared to. The old doubts and distrust began oozing back again. Maybe he had just been curious to see what had happened to me. Maybe he had just come to assuage a feeling of guilt. Maybe the others had told him to come and check out on me. Perhaps he didn't care at all and had only been pretending all afternoon. He had never shown any affection and concern before, why the sudden interest now? I pushed the ugly thoughts down grimly, but they lay there and festered.

That evening I lay in bed staring at the ceiling and going sadly over things we had discussed and laughed over. Tears slipped into the pillow, the loneliness was more acute than ever. Anger and bitterness began to bubble up in me, it would have been better if he had never come. All he had done now was stir up all the old pains and dig around in the wounds. Why did he have to come now, when I was becoming a different, new person and changing from the child I had had to be? He had brought back all the memories of the hate and fear. It was like he had stripped off the mask of what I was trying to be and made me look at the person I really was. I sobbed miserably. Was I really still like that? Surely a person could change, surely I was changing? Surely I was no longer the hateful rebellious brat I had been?

I felt very torn. I didn't want to see him again, and yet I longed for him to call. As the days slipped by, I began to give up hope of another visit. Then one day Toffee Apple came to the counter with news.

"Your brother has asked me permission to take you out for the day, would you like to go?"

I was so excited I forgot all the morose thoughts I had been brooding on. Toffee Apple took one look at my shining face and smiled.

"Well, I obviously have your answer," she said wryly.

"He'll come to fetch you on Saturday at eight thirty, make sure you are ready."

Ready? I was ready by six that morning, impatience crawling in my stomach at the slowness of time. At last his car came up the drive and I didn't even wait for it to stop before I was in. It was a lovely day, just being out of the grounds and driving through the suburbs and the city was an adventure. Charles' wife was quite nice, though I thought she was a bit insipid. We all went on a picnic with his parents-in-law. They were very kind and treated me well, not like a delinquent orphan. Their son was also there, Godfrey, a very good looking guy with dark hair and brown eyes.

I had wanted to ask Charles about our father, where he was, whether he had heard from him, but the opportunity never arose. At one stage he started to say something about my grandfather, but I shouted angrily at him to shut up. I didn't want to know anything about that monster. As far as I was concerned he could rot in hell for all I cared.

When the time came to leave. Godfrey sprang up with alacrity to offer me a lift back to the Mission House. I was secretly pleased. I thought he was attractive and seemed a decent enough person. On the way back he asked a lot of questions about the work I did and the people. It was obvious to me that he was fishing to find out whether I had a steady boyfriend or not. I was amused but impatient with his round-aboutness.

"Look Godfrey," I said bluntly, "you want to know whether I've got a steady? No I haven't. Why don't you just come out straight and ask?"

He looked totally nonplussed, then laughed.

"You're quite a cheeky little piece aren't you? Well, do I get to see you again then?"

The car had stopped at the Mission House entrance by now. I flounced out and leaned halfway through the door to answer.

"That depends on you, doesn't it? You know where I live, thanks for the lift."

With a gay, carefree wave I went inside without a backward glance.

I knew he wouldn't be able to resist that, and in fact he phoned Toffee Apple early the next week to ask permission to take me out, the excuse being that my brother had sent him. So I started seeing Godfrey on a fairly regular basis, but after going out with him once or twice, realised that he was a lot shallower than I had originally thought. I grew to be quite fond of him in a distant sort of way, but I think he also gradually became aware of the fact that we didn't have all that much in common. He was fun to be with and he was an excuse for leaving the Mission House for a day or a few hours, but really that was as far as I felt the relationship could develop. If I had known though what he was instrumental in bringing into my life, I would probably have run a thousand miles away. *Or would I have*???

Looking back with hindsight is one of the most difficult things in life. The word "*if*" is fraught with so much potential heartache, so much destruction.

Would I have chosen differently? And *if* I had, would my life have been so dramatically different anyway?

Perhaps what I went through was a lesson that was set in my way, a lesson I had to learn, no matter which road I chose. Maybe the events that occurred would still have taken place, but with other people, in different circumstances, and in a slightly different time.

Sometimes I think that we have to undergo certain experiences as part of a kind of trial or lessons. *If* we don't, maybe we are put on

230

another road with a different destination, or maybe we even have to repeat the lesson until we have learned it. Perhaps these things are necessary for the particular formation of our character or nature. I mean, wouldn't I have been a totally different kind of person *if* my mother hadn't died when she did?

If I hadn't had to fight my grandfather, I would surely not have the wounds and scars I carry now. *If* I hadn't had to go to the orphanage... *if, if, if.* Those are dangerous words. They lead into a labyrinth of unhappiness, of bitterness against what seems hideous unjust. Life cannot be changed.

Perhaps one of the lessons of living is learning what can be changed and what can only be accepted.

CHAPTER TWENTY ONE

"I'm very pleased to hear from Mrs St Clare that you have settled yourself in nicely and that you are being a credit to the Home here. She tells me that you work conscientiously and well and that so far people have raised no complaints concerning you, but that on the contrary you appear to be polite and well-liked..."

I bridled, wasn't that just like Dragon, back-handed compliments and all kinds of qualifications to positive statements...

"...So far..." as if she is also sitting on the edge of her chair waiting for me to foul it all up.

"...you appear to be..."

Was it so hard for her to admit that people could like me? What was the matter with that female? I couldn't understand why she was so grudging with her good remarks. Was she afraid I might get swollen-headed or something?

I sat chewing my lip as I pondered her letter. I had been most surprised to receive it, the third one from her since I had been at the Mission House. I hadn't expected any more because I had replied to only one of them, and cursorily at that. A glimmer of understanding flickered through my mind as I read it again. She was afraid to put too much hope in someone, in case she was disappointed and hurt. I tried to imagine what it must be like with hundreds of girls passing through your hands as the years rolled by. There was absolutely no way she could keep track of them all, so how come she had chosen to write to me and keep in touch with me? It wasn't as if I had exactly been a model inmate. I gave up the speculation. As usual I couldn't understand her motives. I went back to the letter.

"I trust that the circumstances of your environment and the people with whom you now associate on a daily basis will contribute significantly to the general uplifting of the moral and emotional aspects of your character and life..."

Dragon wrote like she spoke, using convoluted phrases and endless sentences. A thought struck me with an almost physical force, she had wangled this job on purpose! She had constantly commented that she would like to see me married to a minister! The conniving old bag! I rolled back on the bed, rocking with silent laughter. She really was a Dragon. What a choice piece of manipulation! I sobered suddenly as I remembered Roy's proposal. She might very nearly have had her wish granted.

"I sincerely hope that you appreciate the advantages you are enjoying in this, your initial assay into the world and its challenges. I believe however that your years in the orphanage have equipped you well with the knowledge, skills and abilities necessary to handle the daily tasks confronting you. It will please you, I'm sure, to know that several of the girls of your year have found suitable employment and appear to be progressing satisfactorily. Unfortunately however, a small minority are not successfully adapting to the new circumstances and it is to be feared that alternative arrangements will have to be made for them, such a pity that they fail to realise the importance of change, tolerance and perseverance."

I knew Dragon's ways only too well. Trust her to warn and caution me of the need to reform and the dangers of failure, without actually saying it in so many words.

"Grace and Debbie ask to be remembered to you and send their best wishes, as I'm sure would many of the girls who remain here if they knew your current address."

This woman was unreal. She managed to convey disapproval and reproach even while she was wishing you well! She obviously considered it bad form on my part to have broken all contact with the girls in the orphanage and thought I was ungrateful or inconsiderate not to have written to Grace and Debbie. I shrugged my shoulders irritably.

Those were my decisions. I had wanted a clean break, a new start and I didn't want leftovers from the past clinging to me with sticky cords.

"In anticipation of receiving further news, I add my wishes to theirs..."

Despite my annoyance at what I initially perceived as her inquisitiveness and interference in my affairs, I was actually touched that she had bothered to write, and obviously with interest. Hers were not those letters of form that one felt obliged to write. Certainly she expressed herself in a stinted way. I began to believe that she was scared to let her emotions off the tight rein she grasped them with. Maybe she couldn't lighten up any more, didn't know how to.

I decided then and there to go to the lounge and reply to her letter. It was easier than I thought. I told her briefly about Charles' visit and the friendship with Godfrey. Then I spent an agonising half hour debating whether to say anything about Roy. I couldn't quite explain my reticence. In a way I didn't want to give her the satisfaction of knowing how close she had come to having her desires fulfilled, and at the same time didn't want her disappointed, and then I felt it was too close and personal and anyway it didn't really have anything to do with her.

Eventually in disgust I passed over the whole issue without a mention and told her of the evening dinner dance Godfrey had invited me to. It was in about three weeks' time and I doubted whether I would be going since it was a long-dress affair and I didn't think I had either the time or the talent to make a dress by then.

On the way to post the letter I found Mr St Clare sitting with his late afternoon tea. I plonked myself on the chair next to him and smiled as he lifted his eyes over the top of the paper. He always looked so gratified to see me. Carefully folding the paper, he put it down to dedicate himself entirely to our tête-a-tête. We often occupied this corner of the lounge and talked of all kinds of things. I had grown very fond of the introverted, lonely man and frequently sought his advice and opinions when I felt I needed help or another voice in a matter. I hadn't mentioned Roy to anyone, not even to him, but I had brought the subject of Godfrey up. I didn't know much about boys, coming from an all girls school and orphanage, so I suppose I didn't really know what to expect. I could trust Mr St Clare to be straight with me. I had told him of my exasperation with Godfrey's limited range of interests.

"He's so shallow. He doesn't seem to be able to talk about much more than himself. Then he keeps trying to put his arm around me like he owns me."

Mr St Clare observed me attentively. He nodded and sighed.

"Sounds like a typical example of today's youth." He said mournfully, and then nodded for me to continue.

"And so what do you do?" I also sighed and pulled a face. "He's so thick, he doesn't seem to believe me when I tell him I am not his property and don't appreciate it when he treats me as though I belong to him."

Mr St Clare looked highly amused.

"You tell him that?"

I looked up surprised.

"Yes of course, I don't see why I should put up with being manhandled. I tried to tell him that he needs to broaden his mind but he just laughs and says the problem is not with his mind but with my attitudes. I really don't know what to do about him? Do you think I should still go out with him?"

Mr St Clare pondered the matter carefully.

"You know my dear, as long as you can keep him well behaved, it might still be an advantage to keep your options open. He does manage to arrange quite a few pleasant excursions and you never know, you might eventually meet a number of very nice people on such jaunts and outings, don't you think?"

It was the conclusion I had already come to, so it was comforting to have it confirmed. It meant I could go to the party with him this Saturday with a great deal more peace of mind. I loved dancing and was so good at it that people often used to stop to watch and clap in time to the music when I was on the floor. Ever since I was a little girl and my sister's and mother's friends used to come to the house to sing and play piano, I had been a dancer. It came instinctively to me. The music and I became one.

I could feel the notes in my blood. The beat would rise and surge within me and I would feel as though I were floating and swaying in the air with the sound. Perhaps because I was so small, I moved lightly and delicately and people often said it looked as though I hardly skimmed the surface of the floor. Of course the guys queued up to dance with me and that was really the fizz in the champagne!

I had been half toying with the idea of cutting Godfrey off over this particular party and often wonder how my life would have turned out if I had. The chat with Mr St Clare decided me though, so when Godfrey phoned, I agreed to go with him. The decision was to change the whole course of my life.

The music and dancing always transformed me. I sparkled and glowed and could feel the admiring glances thrown in my direction. I was buoyant inside, witty and fun to be with and Godfrey always had a hard time fending off the boys who had come without partners. That night was no exception. There were several people I had met at the other dances but quite a few whom I didn't know. I noticed the one in particular.

He was lithe and slender, with laughing blue-green eyes and a wide smile. His brown hair was a little longer than was generally accepted and it kept flopping into his eyes as he danced. And could he dance!

His partner was no match for him and eventually, she sat down. You could see that he was only just getting started and his eyes searched the floor for someone to dance with. That's when I made sure I came into his line of sight. In fact I practically abandoned the current partner, telling him to get me something to drink and while he walked away. I went straight up to this guy.

"You dance almost as well as I do, it looks as if both of us have worn our partners out, so?" I stared at him expectantly.

I think he was a bit unnerved at my forthrightness, but I had always been bold. It seemed pointless to me to simmer and flutter on the outskirts of something you wanted. It made much more sense to go for it and ask for it outright. That way you saved time and you stood a much better chance of getting it.

"You're a straight one, aren't you?" he remarked. "Well, let's see then if you dance as well as you talk."

And without another word, he whirled me off into the music. It was the beginning of a dream, a dream of happiness, carefree love and laughter that was bathed in sunshine and cooled in the play of evening shadows. A dream that drew me out of myself, scattered the darkness hidden deep in me and painted images of a happy, idyllic life without cares, problems and burdens. The nightmares dissipated. The heavy brooding blackness in me melted away. The bitterness, rebellion and hatred that always lurked in readiness seemed to have drained into nothingness.

Gene was young, light-hearted and so much fun to be with. Yet at times he was so serious it was scary. He could be achingly tender and would then seem so mature and wise. He poured affection out on me unceasingly and unstintedly. I soaked it up like a sponge that had been lost in the desert for years and now floated in drenching rains. It was balm to my soul. It was a heady perfume that intoxicated me. There was a constant dancing and singing inside me.

We spent all our free time together. From the Mission House we took a narrow path across the mountain to the beach and spent hours splashing around in the waves, shouting and chasing one another, splashing clouds of spray over our sun-browned bodies, play-drowning and ducking each other. I laughed so much at times my cheeks and mouth were sore and tired and my stomach hurt. Never had I been so happy!

Never had I been able to give love so freely and so totally.

They must have noticed the change at the Mission House. I know Patrick did, he would greet me with a kind twinkle in his muddy brown eyes.

"Well, I'm glad to see you don't forget old friends," he teased when I came to help him with evening tea and snacks one day.

"Never see you anymore, you gallivanting all over the place, you just forget us here. You make some nice friends, hey?"

He hinted, raising his eyebrows so high into his forehead that it creased like an old newspaper and the whites of his eyes became huge in his black, shiny face. I laughed and nodded happily. He chuckled to himself and carried on with his tea.

I would catch Toffee Apple examining me inquisitively, but her glances were always tinged with suspicion and wariness. She made me feel uncomfortable and somehow always managed to rouse twinges of rebellion and resentment. She obviously didn't trust me.

Gene and I lived on in a dream world of sun, laughter and carefree happiness. I lived for my days off. Even when I couldn't leave the Mission House because of my duties. Gene would come up to spend time with me on the grounds. I tried to teach him to play croquet, but he didn't have the patience. He would end up grabbing the mallet as though it were a golf club and crack the ball so hard it would hurtle over the lawn and get lost in the shrubbery. The first time it happened I was appalled, I went chasing after the ball with my heart in my mouth. What would Toffee Apple say if we lost the balls?

I looked back to call Gene and saw him scuffing the grass irritably and swinging the mallet viciously at the flowers. This was a Gene I didn't know. I pushed down the cautionary voice trying to whimper warnings. I didn't want to know this side of him. It was the first time I had ever tasted the undiluted sparkle of happiness and I refused to allow anything to taint it.

I eventually stopped trying to teach him croquet, because he would lose his temper and hammer the ball violently. I was always the one who ended up scrabbling around in the flower beds and under the bushes to look for it. Those unexpected outbursts frightened me. He always recovered so quickly that it was a relatively simple matter to brush them off. He would burst out laughing, throwing his head back with gusto.

"Amber, watching your expressions is as good as watching a movie," he would tease.

So I would convince myself that he slammed the balls just to tease me, not because he lost control.

"Don't Gene!" I shouted at him one of the last times we played.

"Please, don't hammer the balls like that, you only upset me!!"

For a moment his eyes blazed with a warning anger, as though he were going to hit me next for daring to reproach him. The moment passed in a flash, what I had taken for anger seemed only amusement at my reaction.

"I say, little Amber can get quite domineering when she wants, hey?" he mocked and it cut me to the quick. "What's this, showing me the true colours when you're pressed?"

I'm sure there was a sneer lifting his lip slightly and it should have triggered alarm bells. It didn't. It terrified me. I didn't want to loose Gene. He loved me. He made me feel special. He made me feel wanted and loved. I couldn't bear the thought of his leaving me.

"No, Gene, I'm sorry. I didn't mean it like that, please. Look, please try to understand. I don't want Mrs St Clare telling you to stop coming here. I'm scared she'll see you slamming the balls around and get angry."

It wasn't the whole truth, but it was close enough. For a while the cold look lingered and then suddenly he smiled and gave me a hug.

"Man, do you only get upset about nothing! You really are a funny girl, you know that?"

I clung to him. I loved him so much, I needed him. I would have done anything to keep him. To me Gene was my whole existence. When he was with me I felt a radiance in life. When we were together somewhere, on the beach or walking up the mountain I felt like the clear mountain water tumbling and singing over the rounded stones. When he took my hand I felt like the mad swallows darting crazily at top speed through the blueness of summer.

Gene would have had to be blind and stupid not to realise how completely he controlled me. He was neither. I was too much in love and too naive to understand. So I suppose it was inevitable. It was my day off and we had planned a picnic at the beach. I will never forget that day. I had grown increasingly excited as the week dragged

238

along. Helping Patrick in the evenings I had submitted laughing to his teasing and he had even hinted that if I came to the kitchen before leaving, he would have something really special for us. In fact he did, he had made snacks and cookies and included a bottle of home-made orange juice too.

I woke early, feeling like a bubble floating in the air, reflecting the colours of the rainbow in the yellow-pink light. By the time Gene came to fetch me I was already exhilarated and bounded ahead of him up the mountain path that led across to our special spot on the beach.

It was an idyllic day; there was hardly anyone at the beach and the sun was caressingly warm without being hot. The cold soon went unnoticed. Then exhausted we lay on our towels, drinking in the golden warmth and listening to the rushing splutter and sighing of waves licking up the sand and sucking down into it again.

I was very conscious of Gene's body next to me, I could sense its warmth. Turning my head I watched him lie there, face turned to the sun and eyes closed. My heart beat thickly with happiness and I reached over to touch him. He started, opened his eyes and turned towards me. Again there was a momentary coldness that caught me unawares, but it was a mere spark, and then gone, replaced by the warmth and affection I knew. He fumbled for my hind, then turned his head back up to the sun again caressing my fingers as he lay and let his senses become one with sun, sea and sand.

I believe we both dozed off. I opened my eyes again because I had become aware of emptiness next to me. With a surge of panic I sat up. Gene was gone. I scanned the sea anxiously, but there wasn't a sign of him. My heart beat faster and I was struggling to my knees when someone suddenly grabbed me from behind. I shrieked in fright. He laughed so much at the success of his trick that we both fell to the ground. I was livid and kicked and squirmed like a trapped animal. We tumbled around in the sand till both of us ran out of strength and just lay there, laughing and gasping for breath. Then it was a rush back into the sea to cool off.

The afternoon passed too quickly. It was a haze of warm bodies, laughing eyes, salty lips, cold waves and sandy hugs. Inside me, something had been building up. I didn't know what it was, but it was growing imperceptibly stronger. As we packed to go, Gene suddenly turned to me and gave me a long, hard hug, then kissed me roughly on the lips and stared into my face. There was a heavy thumping in my chest. I sensed that same force in him that was in me.

Awkwardly, I bent to pick up the towels and without a word, headed for the path home. We had just crested the ridge when he touched my shoulder.

"Amber," his voice was hoarse.

I stopped but was afraid to look at him. He turned me round. He had put the basket down on the ground. Gently he unwrapped the towels from my arms and shoulders. I was rigid. I was breathing so fast I felt faint. He draped the towels over the grass and taking me by the hands, slowly but insistently drew me down. I pulled back at first. I was scared. My mouth was dry and I was shaking, he held me tightly and then with infinite tenderness began to kiss me, and caress my hair and body.

I felt a burning rise up from the pit of my stomach. My whole being trembled. I clung on to him and returned his kisses. He whispered his love for me, and I cried mine out for him.

The sun was just setting when we walked back into the Mission House grounds. I was shaken, Gene was tense and silent, almost sullen. He stopped at the bottom of the stairs.

"Well, I'll see you," he mumbled.

His eyes avoided mine; I clutched at his hand and self-consciously darting a look around to see if anyone was watching, he leaned forward and gave me a quick peck on the cheek. But I could feel the reluctance and it was like a chunk of lead dropped into my stomach. I watched him walk away and it was as though he couldn't leave quick enough. I made for my bedroom terrified of prying eyes. It seemed to me as though everyone knew what had happened.

As luck would have it, Toffee Apple was just coming out of the lounge and I almost bumped in to her.

"Hello, Amber. I was just beginning to get worried. Did you have a nice day?"

I was sure there was accusation burning in her eyes. I felt guilty, transparent. I was sure she knew.

"I... yes...uh, yes, thank you, it was nice."

I moved to get past her. She was looking at me very intently.

"He seems a very nice boy, is he working or is he still studying?"

I was in a turmoil, I felt trapped. I wanted to get to my room, to be alone.

"No he's just finished... I think he's applied for a position." I tried again to walk on.

"Well when you've freshened up, do come down to the office, there are one or two matters I need to clear up in preparation for next week's arrivals."

I could feel her gaze burning holes into my back. I almost slammed the door in my haste to be alone. Lying on the bed I began to shiver. The day's events ran unceasingly through my mind. I saw each scene vividly as though I were watching it played out on a Technicolor screen. When I got to the crucial one I didn't know whether I wanted to stop it or not. Confusion swamped me. Fear, love, guilt, awe, excitement, panic - the emotions jangled and jumbled into one another till I lost control completely and could do nothing but turn my face into my pillow and cry.

The last thing I wanted to do was go back downstairs, but I had no option. I made the bath so hot my skin was lobster red and I was literally steaming while I dried myself off. But it helped to drain the tension away. By the time the supper bell rang I had regained control. Most of the residents were already seated by the time I walked into the dining room. It felt to me as though every eye turned and was riveted on me. I was aware of every step I took, I could feel the carpet under my soft shoes, the weight of my body on my feet as I walked. I was conscious of my arms at the side of my body, the touch of the wood as I pulled the chair out, the movement of muscle and limbs as I sat down. I looked up expecting every face to be glaring disappointment and accusation. The smiles of greeting had to be false, those were masks to hide their true feelings. I was belabouring myself with condemnation, anticipating the rejection and disgust. The meal was torture. I didn't want to eat anything. There was a tight hard knot where my stomach should have been and a constant deep trembling that gradually spread into my legs and hands.

"Amber, you're looking pale, are you all right?"

Ken was one of the visitors from the UK and was seated at my table. I nodded quickly.

"I'm fine, just a bit tired from the sea I think."

"You might have had a touch too much of the sun, my girl," he said with a concern tone. "You'd best get to bed early tonight and sleep it off."

I clutched with gratitude at the straw and got to my feet. "I think you're right. Perhaps I did overdo it. I think I'll go to bed right now."

Toffee Apple had missed nothing. Her beady eyes surveyed me with an inscrutable expression.

"Ye-es," she confirmed,

"You're not looking your usual self. Well, the matters I wanted to go over with you can always wait till tomorrow. You go to bed now then."

It took me a long, long time to fall asleep. The nightmares came hurtling at me again that night. I woke drenched in sweat with terror clogging my throat. Afraid to sleep, but longing for the oblivion it brought I lay with heavy limbs and pounding heart. I must have dropped into the blackness of sheer exhaustion, because it was the breakfast bell that eventually shook me into consciousness.

The next few days were agony. Each time the phone rang my being leapt up with hope. The shattering disappointment became impossible to bear when it was not Gene's voice. I didn't know what to do with myself. I couldn't concentrate on the work and kept making mistakes. Toffee Apple berated me a number of times, with growing impatience. At last, five days later, he called. I wanted to reproach him for his thoughtlessness, I wanted to wail and cry and beg him to explain why, why, why he hadn't phoned. But, I clamped up. I was terrified of chasing him away. So I put on a bright, cheery voice and pretended surprise and indifference.

"Oh, hello Gene! How's things?"

I don't know if it was my imagination, but it seemed to me that he was stand-offish. I was holding the phone so tightly my fingers began to hurt. Trying to keep him talking, to keep him close. I wanted desperately for him to say something about that day, about what had happened, but at the same time was petrified that he would be flippant or sarcastic. He said absolutely nothing, as though nothing had happened. His conversation was about trivial things, like he was casting about just to make time pass.

I don't know how long I sat and stared at the phone after he'd hung up. I felt scattered - in pieces, disoriented, confused and bitterly, bitterly alone.

"Hey Amber, there's a parcel for you!"

The voice jolted me back to reality. Toni had just finished sorting the mail. She came over holding a large flat box. I stared uncomprehendingly. A parcel? For me? Who would send me anything? I held it in my hands not knowing what to do, till Toni huffed in impatience and snatched it back.

"Give it here girl! For goodness' sakes, you're enough to make a tortoise grow hair...."

She snipped the string, stripped the paper then shoved it back under my nose.

"There now, open it up and let's see what it is!"

She leaned over, eyes sparkling with eager inquisitiveness as I fumbled at the top

The lid eventually slipped off and I picked carefully at the tissue paper covering the contents. Whatever it was shone a dainty lilac under the flimsy see-through tissue. Bemused, I picked the material up and drew it out of the box. It unfolded in satiny waves of soft translucence. I was stunned. It was the most magnificent evening gown I had ever set eyes on. I held it to my body and glanced down over its silky beauty. The light glimmered in incandescent twinkles over the folds of satin. The length was perfect. I looked up bewildered at Toni, whose face was lit up ecstatically. Her hands were at her cheeks as she exclaimed.

"Why Amber, it is exquisite! Just the thing you need for the dinner dance!"

In the turmoil and suffering of the last five days I had forgotten all about the occasion. It was in about ten days' time. There were two other couples of the Mission House also going.

Where on earth did the dress come from? I draped it carefully on the desk and rooted around in the box. Right at the bottom there was envelope with my name on. I tore it open and found myself staring at Dragon's handwriting.

"I am sending the dress off before replying more completely to your letter, just to ensure that it will arrive in time. I trust it will fit and be suitable for the dinner dance you mentioned. Regards, J. Crawford."

Dragon!!! I gasped. It was just unbelievable! The excitement had quite dissipated every other thought and feeling.

"Oh Toni, please can you sit in at the switchboard for me? I want to go and try it on now!" I begged.

She grinned and patted her grey bun.

"Well now, let me think...

I grabbed her arm and repeated till she pushed me off laughing.

"Go quickly then, and mind you don't take all day!"

I shot upstairs so fast I just grazed the stems. The dress could have been tailored specifically for me. It was startlingly beautiful. Such an unusual shade of lilac that subtly glimmered darker and lighter as I moved. I was entranced! I wanted to float down the stairs then and there and twirl round like a model to show it off to everyone! I pirouetted, keeping my eyes fixed on the mirror in delight and awe, then jerked to a halt when I caught sight of a figure in the doorway. It was Toffee Apple, she was beaming.

"Well, it really does suit you my dear!"

She walked in and pulled a pleat expertly to one side. Then stepping back she surveyed me with a critical look before tugging at another pleat till she had the dress falling in perfect folds.

"There! It fits perfectly," she exclaimed with satisfaction. "Well, I know Mrs Crawford will be pleased."

I began to realise that the two of them must have planned it together. I hadn't told her who had sent it to me, but she knew. I could feel the tears pushing into my eyes. I blinked and looked at her with a new perception.

"Mrs St Clare, it is the most beautiful thing I have ever had!" I said with feeling.

She smiled softly and there was a warmth and gentleness in her eyes I had never seen before.

"Yes, well, now you make sure you don't crease it before you're to wear it. Take it off and hang it up carefully and we'll give it a good pressing on the day itself."

As the days passed I kept opening the cupboard and taking the dress out to wonder over it, stroke its soft beauty and hold it up against me while I stared in awe at the mirror. The colour brought out radiance in my complexion and deepened the glow of my eyes. Yet while I waited in excitement for the big evening occasion, the shadow of Gene and that afternoon clung to my soul and blackened it day by day with growing bitterness. He hadn't come to see me since, though he had phoned several times. His voice had sounded cold and artificial and the conversation was forced. I hadn't mentioned the dinner dance to him because deep down I think I was afraid he would resent the fact that I was going with Godfrey who was quite a bit older than him. I don't know whether it was the mounting thrill of the approaching event or perhaps a subconscious desire to needle him that eventually made me talk about it. The result was astounding.

"By the way," I had said in a half jocular tone, "don't invite me out next Saturday, I'm going out with Godfrey."

I was annoyed to realise that there was hurt in my voice. I don't think Gene was even aware of it. There was a moments silence and then with a lightness that I exulted to notice was strained, he said,

"Oh, where?" before I could answer, he added with a touch of jealous anger.

"How come you're going out with him all of a sudden?"

I purposely ignored the first question and responded carelessly. "Oh it's been a long-standing arrangement. It's a very posh occasion and I suppose he wanted to make sure I would be going with him, so he asked a long time ago."

I hoped it was salt in the wound. My body grew steadily tenser and more taut as I waited for his response. When it came, it was cold. I could hear what could only be suppressed fury.

"So why didn't you tell me about it before?"

"Oh I didn't think you'd be interested. You haven't exactly been such an assiduous visitor lately, have you?"

Then I bit my lip, darn! I didn't want him to pick up the hurt and bitterness. There was no way I wanted him to realise how desperately I longed and ached for him, for his voice, for his touch, for the reassurance of his love.

Very softly, his voice echoed down the line.

"Amber, I have treated you badly. I'm sorry. Can I come and see you tomorrow?"

My spirit leaped up into the evening air, full of light and glory!

"Yes I suppose so, if you want to."

I compelled nonchalance into my voice, but I could feel a deep shivering that was pushing insistently to be released.

"Gene, I've got to hang up now, the switchboard is going crazy." I lied. "See you later."

By the time I hung up I was trembling and felt weak inside, but there was such a delirious exhilaration coursing through me. He was coming! He was coming to see me!

I looked up into Patrick's knowing smile. He was leaning over the counter with a cup of steaming tea in his hand.

"Lo' Nopsie. So nice to see the little madam smiling again," he commented as he deposited the cup. Then with a huge conspiratorial wink he backed out balancing the tray and disappeared down the corridor.

I sighed with happy relief. The world came alive again. Life was worth living, and I was loved!

When Gene came the next day there seemed to be no awkwardness at all. It was like it had always been, it had to be. I teased and laughed and he responded. So why did I feel so drained when he eventually left? Perhaps it was a repressed tension, a hidden fear that all was not well, that something had imperceptibly, subtly changed. There was a nagging question that would not be quieted. Why had he only come when he discovered I was going out with Godfrey?

The evening of the long-awaited dinner dance finally arrived.

Every minute of my pains-taking preparations was a delight. One of the missionary ladies had given me some bubble bath and I luxuriated in the silky water, creaming the froth over my skin and soaking up the fragrance. I still had most of the make-up that the girls from the orphanage had given me and I took infinite care applying it. My hair worried me a bit, but eventually it fell the way I wanted it to.

When at last I stood and examined myself as critically as possible in front of the mirror I could almost see the aura of joy and pleasure. But then I grew nervous, maybe I was seeing only what I wanted to, maybe I was overdressed or too thickly made-up, was my hair fuzzy? I began to feel tremors of panic in me and was considering washing my face and starting again when there was a knock at the door.

"Amber, Godfrey is waiting for you downstairs."

Too late! Oh well, the die was cast, I picked up the pretty white sequinned evening bag with trembling fingers and went downstairs. The expression on Godfrey's face boosted my morale through the ceiling. He was speechless with admiration. I could see he didn't know how to greet me. He couldn't see me as the ordinary sister-in-law of his... any more. He took my hand with a clumsy gesture, was he going to shake it, kiss it or what? I burst out laughing at his gaucheness and it broke the spell. He laughed self consciously and straightened his tie with a sideways gesture of his head, then stared at me again, almost in disbelief.

"Amber! You look lovely! Absolutely lovely! I hardly recognised you, you're all grown up."

I sensed how his attitude towards me had undergone a subtle transformation. I wasn't the comfortable. easy-going friend, to be controlled and dominated. All of a sudden I had become more mature, distant, a bit untouchable and he wasn't sure how to adapt. I was amused and enjoying every minute.

The evening was a huge success. I danced every dance, the compliments flowed all night, and I felt more radiant and more entrancing with each hour. I didn't want it to stop. I gave myself wholly to the music, the laughter the light-hearted conversation and the fun. I clung to each minute as the evening drew to a close, willing it to stay, aching for the hour to slow down, to stop. But eventually it was over and time to go home.

Godfrey had tried manfully to monopolise my evening but had failed completely. I had been whisked from one manner to another and had relished the male competition. From time to time Godfrey would stubbornly butt in and whirl me off, complaining bitterly about female inconstancy. I laughed him off and he had no option but to get over it. Still I could see to my amusement that he was struggling with a sulk!

We drove home with the other two couples from the Mission House and the car was full of hilarity, so he really didn't have much opportunity to plunge the evening into a pit of morose sullenness. I waltzed up the stairs, still feeling the music in my body and lay for a long time reliving the luminous hours.

It felt so wonderful to be alive. Life held so much promise of happiness, love and prospects of fulfilment. My thoughts even embraced Dragon with affection and gratitude and I decided to write her a glowing letter the next day. When I eventually drifted into sleep, my head was still dreamily full of melody and rhythm, of multicoloured flowers, candles and decorations, of gorgeous gowns and smiling faces, it all seemed so wonderfully real and permanent

CHAPTER TWENTY TWO

Six weeks had passed since the dinner-dance evening and by now I could no longer pretend that everything was going to be all right. Each day I woke with tense apprehension and desperate hope and each day the fear drove its roots deeper. Gene had resumed his regular visits, he was the same affectionate person he had always been. Godfrey had become a far more assiduous visitor but was nonplussed by my decided lack of encouragement.

Then the morning came when I felt queasy. I wondered what I had eaten the evening before, but it was nothing out of the ordinary. Perhaps I was over tired, I thought, maybe I had too much sun again yesterday. There was a lurking shadow in me that I simply refused to acknowledge. I went down to breakfast, but the smell of the porridge and frying eggs convulsed my stomach. Before anyone could notice I ran to the toilets and was violently ill.

I stood bent over the basin, saliva dribbling out my mouth and tears pouring in anguish down my cheeks.

"Oh no, oh dear God no, no..."

Maybe it was just because I was tense... But after eight weeks I could no longer pretend and ignore. The nausea grew worse by the day and the other signs were even more vociferous. I sat huddled on my bed the day I had to acknowledge it to myself. I was pregnant.

Oh dear God what could I do? Why had it happened to me? Just when everything was beginning to come right. Just when life was opening up its arms of hope and promise.

Oh God no, no!

I could feel the wailing and tearing inside me as I sat with my lips tightly pressed together, staring into nothingness and hugging my knees to my chest in abject misery and despair.

What was I to do? Where could I go? I had no one. There was no one to turn to, no one to trust. I felt so alone, a crumbling speck in a desert of emptiness. I studied my body anxiously in the mirror. There was no sign yet, my stomach was still as flat as ever. My face was drawn and yellowish. I looked old and haggard. Frantically I washed my face and rubbed my cheeks till they were red. Then with stiff fingers I applied a delicate film of make-up to hide the nasty colour of my skin.

It's amazing how your mind will grab at the flimsiest straws when you are desperate. In my panic I actually thought I could get help from my sisters. I didn't consider Denise at first, because she had always been bitchy with me. So I phoned Charlene. she was completely taken aback at hearing my voice.

"Amber? Well, what a surprise!"

I could hear the questions in the pause between sentences. I seized up. I didn't know what to say or how to say it. Eventually I blurted out.

"Charlene I need to speak to you. I am in trouble and need help."

There was a cold silence, then very diffidently she asked, "What kind of trouble?"

"I can't talk over the phone, Charl. Can't I see you somewhere?"

She hesitated.

"Well... I have to go to town next week for some things. I could arrange to see you then somewhere."

She did not sound enthusiastic, but I was too panic-stricken to care. We fixed a time and place and then I had to sit and wait again. The questions kept hurtling at me like pointed rocks stabbing into my mind.

Should I tell Gene? What would he do? What would Toffee Apple do when she found out? They would throw me into the streets. What would happen then? I had nowhere to go, no work, few qualifications.

What would they think of me at the Missionary Home? What would Godfrey think? How would Dragon react?

Each question brought sick misery and despair with it. There were no comforting answers, no bright solutions. Everything was covered in black devastation. The nausea kept growing worse. It wasn't just morning sickness. I felt constantly queasy. The very sight of food was enough to churn my stomach. I began to avoid the kitchen like it was a place of torment and I could feel that Patrick was upset.

He was also not a child. I think he realised what was happening.

He gave me a long, hard look one day and sadly shook his head. Then he put a confidential hand on my shoulder and looking into my eyes, said softly.

"Nopsie, don't you worry little one, these are good people, they will take care of you."

His tenderness moved me so much I had to turn my head away so he couldn't see the tears. I tried to apologise for not coming to help him in the kitchen.

"Patrick, I'm so sorry I don't come here anymore, but the heat from those stoves makes me want to faint..."

He just smiled understandingly.

"Don't you worry Nopsie. I know. I can imagine..."

And I believe he did know.

He always tried to comfort and encourage me and he was always kind and gentle.

I had to move my day off to another day. I explained to Toffee Apple that my sister would be in town and that it would be the only opportunity I would have to see her for a long time. She must have wondered where my sudden interest in family came from, but I just didn't care.

Charlene was late and I had begun to think bitterly that she hadn't bothered to keep the appointment when she finally pitched up, flustered and irritable. We went to a cafe for tea. I asked for water, because the smell of the place made me nauseous. She was not in the mood for wasting time. We had hardly ordered when she said curtly.

"Well, what is it? What have you done now?"

For a moment I was tempted to get up and walk out. Did she really have no feelings for me at all? I swallowed my anger and hurt, shoved my pride down and took a deep breath.

"Charl, I'm pregnant."

She looked as though I had slapped her. Her eyes widened with shock.

"Oh my God," she breathed. "Trust you to go and do something so stupid."

She put her hands on the table and just looked at me.

"For God's sake, couldn't you have been more careful? Why didn't you take precautions...? Goodness Amber, there's all kinds of things you could take..."

"Shut up!" I screamed.

Heads turned at neighbouring tables. I screwed my eyes shut and hunched my body into a tight spasm. Charlene looked shocked and then embarrassed and indignant.

"Charl, I'm sorry." I lowered my voice.

"I didn't mean to shout, but you don't understand. it was a mistake... we..."

She sniffed superciliously.

"These things always are, aren't they?"

I gritted my teeth. She obviously decided to hurt and humiliate me as much as possible.

"Charl, it happened *once*. I still don't know how or why it's never happened again since then."

I pleaded, but by the way she was looking at me with a slightly lifted eyebrow I knew she didn't believe a word. In her mind I was a slut and that was that.

"So what do you want from me?" she asked coldly.

I was already crying inside, but I could feel the hardness creeping in. Why was it so difficult for me to accept that my *"family"* had never wanted anything to do with me before and would certainly not be changing their attitudes now?

"Charl, I need help. I don't know what to do. I don't know where to go, I don't know who to talk to..."

She had already closed up.

"Look Amber, there is no way I can help you. As it is I am in a very difficult situation. My in-laws aren't particularly fond of me as it is. If I had to get involved with your business now they would start convincing my husband that I was no good for him. I cannot afford to get tangled up in this mess."

Each word tore into me with jagged hurt. In other words, she was saying that her in-laws would say she was the same immoral rubbish she obviously thought I was. Sisters, after all... my situation would reflect on her. She would feel tainted, dirtied... I had heard more than I could take. I stood up.

"Okay, I understand. Good-bye Charl."

She looked momentarily startled.

"Well, what are you going to do?"

I shrugged my shoulders.

"I don't know. I'll think of something. Don't worry."

She picked up her parcels with relief.

"Good, well good luck. Let me know what happens then."

Without a backward glance, she walked away. Never once in the months that followed did she ever make an attempt to contact me.

On the bus home I decided to phone Denise. After all, she was my eldest sister. Maybe marriage and children would have softened her, perhaps she would have some compassion. I didn't get an opportunity to call her that night. By the time I phoned next morning, Charlene had already told her everything.

"Hello.... Who?"

"Oh it's you Amber. Well I suppose I should have expected a call... Yes. Charlene has told me your problem."

I could hear the distaste in her voice and so clearly picture the look of disgust on her face.

"Well, what do you expect me to do about it? Surely you realised what you were doing? You should have thought of the consequences before you started sleeping around."

There was no use talking, no use trying to explain. They wanted to believe that I was nothing better than a whore. I suppose it made them feel superior.

"I was not sleeping around. I'm not that kind of person and you should know it!" I retorted.

Her reply was sarcastically cool.

"Should I?"

It was as though she had punched me in the stomach.

"Well Denise, never mind. I'm sure I will manage somehow."

"I'm sure you will," she replied and hung up.

The desolation of such rejection is appalling. I was a big hollow inside a brittle shell. *I wanted to die.* Their scorn and condemnation burnt death and emptiness into me.

"Hi Amber want some tea?"

The cheery voice shattered into my consciousness like an icy wave. I spun round in shock, dropping the phone. Mr St Clare's placid eyes stretched.

"I say, are you all right? You look very pale."

I tried to smile.

"No, I mean yes I'm fine, you just surprised me, I'm fine really."

He looked disbelieving.

"Come and sit a while, I haven't chatted to you for days now. You have become a real will o' the wisp, always disappearing."

The last thing I wanted to do was sit down in the cosy corner and chat with him as though everything were normal. I wanted to hide. I wanted to close my eyes and let black oblivion swallow me into nothingness. I followed him like a robot. He settled himself comfortably and then beckoned Patrick to bring tea.

I don't know how I managed the next ten minutes. I felt as though another person was answering his questions, talking, sipping the water... while I sat motionless and looked on, feeling the hurt throw huge waves of anguish and bitterness into my being, thrashing around in an insane maze for a way out.

"Gene's on the line for you Amber!"

Tony's voice echoed in from somewhere far away. Mr St Clare urged me.

"Well dear, don't just sit there, the boy will think you're playing hard to get!"

I concentrated on the surroundings to make things come into focus again. When Gene's voice finally penetrated, I realised that I was going to have to tell him. He wanted to visit the next day. I didn't know whether to be relieved or terrified. We set a time and started trying to think up what I would say.

I rehearsed a dozen different speeches, but when it came to the push, I couldn't say any of them. I just clung to his hand in desperation and blunted out.

"Gene, I'm pregnant."

He went rigid, his face was ashen, he stared at me.

"Amber, are you sure?"

When I nodded glumly he was aghast.

"What are we going to do?"

I shook my head miserably. His hands were clammy. It was an awful reality that neither of us were equipped to handle. So, we made stupid desperate plans. We decided to run away, but then realised there was nowhere to run to and no hope if we ever got there.

Gene was still at Technicon, legally he was still under his parents' authority. I was under Social Welfare care. Our situation looked hopeless. We decided to get married, but it was another desperate gamble. It was while we were talking about marriage that I had to admit the truth of what I had been sensing, Gene wanted out. Certainly he felt guilty about the whole thing, but he was looking for a way to squirm loose.

We had decided to talk to his mother about marriage but she was horrified and totally opposed to the idea.

"You kids are mad! You are nothing but children. You have no idea of the responsibilities you would be shouldering... At your age! Ridiculous...! And what about you Gene? You're still studying. What do you want to do, give up your career and go and find some badly paid job? Do you want to ruin your whole life?"

So it went on and on in that vein. I began to notice that Gene's protestations were very half-hearted. He did not try very hard to persuade his mother to change her mind. Strange how it was always a matter of Gene and his life, his career, his future, his happiness... there wasn't a word spoken about me and what I felt.

The next time Gene brought the marriage thing up again, his mother got angry. She glared at me and made some ugly threats, I began to be afraid that she would throw him out of the house.

So I let go. I suppose I'm just not the type to fight a battle that will bring only bitterness and resentment if it's won. I felt the resignation in me. The decision just made itself. I woke up one day and knew that it was settled. When Gene came round that evening, I told him not to worry about it any more.

"Look, what's done is done. Your mother is so opposed to this thing that it would never work."

He looked guilty, but very relieved. I felt as though he had stuck a knife in my gut and was twisting it around.

"Maybe you're right Amber. You know, when I'm qualified and am earning a good salary, then we'll have a better chance..."

The bitterness flooded me so intensely I wanted to puke. He was wriggling away as fast as he could, and trying to throw me a saccharine sop to keep me satisfied. I just looked at him, I think he must have seen the scorn because he turned very serious.

"Amber, what are you going to do?"

I shrugged.

"Don't worry Gene, I won't tell anyone. You'll be safe."

He was totally unaffected by the sarcasm. He smiled at me.

"You're a fantastic person Amber. Let me finish my studies and we can start making plans."

I suppose that is where I really cut loose. It felt like I was severing my own limbs with a rusty saw. I had loved Gene with my whole being. I had given myself completely and totally to him, unreservedly. Realising that he had only used me while it was convenient and served his ego and his needs was more than I could handle. I began to crumble inside. I felt like worthless junk, I loved him with an aching need, but I never wanted to see him again.

I was more than three months pregnant now and I could see a faint bulge, so I started strapping myself up. I wore undergarments that became tighter and tighter so that nothing would show. Not for a moment did it cross my mind that it could be bad for me or the baby. I was completely incapable of thinking beyond the next day. Did I imagine that I could go through the entire nine months and have the baby in secret? *I have no idea.*

It was difficult enough just getting through each day. It was impossible to think of next week. Trying to think of consequences was totally beyond me.

The nightmares returned with vengeance, a thick oppression weighed heavily on me. I felt as though I were mired in black slime. At times I could feel the murk press down on me from outside and send up suffocating mists from inside. The abject despair and encroaching panic were stripping my emotions raw. If only I could just lie down, close my eyes and never have to open them again.

Often at night I would lie staring up at the blackness, willing myself to die. My inner being would yearn and call out for death. At times I was sure I could feel its icy tendrils slowly winding around me. My mind plunged crazily into labyrinths of desperate measures.

Abortion?

Often, so often I turned the option over and over and around and around, but always I came face to face with the wall that had "*murder*" daubed in trickling letters across it. I tried to convince myself. I pleaded with myself, I justified it, pointed to the advantages, weighed the disadvantages, but round every corner the will rose up dark and forbidding. There was no way I could get past it. Abortion was murder. I couldn't bring myself to do it.

Suicide?

Almost every day I stared at this temptation. Somehow it didn't have the same damning aura as abortion. It was frightening, because I was afraid of pain, but surely overdosing would have been a peaceful way to go? The more I surveyed it, the better it looked, I went to great lengths to get hold of pills and one afternoon decided to take the final solution, an escape. As I looked at them the tears began to flow. I wasn't afraid of dying, I knew God was not condemning me like the world was. He knew the truth and He knew me. It was just something in me rebelling, was it refusal to give in? I don't know. I did think that my baby would be deprived of life before she even had a chance. I realised that I would still be killing her. It wasn't even that that stopped me. Sobbing with anguish and loneliness, I flushed the pills down the toilet.

Strangely enough, even such a decisive act didn't put a stop to the thoughts of suicide. In the months to come I think hardly a day passed without my contemplating it, yet there was such a confirmed knowing in me that it was not the answer.

I kept strapping myself up tighter, cried through the nights and dragged through the days. How, I still don't know. In the mornings I would take great pains with my make-up and dressing. Ironically enough the more advanced the pregnancy became and the greater the anguish and desolation, the more beautiful I began to look. Even in the despair and hopelessness of my situation I believed that God was watching over me. I knew that He was fully aware of the truth and I hoped that He hadn't rejected and spurned me like my family had.

I was in reception at the switchboard the day it really dawned on me that I was caring for another life, a life that was totally dependent on me. I had just put a call through to someone when my baby moved.

She kicked me!

The most incredible emotion swamped me. My baby was alive, she was growing in me! Amazement, awe, fear and the most overwhelming tenderness. I looked round quickly, but there was no one there who could have seen and understood my reaction. Tears welled up into my eyes, if only the circumstances had been different... I didn't know if the grief and regret were for me or my baby... or both.

But it also presaged a new stage of development and it was becoming more and more difficult to hide the pregnancy. The more my baby moved and kicked, the tighter I wore the "harness" I had concocted. I began to have difficulty breathing properly.

Weariness and fatigue were weighing me down twenty-four hours a day. I would go to bed feeling exhausted and wake up feeling drained and heavy.

The fear became more acute as the weeks passed. It encompassed every single aspect of living. It made me see accusation on every face, disgust in every expression, condemnation in every gesture. Its intensity would drive me almost to hysteria when I thought of them all finding out.

What would they do to me? Where would I go?

If I lost this job, which was inevitable when they found out, I would be on the streets. What would happen to me? There are no words to describe the oppression that smothered me.

There was no hope I could even clutch hold of unbalanced moments. I knew I had no one. I knew I had nothing. I knew I had nowhere to go.

Then the night came that I reached the limit. I could not go on anymore. *It was over*! I decided to speak to Mr St Clare the next day. By now I was more than six months pregnant. Six months of almost constant nausea and a continuous struggle to stop fainting. I had never seen a doctor, it never crossed my mind that anything could go wrong.

The following morning I took even more care than usual in dressing and making up. It happened that I sat with Toffee Apple and her husband at the main table. He gave me a kind, appraising look and said in a warm voice.

"Well Amber, since you have been with us, you have really grown in to being a lovely young lady."

As he spoke his words seemed to echo further and further away, like I was hearing them through a tunnel. I had been sitting there tense as barbed wire, swallowing desperately to stop from being sick all over the table.

I tried to focus on him, but the room was moving around me. I held on to the table to make it stop. The spinning made me even more nauseous. Voices came to me from a long way away. I could feel my baby kicking, as though she too were protesting, protesting against the tightness of the clothes, against the unfairness of life, against the fear, kicking and kicking and kicking. I could feel a cold, sick sweat pricking out and spreading in a film over my face and body. Waves of faintness washed over me and I felt a growing weakness. Faces loomed and then became tiny little pale dots.

I gave up.

I swayed and it felt soothing to let go.

Then voices and screaming drifted in from far away, but a huge black darkness swamped it all out.

It was beautiful! No pain, no sorrow, no hurt!

I drifted in a mist of peace... I was free! No one could touch me. No one could reach me. I had floated beyond suffering... I had escaped it all!

I opened my eyes into Toffee Apple's face, peering down at me. I felt awful.

It felt as though death were clawing into my stomach, heart and lungs and, I hoped it was.

I gave myself up to it.

Through the physical wretchedness I could feel the accusing look in Toffee Apple's eyes. I knew her husband was there. The sweet aroma of his pipe lingered to reassure me of his presence. I closed my eyes against the bitter accusation of her stare. Softly I began to drift away, then the cold dabbing of water on my face brought reality against my eyelids again.

My thoughts were jumbled and disjointed, but I had determined to say nothing.

Toffee Apple bent over me.

"Amber... how are you feeling now? We have called a doctor. He's on his way now. Do you think you can walk up to your room with our help?"

I said nothing. I kept my eyes and lips tightly closed.

"She must be suffering from shock, my dear," came Mr St Clare's voice from somewhere above me. "Just let her lie still a bit."

Toffee Apple wasn't giving up that easily.

"Amber, what is the matter? Do you have pain somewhere? Is it your head or your tummy, or what?"

Stubbornness had no difficult asserting itself in my mind. I had decided not to answer questions until I had had a chance to think things through more soberly now and nobody was going to force me to say a word until I chose to do so. I let my head loll to the side and refused to give any sign of intelligence.

The doctor arrived and he and the nurse were left alone with me. I suppose it must have taken him all of two minutes to realise what was going on. He cut the strapping off me and called for someone to bring blankets and pillows. His eyes were very penetrating and he was not pleased by what I had done. He spoke to me, but his words simply didn't penetrate. It was such an effort to look at him. I closed my eyes and hoped to float off into nothingness again. There was a prick in my arm. I could hear him talking with the nurse but didn't understand what was being said.

After he left, Toffee Apple came back into the office. Silently, she sat on the chair next to where I was lying. After a while I opened my eyes and looked at her. There was pity and compassion in her eyes, but accusation too. Hopelessness and fear surged in me. It was to much. I couldn't handle it. I dropped my head to the side again and let the tears flow unhindered.

I was so tired of fighting. So tired of becoming hard and resisting. So tired of pretending I felt nothing. A death weariness soaked in to me, like ink in blotting paper.

"Amber," her voice was almost a whisper.

I didn't want to look at her. She spoke again, insistently but still softly.

"Amber, Amber!"

My head felt so heavy, so thick. I turned it in her direction and with effort, forced my lids oven. Her head was shaking more than ever. I suppose the tension of the situation aggravated the condition. The violence of that shaking made me feel awful. I closed my eyes again.

"Amber, who is the father?"

I kept my mouth shut tightly.

"How many months are you now Amber?"

I said nothing.

"Does he know that you are pregnant?"

I could feel the stubbornness bridging on rebellion and even in my misery, feel the resentment beginning to lift its ugly head. I lay silent.

"I feel like death," I thought bitterly, "I might as well act it."

She got not a single word out of me. Yet in all honesty I must say that she never insisted, she never pushed, she never treated me badly. But by then I had withdrawn so deep within myself that I was not prepared to admit anything good in anyone.

I had flung barriers up in panic and nothing and no one would penetrate them.

I felt as though there were a tiny, curled up Amber, hunched into a minute, deep black hole somewhere in nothingness, screaming for help, wanting desperately to believe in their goodness, in their kindness, but as much as I tried, I couldn't.

I couldn't believe that they could want to help me. Couldn't believe that they could still like me. Couldn't believe that they saw me as anything more than the rubbish and worthlessness my sisters had made me feel.

After a long while, I felt her hand under my head. Gently she was trying to lift me up. There was a glass of water in her other hand, close to my lips.

"Amber, do you think you can sit up? Try to drink some of this. The doctor says a little sugar water will help."

I tried to strain my head up, but the boiling clouds of blackness pushed nauseatingly down on me. I fell back, feeling the tears rolling like a stream, vaguely I wondered how there could be so much moisture in me. I don't know how many times they tried to get me to sit up. They were not unkind about it. I think now that they probably were concerned, but I don't think I was prepared to see it as concern at the time. Eventually after a hushed confabulation, they must have decided it was best to leave me there for the night.

I was feeling very drowsy and detached from my body. Perhaps that was the stuff the doctor had injected. It was such a gentle, peaceful blackness that slowly filtered into and over me.

It was easy to embrace it!

I opened my eyes to see daylight seeping in through the curtains. At first I was disoriented. My field of vision included table and chair legs, and the lower part of a body sitting on one of the legs. Toffee Apple was still there. I found out later that she had watched over me the whole previous day and all night. Her voice was gentle and kind. Why was I so completely incapable of believing it? I was expecting her to lash out at me. So I couldn't receive what she was giving, I had thrown frantic, aggressive defences against attacks I knew had to come. When they didn't, my mind said they must be there, and tried to interpret every word, every gesture as antagonistic. The confusion was horrendous.

All my past experience rose up like a Hydra with a thousand heads shaking warnings. I believed that it would be the old story again. I would have to stand with my back to the wall and fight tooth and nail against everybody and everything. I would be completely alone again. I would have to lash out, hit back. I would have to scrape myself into a position to be able to live, be an individual, be recognised as having a right to live and breathe. It would be one bitter battle after another, against condemnation, unjust accusation, judgements, against punishment and the rank unfairness of life.

When none of that materialised I somehow had to make it, I had to believe it was there. It was impossible for me to believe in the compassion that confronted me. It had to be some kind of scorning pity. Dear God, how intensely I wanted to believe it, but the fear trampled the believing to shreds. Fear of hurt, fear of rejection, fear of being disappointed again, naked, stark fear.

Toffee Apple's daughter-in-law came early that morning. She was quite young, attractive and dressed in a smart, clean-cut way. She helped me to my room and stayed there while I bathed and dressed. I had been expecting to be addressed as some kind of cheap slut, but there was no suggestion of that at all when she spoke to me. Shortly afterwards the doctor came back to examine me. I didn't like the look on his face. When I asked him if everything was all right he fobbed me off, but I could sense the unease in him. It was plain to me that something was wrong.

There was much whispering and conference outside my room and the odd word I managed to catch confirmed my suspicions. They were worried about something. The doctor gave me another injection and left some tablets for me to take. I felt so much better that I got up later in the morning and went down to attend to my duties. Patrick was waiting in front of the office door. When he saw me come down the corridor, the heavy folds of worry on his forehead uncreased with a brilliance that made me laugh. His face lit up like a shiny black shoe. He was so pleased to see me I thought for a moment he was going to kiss me! He grabbed my hand and pumped it energetically.

"Oh Nopsie, I'm so glad you're better. Nopsie they said you were very sick. I was so worried. Oh I'm so pleased you're better! Wait, I made you something special!"

He rushed back from the kitchen within minutes with a tray loaded with the special snacks he knew I liked. I wanted to cry. Instead, I laughed and shook his hands again and patted his shoulder and thanked him profusely. The medication had even done something about the perpetual nausea, so much to Patrick's delight. I was able to munch on a few of the delicacies he had prepared with so much affection.

It happened to be a busy morning. The phone rang constantly, so I didn't have much time to sit and mull over the circumstances. But I was relieved. I felt as though a huge, ugly weight had dropped off.

Now that the truth was known, I felt that the matter was out of my hands. I was no longer the one who had to make the decisions. It was done. There was nothing I could do about it anymore, and it was a relief.

Soon after lunch, Toffee Apple sent for me. Her daughter-in-law was in the office with her.

"Come Amber, sit down."

Her voice was kind and perfectly normal, but I tensed and expecting the worse. I didn't want to hear the kindness, I was prepared for grim punishment expressed with repugnance.

"You've already met Annie here. She and her husband Mark have just been giving us a hand with arrangements. How are you feeling now?"

I smiled weakly albeit defensively, because I couldn't figure where this was all leading to.

"You won't be able to keep on working here for much longer, because you and the baby will need professional attention. We know of a home where unmarried mothers are very well taken care of and we think that it would be the ideal place for you to go until your baby is born."

I didn't know how to react. On the one hand it was somehow comforting to have someone else thinking and making decisions, but on the other hand I wanted to rebel against the fact that others were arranging the course of my life.

"Amber, we realise that you don't want to talk about it, but I just want you to know that if you do not wish to disclose the identity of your baby's father, no one is going to force you to. I wanted to know because I felt that he should know and that he should be required to assume some responsibility in the matter. However, if it is against your will, I respect that. Should you ever change your mind, please don't hesitate to come and talk to me. I will always be here for you."

I heard the words, but I didn't believe them. They just weren't possible. If my own sisters could spurn me without a backward glance how could this woman, who was a stranger, treat me any differently?

Toffee Apple leaned over her desk.

"I would like you to think about what I've just told you, because I don't want you to feel that we are chasing you away or that you have to do what we want. Annie will tell you a bit more about this home, which by the way is a private one, it is not run by the government, and then you can decide what will be best for you and your baby."

Thoughts were thundering and churning through my head in a stampede of confusion. Everything was happening so quickly. I wanted to shout to her to stop and let me breathe, let me think. "*Private home*" - that meant money. Where was I going to get money from? My family certainly wouldn't contribute, so if she thought I was going to get help from that direction, she was badly mistaken. I was opening my mouth to say something, but Toffee Apple motioned for me to listen.

"The home is not far from here. Mr St Clare and I would like to come to visit you so that we can look after you and help you until it is all over."

I stared at her, not believing, but crying out for it to be true.

"We will pay what is required, so you don't have to spend nights fretting about money."

I could feel hot tears burning into my eyes, then she smiled. It was actually weird, because her head was shaking with that nervous twitch and the smile danced with each movement of her head. She reached under the table and drew her hands out holding a big parcel that she pushed towards me.

"Look, we've been busy this morning," again she smiled.

Bemused, and not understanding, I fumbled at the parcel.

"Open it," she encouraged and Annie leaned forward to give me a hand.

When the wrapping came off I was staring at a pile of baby clothes, yellow booties, blue and pink bibs, tiny jumpers and minute bonnets. I had been expecting anger, disgust, scorn, contempt. I sat clutching the baby clothes and the tears fell unhindered.

When I looked up, it was to see tears in Toffee Apple's eyes. Annie had turned her face away, to look out the window. But her hands were clasped tightly in her lap.

I felt so low, so abject for having distrusted Toffee Apple. I wanted to cry out for her to forgive me, and yet still, lurking in the depths of past rejection, doubts and misgivings held me back. She blew her nose and smiled at me.

"You will still be working here for a week or so, so don't think you are getting off that lightly! But you will only be required to do the switchboard for now. As soon as the home has a vacancy, they will phone, and then we will be able to take you. Now I would like you to sit and think it all over, and when you are sure in your mind and heart, then you can tell us what you decided."

What was there to decide? Where else could I go? What else could I do? By now I had realised too that these people wished me well, they were genuinely helping me, they were not throwing me out in to the street. I swallowed and took a deep breath. Speaking almost felt funny, because I had been keeping such a carefully guarded silence.

"Mrs St Clare I don't need time to decide. I want to thank you so much for your trouble. I'll go to the home."

I couldn't say any more. There was too much crying in me. She smiled with relief and pleasure.

"Well then, that's settled."

She and Annie looked at one another with big smiles.

"Well then my dear, it's life as usual now. Certainly you are going to have to be strong, but then, I don't think that is something new to you. Here we will give you all the support, strength and encouragement you need. So you can know that you are not standing alone and you do not have to go through this without any help. We will stand by you."

INTERIM

Never for a moment did I think that opening the doors on the Past would be so traumatic. I feel drained and brittle, like an old, cracked eggshell. The nightmares have doubled in frequency and occur with a vividness that leaves a frightening disorientation. I have had to force myself to keep going. Scores of times a day I get up trembling, unable to continue, screaming inside to stop. But I feel that if I don't carry this thing through, I will somehow be frozen back there in time, I'll be trapped.

The faces float into my mind, then I see them reflected on the screen in front of me. The emotions that scarred me rip open the deep, buried hurts again. Sometimes the reaction is so violent I cry out. People I had forced myself to forget, experiences I had ran from, psychologically and emotionally. I get up after a few hours writing and the exhaustion has seeped into the very marrow of my bones. I feel as though a storm has lashed through me. My eyes are red, burning and scratchy. The flat presses down on me. I get almost hysterical from claustrophobia and feel desperately that I have to get away, out, anywhere.

But where do I go here, in the middle of busy streets and crowded malls? I walk down the pavement, but the jostle and noise is oppressive, threatening. My breath starts to choke at the back of my throat and my mouth is as dry as ash. There isn't even a park where I can sit in peace. I find a café in the mall and sit in the back corner, as far away from people as possible. But there is no escape, not from the world around me, not from the one inside me.

I feel tattered and torn, as though I were bleeding inside. Cigarette after cigarette, one cup of tea after another. I try to read the paper, but can't concentrate. There is so much death and destruction in it anyway. So I watch the people hurry past, laden with parcels, carrying officious briefcases, strolling along with babies, chatting and laughing in carefree groups. It gets overwhelming because I feel the weight of each life, as though the dreams, hopes, problems, aches and longings of each individual leave a ware that drifts in and settles around me.

I don't know what to do with myself. The flat feels like a prison. The streets are making me hysterical. The malls are oppressive, the people crowd in and suffocate me. I don't know where to go or what to do. Faster and faster I walk till I'm half running, then I find a quiet back street, where the Jacarandas and Syringas shade the street under huge old branches. The noise from the main streets are muted. My heart is pounding painfully and my eyes are watering. I sit on the curb, light another cigarette. A black domestic walks past on her way to do the madam's shopping, glances curiously at me out of the corner of her eye. I couldn't care less.

I sit there for a while, puffing at a cigarette that tastes awful till my heart calms down. I'd heard the expression about "Demons from the past" haunting you but it had never really meant much. Now the phrase burns in on me. I pray to God that writing this book for you will dredge it all out forever and release me. I don't want the pain and fear anymore. I don't want the bitterness and hatred. I hope desperately that this agony will be the last of it. You know when a boil is excised the pain is excruciating, but I remember being told that unless you squeeze all the puss out with the core, it will grow again. Maybe that's what I'm doing with this book. Then dear God, please let it all come out.

Looking back with hindsight is perhaps one of the most devastating experiences I have undergone. One is so tempted to indulge in the *"if only..."* syndrome. But that is such a vicious trap. Knowing me, I can guarantee that even if I had chosen differently I would have ended up making another equally destructive mistake and the result would still have brought suffering and disaster. I believe that there are some things that we have to learn in life, that's all. I tend to think that there is no avoiding certain kinds of experiences and problems. Some of us make more mistakes than others, so it takes us longer and we hurt more.

It's not always easy to see people and circumstances without the accumulated experience and wisdom of the years that have since passed. I find I want to analyse, try to understand, explain and see things in the light of what I know and am now. The Amber of those days still had so much to suffer and learn and I find myself wanting to narrate from my own perspective of today. I even found myself doing that, but when I realised I was trying to find excuses, justifications for myself and for you, I tore up the pages in fury. There was something unclean and ugly about it, like it was dishonest. I don't want to make excuses. I don't want to lay blame at other doors. I know that I am responsible for the choices I made. I have made myself what I have become, both the positive and negative aspects.

By looking back now, I just have a greater understanding of why I made the choices. I have a clearer perception of people and their motives. Certainly, in many ways I have to fight the bitterness that wants to shove its way in, because I can now see the selfishness of people, the lack of compassion, the conscious exploitation and the other ugly characteristics that are part of human nature. I remember my own naiveté. I remember how I used to weep to myself in the privacy of my room, feeling the fear and loneliness of a child in an adult's world who has to behave with the maturity and poise she knows are masks. I remember how lost and alone I used to feel. I remember how I used to force myself to keep control, act adult, when all I wanted was to run away and hide in someone's arms. How I used to long for my Mom! I missed her with such painful intensity.

It's only now, in reliving those dreadful days that I realise how tired I grew of always having to be mature. I never had a childhood. My grandfather stole that from me. And the years in the orphanage left little room for the carefree love that "*normal*" children take for granted. From the orphanage it was straight out into a world that I didn't know would be so hostile. I was so full of hopes and prospects for a bright and glorious future. Perhaps I had just read too many novels and had consequently developed expectations that were unrealistic, romantic even. I was a voracious reader and identified myself totally with the characters in the books. They always managed to struggle through sometimes horrendous circumstances, so I assumed I would be able to as well. And of course, there was always a happy ending, there was always a knight in shining armour....

I haven't been able to sit down and take up the threads of the story for some time now. I get agitated and terribly restless even recalling that time, when I think of the sparkle and promise of the hopes and ambitions and then the crushing blackness of reality.

I suppose I'm over-reacting. So many years have passed since then. One would think the pain would have been dulled. the anguish stilled, yet I can see how those early years have stretched a cancerous shadow over my whole life. I wonder whether many other orphanage kids experience the same emptiness, the same search for acceptance, the constant cry for affection and the unhappy restlessness that keeps driving you from one place to another, in search of what? Even you don't know, except that it might just be there around the next corner, waiting with the next acquaintance.

I believe that all of us are aware of the huge reservoirs of love in us, love we ache to give but are afraid to, afraid of the rejection or afraid of being used, like so many of us are. So what do you do? Take refuge in cynicism and distrust? Keep reaching out and being burned? There must be a middle road somewhere, I just haven't managed to find it.

I have been sitting in front of the computer this week feeling hopeless and impotent. I don't know how I am going to manage telling you of the next few years. I think it is only because I have found you again that I can even bear to think of them. It's knowing you are alive, that you are well, that you have a family, and more than anything, that you love me which is giving me the courage to go ahead. It's the only thing that gives meaning to the torment, that I've found you, I've seen your face, heard your voice. Now I can tell you of my love for my daughter, a love that has burned constantly, that has kept hope and determination flickering despite horrendous circumstances. A love that has been so deep and so strong that nothing has ever been able to obliterate it. It is that love that spurs me on now. It is my love for you that keeps me at this task, because deep down I know it is important for you to know the truth. For you and me, and for your children.

Truth hurts at times. but it also cleanses. It brings life and meaning with it. So tomorrow I will get up early and I'll sit at the computer and write, until the years are laid bare and the festering sores cut open to be drained and healed.

I love you -- Mum.

CHAPTER TWENTY THREE

There had been a heat haze hanging sweetly over the tar road. But here in the garden, huge, ancient trees spread cool shadows majestically over lush flower beds and thick lawn. The home was a double-storey house, tucked away from the street under the protection of tall indigenous trees. When Mr and Mrs St Clare had finally entrusted me to the care of the nurse, he had held silently on to my hand, squeezed it gently and let his encouragement and affection flow into me. I stared unseeingly at him through tear-filled eyes.

Conflicting thoughts and emotions had churned me into confused turmoil. Part of me wanted to hang on to them and was terrified of seeing them go. Another Amber yelled hysterically inside that I was just a calf being fattened up for the slaughter. Yet another voice argued that it was a new start, a new chance.

A deep weariness cried out that it was enough... enough... I was tired of fighting. I wanted everything to stop!

The light, the noise, the voices, the hurts, the fears. I sat there without moving and without saying a word. The St Clares had packed all kinds of unexpected gifts and treasures in my luggage. As she left, Toffee Apple had also awkwardly shoved an envelope into my hand and told me to put it in my bag. I obeyed mechanically, I was in no state to think, react or protest in any way. Later when I unpacked, I found they had given me two months pay, filled boxes and packets with all kinds of cookies and candy and loaded me with books. I had always had a reputation for being a voracious reader.

I sat with the presents spread out before me. I was hurting so badly I felt as though I was being physically torn into fragments. Yet the distrust had dug its claws insistently and suspiciously into every crack of my shattered being. I was moved and grateful, but felt that ugly distrust leaking in to every thought and emotion.

Once again the awful weariness began to drain life and strength from me. All I wanted to do was lie down. I was so tired, the lady at reception had told me to unpack and come down again, but I was so tired...

As I sat trying to muster energy to move, that wonderful feeling of drifting floated down on me again. It was beautiful, I welcomed it with an open being.

When I opened my eyes I could barely distinguish medical-looking objects, like in a surgery. It was already dark outside. It felt like a dream, I smiled - it was so soft and gentle, I felt separated from my body and it was so good. Then slowly reality inched forward from the shadows of memory.

I recalled the garden, the steps to the home, the reception...

Then a face bent over me, lined and tired. The voice echoed down a long hollow tunnel so that I could hardly distinguish the words. Faintly the meaning impinged on my drifting senses. Someone had to leave me where I was and stay on duty till morning. My eyelids were so heavy... with an effort I forced them open again. Such a beautiful lady... she was in shining white, so lovely... she was like an angel...

I woke up with a hard shock in the cold light of dawn. My mouth felt like baked clay. My tongue was dry and stuck to my pallet so that I couldn't talk properly. All around me the smell of disinfectant and medicine permeated the air. I felt it was suffocating me, thick panic convulsed in clots from my stomach to my chest and wide-eyed I struggled to sit up.

Gentle hands on my shoulders pressed me down, quietly and firmly. This lovely lady smiled and smoothed my hair down with a soft touch.

"Don't worry now," she whispered. "It's all going to be all right."

The fear exploded in my head. I've lost my baby. I went rigid. Tears long suppressed broke through every barrier, weakened by fatigue, hopelessness and rejection. I began to sob, bitterly and brokenly. The nurse took me into her arms and pulled my head onto her breast, like a mother with her little child.

"Let it go, girl," she whispered. "Cry it all out now."

The dams within me collapsed. With shuddering sobs and moans, the buried pain and fear racked my body. Remorse and grief for the hurt I had caused others, loneliness and rejection for the hurt and abandon I had suffered - they came tearing out, clawing their agony into my mind and soul.

The injustices, the unfairness, the resentment and hatred I had had to carry since my mother's death, the bitter aloneness of the constant fight to prove my right to be, of earning my right to live, of demanding my right to be noticed, to be accepted, to be wanted, and the crushing disappointments and pain of constant, constant rejection, negation, derision and misunderstanding. All the people who had contemptuously thrust me aside, discounted me, considered me worthless and tried to break me now seemed to press in on me in a concentrated surge of hatred and resentment. I wept till there were no more tears to cry. Just a dry, empty hollow of brittle agony. Nausea rushed up to engulf me and a sick headache was crushing my skull. All this time the lovely lady held me, crooned and comforted me. When only dry, harsh sobs shook my body intermittently, she laid me back on the pillow, caressing my hair.

I said nothing, but I could feel that she knew what I felt. She knew what I was going through. She brought me a cup of tea and biscuits and I realised how hungry and thirsty I was. The constant nausea and vomiting had put me off food altogether, so it was a long time since I had eaten. It was obvious she knew that, though she said nothing. The way she offered me the tea, it was plain that she could feel my hunger and thirst. When she spoke it was like hearing my own thoughts. Always she was gentle and soft-spoken, with an inner warmth and compassion that made me want to trust her. But always that wariness put distance between me and others. I had simply gone through too much. I wasn't prepared to trust anyone ever again. As the weeks passed though I grew increasingly aware of how she identified with us. I wondered sometimes whether she herself had been in our situation or whether it was just that she had dealt for so long with unmarried mothers that she felt our emotions and knew our fears so intimately. Perhaps in a way our heartache and emotional stress became her struggle too, so that she felt and thought like we did.

Gratefully, I sipped the tea, but I was a bit cautious because I was afraid the nausea would bring it all out again. But she smiled reassuringly.

"You won't be sick again, don't worry, just sip slowly and let the liquid moisten your mouth and tongue before you swallow."

Her presence was comforting, encouraging.

"You're going to like it here, sweetheart. There are only about twenty girls and you'll find that you are all more or less the same age, just a few years difference. No one here is going to accuse you or make you feel bad. Everyone is in the same boat, you know. You'll be receiving a lot of encouragement and strength from girls who arrived before you and I'm sure that you will also be able to lift up others from your own experience. We learn to come through the pain and difficulties here. We learn how to give and share, and that helps us become better and stronger too."

I began to drift again... concentrating was too difficult. I smiled tiredly and let my eyes close. There was a glimmer of hope in my heart now though. Knowing that I would be with others in the same predicament made me feel a bit better. Perhaps I wouldn't feel so desperately isolated anymore...

Yes! I suppose it did help, being with others in the same circumstances, but nothing has ever been able to shatter the shell of loneliness that still encompassed me. I had always been a very private person, able to shut myself off when things became too difficult to bear, and always alone. But loneliness such as that which engulfed me at the home I had never experienced, not even in the most climatic moments at the orphanage.

There were times I knew that I was totally alone in creation, the only person God had ever made.

Life, and living things were as foreign and distant as tiny stars faintly flickering in an immensity of blackness. My breathing filled the whole expanse of the universe and my heartbeat throbbed in space, the only sound in all existence.

No one to hear me. No one to touch me. Not a soul who cared!

Perhaps I was slowly losing my mind. I know then that it was only the determined kicking from my baby that could break that annihilating nothingness.

As I got to know the other girls, I was drawn into their bond of affection and unity. We were similar in many aspects, condemned by society, rejected by family, scared, heartbroken, hurting, facing now realities we didn't know how to confront, all torn and broken inside while trying to show a brave face. I looked at them often, crying out for... someone to really confide in... someone I could pour my heart out to. For so long I had buried it all inside, been afraid to look at it, shoved it aside, pretended it wasn't there.

Carrying this awful heaviness had made me so tired. I wanted to talk it out, make the burden lighter.

I was so tired of struggling on my own. Little by little I spoke to the nurse or the matron, but, I could never open up completely, always a shutter would come clanging down and I would clam up inside. They never pressed me. I believe they understood a lot more than I ever said. They felt for us, there was an empathy and compassion there that was so genuine. It was balm, it was far better medicine than any doctor could ever have administered.

Some of the girls came from very good homes. Others were homeless and poor like me. The social differences lost all meaning there. We lived together, helped one another where we could. It was actually there that I learned what it really meant to share, without having someone push it down your throat. I learnt that sharing was not just giving someone a physical part of some material thing you happened to have when they didn't. I discovered that sharing came from within your own being. It was a reaching out, not merely physically or materially, but emotionally, spiritually, morally. It was a holding up of those who couldn't stand or walk any more. It was a joke at the most unexpected moments, a sometimes totally irrelevant remark that yet somehow hit home with truth or strength or encouragement.

I often experienced it myself. When I had got to that point where I was contemplating putting an end to it all, someone would come along or something would happen to give me courage to carry on, and then suddenly the pitch black cloud over my spirit would be transfused with a new light. Then, another day, I would find myself bringing the same spark of life to a girl lost in hopeless defeat.

Despite the problems and sorrows, the home seemed filled with sunshine. I knew it was there that I learned to laugh again, and yet when I think back, there seems so much agony and darkness in my soul. There wasn't a large staff, they were fairly firm with us, but never harsh or rude. The matron is imprinted in my memory, strength and understanding emanated from her. Now... I better appreciate the gentle wisdom that gave birth to all her counsel.

When I first arrived there, I was fiercely defensive, almost aggressively protective where my baby was concerned. I had made up my mind that this "*home*" people wanted only to snatch my baby from me and sell her to some barren woman. The thought agonised and appalled me. It was my baby! The thought of some strange woman holding, feeding and hugging her made me shrink with fear and horror. When anyone said something that could even only vaguely be construed as a remote reference to babies I would seize up inside and switch off.

Little by little somehow the realisation began to penetrate that no one had any intention of threatening me and my baby. No one was going to coerce or manipulate me to do anything. Being with the other girls, listening and seeing their reactions to thoughts about the future, about the chances for their babies brought me to an admission I had never ever made before... I had been wrong. I had been wrong about the attitude of the matron and staff at the home. I had been wrong about their intentions towards me and my precious child. It was a strange experience, I had never been able to admit to being wrong before. Yet now it even brought a kind of peace with it.

I began to see the staff in a different light. I could feel the defensiveness gradually diluting. As I opened up more to them, I started to perceive their genuine compassion and care for us.

They seemed to understand what we were going through. It took me a while to accept that, because all my past experience shouted angrily that no one could understand or feel what I did, that they didn't want to, weren't interested enough, couldn't be bothered. Yet, every time those protective accusations reared their scraggly heads, I was confronted with the reality of an understanding that went so deep I couldn't deny it.

Sometimes one of the nurses or even the matron herself would come right out and say the very thoughts and worries I had been grinding over and over and over in my head. Say them as though they really knew what I was feeling, not as though they were phrases they had learnt in some textbook. It was like they had lived through the same things.

Warily and with infinite caution, I reached out a very tentative feeler, ready to retract instantly. For the first time, I initiated a discussion with the lovely nurse that had sat with me that first night. I Suppose my idea of defence was attack. I reasoned that if their behaviour was all a put-on, then storming the walls was the best way to make it disintegrate. Yet so much depended on her response. If she reacted like I expected her too, that would be the last time I called for help and understanding.

"What are you going to do with my baby?" I demanded harshly as she took my blood pressure.

She didn't wince, flinch or even interrupt the smooth flow of her actions. She looked straight into my eyes and saw right through me.

"Amber, you still have more than two months to go. There is time still for you to give the matter a lot of deep thought and even to pray about it. Talk to the other girls. Be honest with yourself. If you want advice or a second opinion, come to me or to matron or any of the other staff. Talk to the doctor. The more opinions you hear, the better you will be able to weigh up the pro's and con's and make your decisions. Your baby is yours, not ours."

I stared at her, not fully understanding, was she washing her hands and condemning me?

She obviously saw that I was confused, and shook her head. She put her hand on my shoulder and bent down to look into my eyes.

"Amber, no one is going to do anything with your baby. We are going to make sure you have a smooth, easy delivery, that you and your baby are well cared-for, healthy and that you have every single opportunity possible to decide what you think is best for you and for your baby. That's what I mean when I say the baby is yours. No one is going to take it from you or influence you to keep it or give it away. You hold a life in your hands my dear, two in fact, yours and the baby's. You are the only one who can make the decision concerning your life and the baby's. We are here only to help and support. We have the experience of many years that we will give you. We have seen hundreds of girls in the same heartbreak, the same uncertainties and doubts. We can give you the benefit of their agonies and their decisions, but the final decision is yours and yours alone. Do you understand?"

Through the tears I nodded, I believed her. The crushing weight of fear and suspicion crumbles, relief filtered slowly into its place. It doesn't mean that the doubts all disappeared, they kept surfacing with oily suspicion, but it was so much easier to accept the affection and care the staff showed. I found my mind was clearer to consider the alternatives now. There was still so much confusion though, so much hurt. I still found it difficult to give anyone any real amount of trust. It seemed to me that all these people that I had trusted had just been amused at my naiveté and had ruthlessly exploited and abused me, having no qualms about mockingly tossing me aside when they were sated. I still cried a great deal. There were times I thought that there was maybe some truth to those old myths and legends about the seas being made to the tears of sorrow and pain cried by the lost and lonely. I was becoming better able to think about the future and started communicating with the other girls more. Decision making was still beyond me, so I settled in to the daily routine of the home, so grateful that I could speak to understanding grown-ups and be treated as an individual who mattered.

In many ways, the home was like the orphanage. We all helped in the daily running of the place, and each had chores to accomplish. Except that here no one tried to find excuses to offload their duties on to someone else. There was a different atmosphere, a desire to help each other, to strengthen and support. All of us were conscious of the shortening number of days before our babies were due. We were all frightened and apprehensive about the event. It wasn't all work and no play, there were specially designated periods of rest, there were the meal times and times off.

Though we tended to be considerate of each other, we all had those days of unapproachability. Perhaps I was more subject to these "off-days" than others because I was dealing with such a load of deep-seated bitterness about the hand life had dealt me.

It came naturally, I think, for us to withdraw from the others then I know that I kept away because I was afraid of lashing out and hurting others even as I struggled to cope with my own hurt. We developed a kind of sensitivity to this need for isolation, when someone drew into their shell like this, we left her alone. Physically I felt a lot better now that I no longer wore the tight constricting harness, but I still had to make wild dashes out of the dining room. The nausea remained a constant right to the end. I didn't look very big, rather as though I had been over-eating for a while and had developed a boop! As the weeks rolled by though, the swelling increased and I somehow thought I must have looked more awkward than most because of my height, or rather lack of it.

We were allowed free access to the kitchen, especially in the evenings. Many of the girls developed a craving for fudge, perhaps because of the intense sweetness, or maybe because it was easy and fairly inexpensive to make. I was an expert at fudge-making thanks to the orphanage experience, so was often in demand here. I recall those times with a smile now because we actually had quite a bit of fun and when I picture how we must have looked then my smile grows broader. Some of the girls were very big and clumsy and there were always jokes about tummies getting in the way.

Most of us had very little in the way of money or material things, but we shared what we had and did so willingly. Those were undoubtedly the most unselfish people I had ever met, perhaps common tragedy and suffering do bring about a sense of oneness that normal living doesn't.

We did our washing by hand, including the sheets and towels. The girls who had already given birth dealt with the sheets from the labour room. It was hard work and my hands were often chapped and bleeding, but I can't remember that any of us ever complained, not with any meaning, perhaps just as matter of course.

The labour room was on the ground floor, next to the surgery on the right of the passage that led from the main entrance. The nursery was the first room on the left, right next to the door. I think it was designed that way on purpose, so that prospective parents who came to adopt the babies wouldn't have to come right into the home, so that we were affected as little as possible.

For that same reason the home was equipped to meet every need. The surgery had all the necessary facilities and all the girls had their babies in the labour room in the home. They tried to protect us as much as possible during this very fragile and vulnerable time, knowing full well that when we left the walls of that cocoon, we would walk straight into the censure and contempt of society.

The doctor visited every Monday and spent time with each one of us, giving us a thorough check-up and prescribing medication where required. From the start he took special care of me. He was a kind, grey-haired man who was a real gentleman. Never did he make me feel like lady muck, but always had a kind word and sometimes a joke. I think he joked to hide his concern though. I wasn't so thick that I couldn't sense the preoccupation and the serious expression that flitted through his eyes when he was examining me.

They tested my blood constantly. I knew something was wrong because I was always tired and faint, and none of the other girls seemed affected by the sapping fatigue that leeched my life away. Almost every day I had to struggle against fainting, sometimes clenching my teeth and pinching myself to resist the thick black waves that washed so freely over me.

At first I welcomed them with relief and almost joy. From the time I had first experienced that wonderful drifting sensation and the release from pain, fear and hurt it had seemed an escape. But gradually it lost the pleasurable response. The fainting brought cold and blackness with it now. It left me sweaty, shaking and pale. There were times I wondered what it did to my blood, because it made me feel as though there was just water in my veins. It sapped the little strength I had left and it left residues behind it, as though the fainting had inserted sticky tendrils into my nerves and tissues. Bit by bit it started to instigate headaches: at first just a thick, almost numb feeling in my head, then an overall pressure, but heavy, like my head was stuffed with wadding. Then a dull ache, and eventually an all consuming pain that trotted out every thought and every emotion except agony.

In flashes of lucidity I remembered how some of the missionaries had lain and suffered in the cool twilight of their rooms, recovering from malaria, or yellow fever on some other North African or tropical disease. One in particular had tossed moaning in agony and despair for days, complaining of the terrible pain in his head. I wondered dully if I had perhaps somehow caught his disease.

I was afraid of losing my baby. I think at the back of my head was the idea that if I had a miscarriage it would be punishment, it would be my fault for having thought of abortion or suicide, or because of the way I had trussed myself up. All kinds of mangled thoughts and suggestions limped or slipped through my head, creating confusion and bewilderment that made it difficult for me to understand what the doctor tried to explain.

"Your blood-type is Rh Negative, Amber my dear. This makes it a bit complicated because it is a very special type that gets very choosy about the other kinds of blood it mixes with. It will for instance on no account mix with positive blood."

I gazed at him blankly.

"So?"

What difference did it make whether my blood was one kind or another? Were they afraid I would bleed to death when I gave birth? Frankly I was so disoriented at the time that the thought even seemed attractive. But it appears that was not the problem, the problem was the colour of my baby.

"It means," the doctor sighed, "that you will give birth to a blue baby."

I smiled sweetly at him, a blue baby? It would look so sweet; I thought of the blue bib and bonnet that Mrs St Clare had given me and wondered whether the shades would match. Well at least then she won't have a headache I thought to myself, that would really be too much, a headache on the day you're born.

Even when they explained the facts to me, it didn't seem to make much sense. I had the information but not the understanding. My mind just seemed to close up about the whole issue, like a temporary paralysis.

What they didn't tell me was that I was in for a terrible delivery. The foetus was not turning the way it was supposed to. When I think about it now, I can only presume that it was the result of the harness I had trussed myself up with to camouflage the pregnancy. Or perhaps it would have happened anyway. All I knew then was that I was petrified. As the days approached for me to give birth I took less and less interest in what was going on around me. I spent so much time crying that I began to see the world only through a film of tears. I tried to lose reality in the world of books. I went through one book after another, but registered nothing. I just saw words strung together from the top of the page to the bottom. They made patterns and shapes on the page, but no sense. I would get to the end of the book and have not the faintest idea of what I had read. People would speak to me, I would hear the words but they meant nothing. It was as though the sound came from a long way away, echoed hollow inside my head and then drifted away. I would look uncomprehendingly at the speaker until they went away.

I worked automatically, finishing my chores in a kind of trance, detached and unthinking. All I saw was red blood cells and white blood cells fighting each other. Antibodies insinuated themselves in there and added to the "*mayhem*". I struggled through the weariness to understand, but it was useless, it meant nothing. I was always tired, so tired... I just wanted to lie down, close my eyes and let the waves of blackness engulf me. I just wanted to stop! Dear God couldn't it all just stop?

Then something from so deep - I didn't even think it was possible would come struggling up and push me on.

By this time they had assigned only the lightest duties to me, laying the table, making beds and so on, because the slightest exertion would make the hole of unconsciousness swallow me up.

I think I had been at the home for about two weeks when one of the girls went into labour. I sat rigid and listened to the sounds with growing horror. Suddenly there was one piercing scream and then silence. I was scared out of my mind, I scrambled to my feet and shouted incoherently about someone having to do something because she was dying. The girls calmed me down, but the seed of panic was sown. I tried to avoid walking past the labour room as much as possible. My imagination ran riot when some thought about the birth managed to creep past the barriers I had created against them.

Next to the labour room was a special "*waiting room*" which the staff in the home had prepared for the girls who were about to give birth. It still amazes me that in the midst of the hysteria and immaturity of emotionally wrought and often disturbed girls the staff could have stayed so calm, so level-headed, so much in control. Matron had a sixth sense about whose time had come and she would move them down into that room beforehand as a kind of psychological and emotional preparation. It was a two bedded room beautifully decorated as well as equipped for any emergency.

There were night lights and a bell to the sister's room as well as such items as oxygen and so on.

One of the beds was for the mother-to-be, the other was for one of us. It was the custom for one of the girls to sleep in the same room, so that if anything happened during the night, the sister could be called immediately. It took a lot of the pressure off the staff who of course had their daytime duties to accomplish and simply couldn't stay awake at the bedside all night long.

I had a pathological terror of that room. I prayed wildly in the depths of my heart that they would never ask me to sleep there with someone else. The thought of the approaching birth flooded me with fear, the memory of the screams and moans of the first birth I had heard shrivelled my soul. Whenever someone went into that room, I made sure that the next day I would find something to do right down at the far end of the garden, as far away from the labour room as physically possible.

I sat there one morning when I had one month to go, straining to block out the sounds. Thinking a thousand haphazard thoughts to get my mind off what was going on in that room. I concentrated on my own baby that was squirming and kicking like a dervish.

What name would I give her?

It was a common topic among the girls and I had no lack of ideas, but none of them were suitable.

I had been reading a book about Marie Antoinette and had thought rather caustically at the time that in a way I was like her, she might have lost her head physically, but there were certainly times when I felt as though I was losing mine, in less material ways. There were days that I drifted through mists of total alienation, I understood nothing that was said to me. I tumbled in the whirlpool of my own disjointed thoughts and the only thing that pushed itself insistently into my awareness was a mocking refrain.

"I must be losing my head... I'm losing my head... I must be going off my head...!

I ruminated about Marie Antoinette and decided that I was going to call my little girl "*Martoinette*" - "*Mar*" for the month of March and "*Toinnette*" after the unfortunate headless queen and her own increasingly headless mother. I had no doubt it was to be a girl. In fact when one of the girls asked how I could be so sure I was surprised that she should even query my certainty.

"I just know. It's a girl, I know it is."

A week or so later one of the girls was booked into the waiting room. As she went down the stairs with a pile of washing in her arms, sister called to me.

"Amber, please will you take your things and go to the waiting room with Cynthia?"

I was appalled, nausea and fear convulsed me, but sister was already out of sight and Cynthia grabbed my arm.

"Oh that's good! I'm glad you'll be with me Amber."

Before I could say anything she went into her room to fetch her things. Whether it was the shock of the experience or not, I felt steadily worse as the evening wore on. I must have looked bad too.

Matron came along taking blood pressure, temperature and so on. I just lay and let them prod and push, I felt the big forbidding walls going up around me and the little spark that was me became smaller and dimmer and hunkered down somewhere in a remote, desolate hole where no one could find it... and, either extinguish it for good or try to fan it back to life again.

The doctor came the next day and after he had gone through the pushing and prodding routine looked more serious than usual. He forbade me to leave the building. I felt so distressed, I had been planning to hide at the bottom of the garden to avoid the trauma of Cynthia's delivery. I lay there listlessly, feeling the sickness and malaise thicken and spread. That night they gave me an injection for sleeping, the darkness was haunted by phantasms - formless figures, wisps and shadows that left terror and whispers of death and blackness behind them. I dragged myself awake feeling that death in me; I tried to claw myself out of bed to escape the sticky tentacles of that nothingness, everything was wet and sticky, drifting with the formless figures calling out to Cynthia, calling, calling...

Calm hands pushed me back into the bed, soothing words placated the terror. I felt a prick, soon a type of peace crept into my breast. Someone leaned over me, I opened my eyes to see the doctor's face. The fear rushed back, something must be wrong - why was he here again? He was here only yesterday, they must have called him. Did I fall asleep? Was Cynthia okay? He said something, I saw his mouth open and move and heard the sound, but his words didn't register.

Something in me was refusing to react, refusing to think. I tried to detach myself altogether, I wanted to run away, refuse to go through with this thing.

If I switched off then it wouldn't happen to me, it would take place somewhere else, without me. I wouldn't have to do it. I searched for the waves of unconsciousness that always came to release me; there were none. Just a stark, terrifying awareness pushing against my closed eyelids.

I opened my eyes again and stared at a masked face, I screamed and thrashed to get off the bed. Strong hands pushed me back. I heard voices and then the pain started. Excruciating pain tore through my body, almost paralysed I fell back on the bed. The pain was all consuming, it was a pounding ocean, a crushing mountain that shattered into jagged rocks piercing and tearing me. I could hear screaming and slowly realised it was my voice. Then there was another high-pitched sound floating closer and closer till it was louder than the screaming.

Ambulance sirens???

"There must have been an accident." I thought stupidly.

Then many hands lifted me up, I was moved on to a stretcher. With jerky movements the ceiling moved over me, then the door lintel, then the corridor, then it dawned on me that the ambulance was coming for me. The panic began to suffocate me, why were they taking me away? All the girls gave birth in the home. I struggled again to get off but the pain crippled me and I fall back breathless, my heart thudding agonisingly in my chest and throat. As they settled the stretcher in the ambulance the pain lifted. I felt like a lemon, grated and squeezed dry.

Oh dear God, at least it would soon be over, it was just matter of hours, I only needed to hold on for a few hours. My body was already limp and useless from the pain but I already no longer knew what happened. Suddenly the pain clawed me again, the scream echoed with ear-splitting intensity in the enclosed space.

Then there was nothing.

I woke up to the movement of the stretcher being carried through long corridors, endless ceilings and square lights flashing into view and out. They brought me to some place where a woman in white pulled me unceremoniously to a sitting position and made me drink some foul tasting orange juice. My stomach registered its disapproval. Only her quick reaction saved her from the spray as it was decisively rejected. I don't know why they kept trying to get this stuff down my throat. At one stage I was vomiting so much I felt as though my stomach and everything else inside of me had been puked out.

The pain grew worse. Someone was tearing my body into fragments and each piece was being shredded with infinite cruelty. I had great difficulty breathing. Blackness took over, curved talons of pain lacerated the blackness into blinding shards of agony. I hurtled through inky depths, I felt my body plummeting into nothingness and lost consciousness.

They told me later I was in labour for two days. I have no recollection of the birth itself. I hovered on the brink of death and only by some miracle had they dragged me back to life. I was told by the doctor that I had an *"instrumental breech-baby"*. I didn't fully comprehend what he was telling me. Even now it feels vague, as though it applied to someone else. I just felt this overwhelming tiredness, all I wanted to do was close my eyes and sleep. I didn't care whether I was alive or dead. It didn't seem to matter that the baby was born, all I knew was that the pain was over and I could rest. As I began to focus on my surroundings again, I missed the other girls intensely. I had come to learn that when they said they were happy or sad, they meant it. Truth was a very precious thing to me and I valued it in a relationship.

Their friendship was important to me and I yearned hopelessly for it. I longed for the protection and comfort they had always provided. Here I felt vulnerable, defenceless - there were a lot of strange women in the ward with me. I felt outcast and terribly alone. I needed to defend myself but I was so tired... I closed my eyes and feigned sleep most of the time. When one of the women come to sit and talk or introduced herself I would take refuge in the silent blackness until eventually they gave up and left me alone.

It was a strange feeling, to feel the need for someone and to miss them. I had learnt to be self-sufficient. From the day I had been left to face my pregnancy on my own I had blocked everyone out and stood alone. In my strong-willed obstinacy I had determined to fight this thing through on my own. So I found it horrendously difficult now that I cried out for comfort and help being isolated and alone. Now that all my defences were shattered, the hurt seethed up unhindered. From the deep roots of childhood the bitter injustices, the unfairness, the cruelty of people and the suffered wrongs surfaced, scathing and blistering my emotions. I was so lonely, so hurt I felt like screaming myself into oblivion. Inside I cried out for my mother. It became unbearable, I felt that I was going mad. When people tried to approach me I would either cut them off in total silence or lash out with a viciousness that would guarantee they stayed away from me in future.

It was a hideous process, learning to control the emotions, learning to push the memories down, suffocate the hurt. I told myself I would be like a cat - it didn't matter if you threw it or dropped it, it would always land on its feet. I decided that that's what I would do. It didn't matter how long it took, I would get to the top, if I had to scrape myself there by tooth and nail. I promised myself bitterly that it didn't matter who got in my way or tried to stop me. I would trample on them. They would not push me around or stop me from accomplishing my goal. I was lying curled up into myself one afternoon shortly after the birth when a hand shook me gently and a familiar voice called.

"Amber, Amber turn over... look who's here."

The St Clare's were standing at the bedside, Mr St Clare looking self-conscious with a big bunch of multicoloured flowers clutched awkwardly before him. I couldn't get my fill of looking at them. They had brought a number of presents from the people at the Mission House: cards and good wishes, sweets, little items for the baby. I wanted to talk, but couldn't always get the words past the tears. I was so determined that they would not see me crying, so I would swallow and take deep breaths. Mr St Clare looked worried, I gathered that they had heard how close to death I had come, they were so gentle and kind. After they left I buried my face in the pillow and let the pent-up tears pour out.

My longing for the girls at the home grew more intense, they would know how I felt, I knew I would be able to speak to them. I felt like a hand cut off from an arm - detached and helpless. I knew that they would infuse me with strength and the will to keep going - they had done so when I was low, they would do it now that I could feel hope and life itself ebbing away. We had laughed and cried together, sometimes we had laughed because we were crying... one does such weird things when one is lost, sore and lonely.

Lying there and gradually making contact with myself and reality again, I realised that something was wrong with my body or my muscles. I couldn't move properly, I think it must have been the second or third day after I came round that the pressure of being in with all those strange women started smothering me. I wanted to get up and run away, I couldn't get up. My legs refused to respond properly, I thought it was the drugs or something so I rang for the nurse and asked her to help me.

As soon as my legs were over the side of the bed, I pushed her away and tried to stand. She grabbed me as I started to collapse and supported me a little distance. Then determined to walk on my own, I shoved her off again but I dropped like a rock to the floor. Another nurse arrived on the scene and together they got me back into bed. It was only minutes before the doctor arrived.

The curtains were drawn around the bed with a clatter of the rings rattling on the rods. By the time he straightened up from his examination I was almost shrieking with pain and his face was grave.

My pelvis bones were broken. At first they wanted to set me in a cast, but after consulting they decided that shifting the bones, in fact breaking them where they had begun to set, and the consequent operation would have been too much for me. The only alternative was for me to lie dead still until the bones knit. I felt trapped, I had been expecting to be able to leave in a day or two, now they were telling me it would be weeks before I could go back to the home. Fear of every description started crawling over me, like an army of soldier ants, fear and rejection by the women in the ward, of their contempt, of being hurt, of having to fight again, of defeat, of being alone, fear of being with people. Since I could remember my defence had always been to attack. So, the harsh, selfish, cheeky Amber pushed herself to the fore again. I knew I would have to be strong to face the other women, I would have to fend them off before they attacked.

I began to wonder who the real me really was. As situations changed so did I. My nature, my personality would adapt accordingly. I lost myself. There always seemed to be some other me waiting to take over a situation as it occurred or changed.

The St Clare's visited me several times. I found myself looking forward to those visits despite the fact that I spent a lot of time convincing myself that all they felt was pity, that it was nothing more than a duty, that they felt obliged to come. Mr St Clare never said much in front of Toffee Apple, but he would hold my hand for minutes at a stretch and pat it in a comforting way.

Toffee Apple brought me an Easter egg - it was nestled in a basket with a chicken brooding on top of it. I didn't know how to take it. Was she implying something? What did she mean by it? The hurt made me closed and suspicious and I didn't know how the gift was meant, so I didn't touch it. I left it on the locker and looked at it from time to time. It seemed to me that I destroyed everything I touched anyway.

I was so pleased when the matron from the home bustled over one afternoon. She was full of smiles and brought a sparkling, zestful life into the place. She had messages from all the girls, I could hardly bear the ache of longing.

"Matron, when can I come back? I miss the home and the girls so much. I want to leave here and come home now."

The tears forced their way through the barriers I had thrown up against showing emotion. She smoothed my hair back and carefully wiped the tears from my face.

"Doctor says you must lie dead still for a while yet my dear. Rather listen now and let the bones mend properly, otherwise you will suffer for the rest of your life. It might even affect your ability to walk at all. So hang in there now, I know how alone you feel, but really we are all there with you, you know that."

I nodded bleakly, I knew she was talking sense, but that didn't make it any easier to accept.

The staff in the hospital were kind to me; I'm sure they knew my story. In some eyes I caught a pernicious kind of glee... *Schadenfreude* the Germans call it, but I was past caring, they could think what they liked. Others treated me with a kind of pity that was more difficult to handle but there were some who were genuine. No one asked questions, though I could sense that they thought Toffee Apple was my mother.

It was one of these sincere, compassionate nurses that brought Martoinette to me the first time. It was quite a few days after the birth, so she didn't look red and wrinkled like the pictures I had seen of new born babies. She was exquisitely beautiful. A fluffy nest of fair hair was ruffled over her head. I was astonished to see how exactly she resembled the photographs of me as a baby. She had the same bottom lip too. I laughed in a funny, jerky kind of way, feeling the tears in my voice as I delicately traced the little lip. Her fingers were so tiny, it was almost hard to believe that such a little mite could even breathe on her own. As gently as I could I put my finger into her palm and my heart lurched when her fingers grasped and held on.

This was my little girl! I wanted to crush her to me, but I held her so carefully, in case she broke or something. I didn't want to let her go. I stared and stared at her, absorbing every detail of her funny, chubby little body. I couldn't get over the perfection of her limbs. When she screwed up her face to cry I laughed and cried with her. I know that if any child ever needed love in order to survive, then Martoinette would have lived for hundreds of years. I felt a powerful, possessive love for her. It engulfed me and I could feel it flow out towards her to cover and protect her. She looked so small to me, but the nurses said she was big - eight pounds and a few ounces.

The cartilage between my pelvis bones had been severely damaged. I was quite a fighter and holding my daughter in my arms had brought a fresh determination into my life. I began to climb back from the edge of nowhere. Courage began to put roots down again, and my body began to heal. The nurses took turns helping me to walk again. They would support me as I concentrated on dragging my legs forwards.

At first it was an old man shuffle that lasted for only a minute or so before exhaustion made me give up. But gradually the muscles began to strengthen. My legs grew more accustomed to taking my weight, not that there was so much weight there. The nausea and sickness had seen to it that I was not much more than a loose collection of bones, weighing about sixty-eight pounds.

The food was staying put now, and though the meals were still ludicrously small because of the size my stomach had shrunk to, they were regular, strength was crawling back into my body.

I've heard people speak of the resilience of youth, I suppose that also had a lot to do with it. In time the only sign that I had been through nine months of unadulterated hell was the fact that I was holding a baby. I walked stiffly with an odd sway because of the pelvis damage, but I was walking, and there was no more pain. To this day still I walk like that.

There was one lady in the ward who was different from the others. I watched her walk up to my bed with a huge bouquet of flowers in her hands. While I observed her movements, she put it on my locker, pulled at a few flowers to rearrange them and then smiled at me.

"They've brought me so many flowers I don't really have room, so I thought how much nicer this bunch would look here."

It came naturally to accept them, I could feel the sincerity in her gesture. She wasn't artificially nice like the other women, she was genuine. Often she would shuffle cautiously over, sit on the bed and start chatting. She accepted me as I was, never asking questions or insinuating anything.

I admired and like her for that sincerity. When she left I closed up completely. I think the other women eventually thought I'm deaf and dumb or just plain stupid. They gave up talking to me and obviously learnt that it was useless asking questions. I lay within my own being, talking only to my beautiful daughter or the nurse who brought her. That's probably what helped me keep my sanity. The women in the ward came and went, I stayed, till the days flowed into weeks and I began to despair of ever being able to leave.

The doctor and the matron were very kind and understanding, he often came over to talk to me and look at Martoinette when she was with me. He explained that I had been very lucky that she was born normal. He went to great lengths to impress on me that I would never be able to have a normal birth again because of the damage to my pelvis. He also stressed that the chances against another normal baby were huge.

"People with your blood group seldom have two healthy babies. Maybe if you took great care there could be a chance of one healthy baby, but then you will have pushed your luck beyond the limits. If you have more children after that it is almost certain that they will either be stillborn or will have some kind of defect."

I listened, though I didn't always understand immediately. I meditated on the things they said and eventually it all penetrated. In the long run I probably had a better grasp of the consequences of my condition than most in the same situation. I enjoyed the visit of the doctor or matron, I think they must have realised how immature and naive I still was.

They never scolded or condemned me, they were always so understanding and compassionate. Thinking about it now, I realise they probably treated me as though I were their daughter. They related to me like parents to a child, they were always very frank and patient with me.

Matron took time to teach me how to care for Martoinette. She discussed a number of things with me like no adult ever had. She never asked me in an ugly way what I thought I was going to do now, but I think she could see that the question was now beginning to push an urgent face into mine.

One day, out of the blue, I said,

"Matron, what do you think I should do?"

She knew immediately what I meant and didn't pretend the question came as a surprise.

"Amber, first you need to get properly well. You cannot make decisions while you are sick and don't have a clear view on life. Then you need to get back into the home among people who love and care for you, who have experience you can draw on and wisdom you can trust. You need balance in your life before you will be able to make decisions that you will know are the right ones. But I want you to know that any time you need to talk or need advice, we will be here for you."

I knew she meant it, and it was a great relief.

At last the day of my discharge dawned. One of the less pleasant specimens of nursehood instructed me not to leave before going to the accounts department.

"Otherwise they have the extra expense of having to send you the bill."

A very sick feeling crept into the pit of my stomach. How on earth was I ever going to be able to pay? The account must have been enormous. I knew it had been a complicated procedure with me and that it had been touch and go for days - then there was the long period of immobility and nursing... I felt awful.

Matron came bustling in, to speed my packing. She took one look at my face and with immediate concern asked.

"What's wrong Amber? Are you not feeling well?"

"Matron, I haven't got money to pay for all this..." I started.

She smiled and brushed the whole matter away with a careless wave.

"Don't you go worrying your little head about that. You won't have to pay a penny. And, I'll tell you another secret... She leant conspiratorially towards me and whispered with a grin... neither will the home!"

She straightened up with sparkles in her eyes.

"We decided that you had been such a challenge and such a learning experience for us all that we wouldn't charge anything!"

I gaped, scared to believe.

"But that's not really the whole reason Amber my dear. You see, it's because your life was worthwhile fighting for. You were worth saving."

No one had ever said anything so overwhelming to me before. I couldn't contain it, she knew what it meant to me and her arms were ready.

CHAPTER TWENTY FOUR

I had three months in which to make a decision concerning my baby. That was the maximum amount of time we were allowed to stay in the home after giving birth. Physically I felt as well as could be expected, but was not yet able to handle the more onerous tasks. Emotionally I was a mess. The understanding and compassion I had received both in the hospital and in the home were helping to stabilise me but I still couldn't sort through the jumble in my head and my feelings.

I thought how much I had loved my mother, how much I still missed her and wondered how Martoinette would feel if I had to give her up and she found out. I couldn't stand the thought. But perhaps she wouldn't find out. Perhaps the lady who adopts her would love her and give her opportunities in life that I couldn't. Fiercely I denied to myself that I could ever fail my precious daughter, this little being who owed her life to me, and in fact, to whom I owed my life. But then deep down I would have to admit that there was very little I could give her then and there. I had no work, I had no material possessions. I had nowhere to stay. I had no one to look after her if I did find work. In fact I even doubted whether Social Welfare could allow me to keep her until I could provide something more stable and secure for her.

When I had come back to the home the girls had received me so warmly it had filled me with happiness. They cooed and crowed over Martoinette who was without doubt the prettiest baby in the nursery. It was a friendly room and we could go there at any time during the day, except when visitors came to see whether they wanted to adopt one of them or when the parents-to-be came to take away the one they had chosen. Those were dreadful days, even if it wasn't your baby they were taking. You lived through every moment of agony with the mother. The experience became so vivid in your own mind that it only confused your decisions all over again. I so desperately wanted to keep my little girl it was a terrible, tearing conflict deciding about the future.

I was knitting in the lounge with some of the other girls when I was called to the reception room, someone had come to visit. To my astonishment, Godfrey was standing there. I was overcome with conflicting emotions. The first thought that leapt to barricade me in hostility was that he considered me immoral, a *"fallen girl"*, worthless. So I greeted him very coldly. He was entirely unaffected. There was no doubt that he was very pleased to see me. I found out that he had been repeatedly advised not to come and visit until after my baby's birth, and that he had phoned insistently to enquire about me. I was surprised; why on earth should he have wanted to do that?

We walked in the garden, I was very tense waiting for him to explain the reason for his visit, trying to fathom the motives. It was wasted tension. All he did was chat like an old friend. He joked, he talked, he tried to put his arm around me. When I jerked away like I'd been scalded he didn't seem to take offence.

Then after about an hour he said he would have to go and asked whether he could come and visit again. I was nonplussed. What did he want? I was very suspicious.

Matron was all smiles when I came back into the lounge.

"Such a nice young man. He phoned almost every day while you were in hospital you know and was actually most upset when we didn't want to allow him to visit you there either."

Now bewilderment joined the distrust. What was up with this guy? I still don't know why it was so hard for me to believe that his motives were nothing more than what they appeared.

It only took a few days for Godfrey to tell me he loved me and wanted to marry me. I felt as though I'd been hit by a falling rock. Was he crazy? Did he have no understanding of what I had gone through? Didn't he have the faintest inkling of what was in me now? I looked at him with pity.

"Godfrey you're out of your mind." I said bluntly. "Forget it," and walked away.

He was not to be put off and kept visiting, but I had switched off totally. Eventually I think Matron advised him to let well alone. I wanted nothing to do with him or any other man. I wanted nothing to do with my life before the home. I was not prepared to countenance anything except trying to get back on my feet and find myself, find my direction, find meaning. How did he think I could do that lumbered with someone else? Someone who would probably expect me to serve him and slave for him. He was crazy, so I shrugged him off.

Then another surprise visit shook me. When I came downstairs one morning it was to find an old friend waiting for me, Gene's little sister. She had always looked up to me and was very fond of me. I froze. I could imagine what they had told her. I didn't want to see contempt or condemnation in her eyes. But there was only affection and pleasure. I was very stand-offish, because I didn't know what she thought of me and I didn't want to hear anything about Gene. She was too young to have any kind of tact.

She burbled on about how broken up Gene was, how much he missed me, how much he kept talking about me. My reaction was only bitterness.

"Yes sure." I thought to myself. "It's easy to miss someone who in carrying the whole load. It's easy to talk. I wonder what exactly it is that he's missing."

The bitterness swamped out any longing or tenderness I could still have felt for him.

"Amber, all he talks about is visiting you, but they wouldn't allow him."

"I should hope so," I grated. "He wouldn't have been welcome."

She was surprised and with big eyes exclaimed.

"But Amber, he loves you and wants to marry you! That's what he keeps saying."

"Well let him keep saying it. I'm not interested."

I refused to say anything about it. When she tried to insist with the subject I cut her short harshly. She looked at me hurt and not understanding. It hurt me to see her reaction, but I was really not prepared to be dragged back into the hurt, recrimination and rejection of the past. He had been more than ready to squirm out of all the difficulties and the horror. Now that it seemed over he wanted back in again? What did he think I was, some kind of idiot that never learned? As far as I was concerned what was done was done. It was over! It was finished! It was dead! There was no way it could ever be resurrected.

I eventually told Matron she must please tell both Godfrey and anyone else to stay away. I didn't have to go into lengthy explanations about the reason, her sensitivity and intuition told her. She nodded, gave me an encouraging pat on the shoulder and said nothing.

A few days later, I was told about the job they had managed to procure for me. I didn't like the thought at all. It was not what I wanted for myself. The claustrophobic feeling of being trapped came washing over me again and all I wanted to do was run. But there was nowhere to go. I had no choice. I had no doubt that given a chance, I would have been able to do well in any job and work my way to the top too. Everything in me rebelled against being pushed into something I was not ready for and willing to confront.

Martoinette's life, her future began to plague and haunt me. Dear God, what would be the right decision? I died inside when I thought that perhaps one day she would think I had simply abandoned her, hadn't wanted her. It tore my soul to think that she could perhaps one day suffer the aching sorrow of rejection that hounded me. I didn't want her to experience the hurt I knew.

I would have given her my life if I could. I knew that at that stage I could not give her the opportunities and the chances I desired with all my heart for her.

There were no restrictions on our movements at the home, we were allowed to go out, walk to the shops and so on. So one morning, taking my resolve in both hands, I went back to the hospital to speak to the Matron and doctor. It was not for lack of trust of the Matron at the home, I suppose I thought that their years of experience in the home most colour their opinions. I wanted a totally unbiased, outside opinion from someone who knew and cared for me, but didn't have such intimate knowledge of the situation.

She was delighted to see me and fussed over me and Martoinette.

"She's grown already! And she looks just like you too, goodness there is certainly no doubt about who her mother is!"

The words cut to the quick. I smiled to hide the pain and followed her to the doctor's lounge where she offered me tea and biscuits while we waited for the doctor to arrive. He was also impressed by Martoinette and I know he was sincere, I pick insincerity up very quickly.

They knew why I had come, so there was no beating around the bush. I took a deep breath.

"Matron, I have to decide, I've got so many different thoughts. I don't know which would be the right decision. I don't want her to grow up thinking I didn't love her, didn't want her, just wanted to get rid of her. I love her so much it hurts. I want to keep her and look after her, teach her and help her so she doesn't make any mistakes. I want to be with her all the time so that she can know what it means to be loved and cared for. I don't want her to be in a position where people can misuse her and abuse her trust. I want to be there to protect her and care for her and..."

The words and emotion choked me up, I raised a pleading look at them. They were watching me with very earnest expressions and obviously understanding my confusion. I sobbed brokenly.

"I don't know what to do... I don't know what will be best for her. Please help me..."

We talked for a long time. Together we examined the pro's and con's. We made a list of advantages and disadvantages so that I could see and grasp them as clearly as possible, try to understand the consequences, imagine the repercussions. It was the most painful and most difficult afternoon of my life.

At last I knew what I had to do. If I kept Martoinette, I would be subjecting her to the very life I was trying to run from. I would be stealing her chances in life. I would be handicapping her. I couldn't face the thought of seeing her dealt the same injustices and unfairness I had suffered. Her peers would crucify her because she had no father. It was no use my trying to pretend that I could move and no one would ever know the truth. I knew from bitter experience how people always found out things like that. It would be my fault that she was marginalised, outcast, rejected. I knew I could offer her nothing more than the immense, overwhelming love I had for her. The inevitability weighed in my stomach like a huge cold rock. Matron was hurting with me. I suppose the final factor that made me accept the decision was the assurance both she and the doctor made repeatedly about prospective parents.

"Every single person is intensely screened, Amber. They don't allow just anyone to adopt children. They go into their background, their financial status, their relationship with one another, their religious life, their friends and social position. It is a very thorough investigation, and Social Welfare checks up regularly to make sure the children have been totally assimilated into the family and are being treated as the biological offspring."

Every word was another jagged tear inside. I knew she was right, but the very thought of having to give my precious daughter to a stranger was lacerating. But wouldn't it be much worse if I failed to provide for her and one day, when she was bigger, could see what was going on... and, I had to give her away then?

There was no way that I could even contemplate being the cause of hurt for her. The decision was made, now I had to prepare myself to confront and carry it through.

Without saying a word to a soul, I went and signed the papers that would release my child for adoption. A piece of me died then, it was like signing my own life away. No one knew what I had done and I carried on with my life at the home as usual, completing my tasks, helping out where help was needed and waiting in agony for the day my daughter would be taken away.

Encouraging and uplifting the girls who were still pregnant or suffering with nausea helped me to get my mind off my own grief. I spent a lot of time with them, getting stuck in where I could, making them laugh, helping other girls with their babies. Not all of them knew as much about caring for them as I did, because Matron and the doctor at the hospital had given me a lot of tips and hints that I was able to share with the others. At night we had the babies in cots next to our beds. When Martoinette woke up and cried with her pathetic little call, I cried with her and let the tears I had pushed down during the day come flooding out.

When the sun rose there was no more crying, then I closed the hurt off and put a smile on my face and let the weeping take place inside, where no one could see or hear.

I found myself doing things automatically again, as though I were detached, apart from life and the people in it, an observer mechanically going through the motions of working and living. I spent as much time with Martoinette as I could. When she was awake all I wanted to do was hold her, go into the garden with her, let her see the colours and smell the scents. I talked unceasingly to her and thrilled when her lips stretched in her funny rubbery smile. All the time I was trying to brace myself for the day I knew was coming. She was such a beautiful baby, I knew she would be the first to be adopted.

And so she was! Matron came to tell me. The preparations had been useless. I fell to pieces. My life felt like a jigsaw that had been broken and scattered. I stopped eating, I couldn't sleep, tears flowed without cease. Eventually the doctor injected me with something that put me out. When I came to, I don't know how long afterwards, I was on a drip and the lovely nurse was by my side. When she saw my eyes were open she leaned over and whispered.

"Amber, you have to keep going. For Martoinette's sake, you must get up and start again."

A long wail echoed inside me, I didn't want to. I wanted to stop. I didn't want to start again. But the thought of my little girl gripped down deep into my being and out of some unknown reserve, squeezed courage, and the growing determination to get up and make it.

There was a job waiting for me. If I was going to succeed then I would have to start becoming myself again. I made myself eat, I began to look after my body again. I had a lovely figure and with a bit of make-up could look very attractive. One of the girls gave me a beautiful apricot-coloured dress with a very broad waist band that no longer fitted her. I looked good in it. It was little things like that that helped to make the sun shine again. I packed my sorrow into a tight bundle and shoved it down as deep as I could. I remembered that I had made myself promises, I swore I would not break them. I felt that I owed it to Martoinette to succeed. Perhaps one day we would be able to meet again and I would want her to love, respect and be proud of me.

Then, as later, Martoinette became an inspirational factor in my life. So often when I was tempted to give up, when I had reached the end and wanted no more, the thought of my child would come floating up from the depths and I would force myself to go one more step, to hang on to life and push back from the brink. I gave her a gift, "*LIFE*", it was true, but I can say in all honesty that on many, many occasions, I have owed "*MY LIFE*" to her!

One of the jobs that I did for the home was to help with the street collections. It was one of the ways that we raised money for the Home's various needs. I was an effective collector and also came back with large sums of money, because I was pretty, dressed neatly and smiled sweetly at the people. Inside though I was seething with anger, hatred and contempt. Hypocritical sods, all of them, I would spit derisively. Holier than thou, snotty self-righteous asses... and a host of less kind expletives. I had a rich vocabulary, and I exhausted it when thinking those..."*kind contributors*".

"Oh, the girl's home!" they would coo.

"How sweet of you my dear to collect for them!" They treated me like a lady, because they didn't know I was also..."one of those girls".

"Shame those poor things," they would tutt-tutt.

"I feel so sorry for those girls who go astray like that."

Then they would dig around for something to drop in the tin while I was trying to control the shaking that came from suppressed rage.

"Well, I'm sure they've now learnt a thing or two."

"It's a tragedy that some people can be so immoral, so loose and insensitive to consequences."

I had to clench my teeth to stop me from throwing the tin in their faces. I wanted to scream dirty names into their arrogant, pompous faces. They infuriated me with their hypocritical piety. But the real hatred for society took off when I came across the others, those who refused to contribute and said why.

"Give money to those street sluts, you must be joking?"

"Contribute to them - what? They want us to support their sins now?"

"Give to the Home, I wouldn't dream of it, money down the drain. Girls like that never learn. In a few months they'll be right back where they are now..."

And so it went on until it was as much as I could do to keep my mouth shut and not throw myself at them and tear them to shreds. I wanted to dig my nails into their faces, leave deep, bloody scratches.

How can people go and sweep somewhere else when their doorsteps are laden with filth? I wanted to hurt them, physically. I knew these are the kind of people who will sit piously in church Sunday after Sunday and mouth religious platitudes, but not lift a finger to do what Jesus said to do, and then have the nerve to call themselves Christians. They were no more Christian than "Grunt and Grunt", the two pigs my grandfather slaughtered in front of me. I remember Jesus having compassion with those who had fallen. I never read of His condemning anyone. Hadn't these people ever heard of the Good Samaritan? I was prepared to bet that a peek into their own lives would reveal heaps of stinking sin which they found it very easy to justify and live with.

Bitter and furious I would return to the home, clanging my full tin and praying for the opportunity to be able to get even. I pushed the thoughts and feelings down and kept the smile on my face, and the money came in for the Home. I felt it was the least I could do in return for those who had done so much for me.

I don't know whether it is just a sense that my experiences have caused me to develop, but there is an innate knowing in me when people are genuine. I sense insincerity and hypocrisy instinctively.

There is something about the expressions in a person's eyes, in the intonation of their words, the way they gesture that reveals the truth. So I learnt to change myself into the person they assumed I was, fitting into the circumstances as required. It was an ugly, horrible way to react, because it was like living a lie, like denying your true self. You have to be you without being you, leaving your real self in a kind of limbo while you are being someone else. Nowadays of course they have such a pretty euphemism for it, they call it "*adapting to circumstances*", but it boils down to the same thing. If you don't have a pretty strong character and clear knowledge of who you are, what you believe in and what you stand for, you end up being nothing and no one. You become what people want you to be, so you end up as some kind of insubstantial meaningless shadow. I've met so many people like that, they are worthless, transparent and superficial. They tend not to have an original idea in their heads and they will say whatever they think will impress or please you. I despise them with all my being.

The day came for me to leave the Home. I moved into a boarding house not far from the office where I was to start my new job, but from the day I set foot in there the rebellion took root again and grew vigorously. From the word go I disliked the people there. Their initial greeting reveal the contempt and distrust they harboured for "girls like me". They made no attempt to disguise their ugly suspicions either. I felt like a prisoner under close surveillance. They made it so obvious that they expected me to behave like some low class female of no morals, the way they spoke to me and spied my every movement.

I hated the work, it required no initiative, no thought, no effort and provided no stimulus whatsoever. Something with half a brain and one eye could have done it in their sleep. To make matters worse, I had no privacy whatsoever, not even a room of my own. My roommate must have been twice my age and her attitude reflected that of the boarding house keeper. We had absolutely nothing in common and from the start there was animosity and resentment between us. She would try to upset me, slide subtle needle-like insults into me, then get angry when I refused to reply or react in any way.

I loathed coming back to the room, and again the debilitating weariness began to encroach me. I would go back to the boarding house as late as possible, to avoid the harridan in the bedroom, then get up long before dawn and leave. I wandered aimlessly around in the streets, looking blankly into shop windows, watching leaves in the gutter, staring at my own feet as I walked, till it was time to go to work. The dizziness and fainting spells returned. An overwhelming weariness eventually swallowed everything in its possessive maw. I no longer made an effort to cope with things. I fell asleep at work. Sometimes I would be so tired I would fall asleep on my feet. I would sleep like a log at night, but wake up feeling tired and drained. I always felt as if there wasn't enough air to breathe. I kept wanting to faint, and not caring whether I did.

One of the girls at the office was more friendly that the others, and she invited me out with her. She took me to a night club type place, where you could dance and listen to music. That's why I had accepted the invitation, but looking around me, my flesh crawled. There were people there that I wouldn't greet outside those doors. I could feel trouble and unpleasantness as though it were painted in thick, shoulder-high letters in the air and on the walls. I didn't want to go the second time, she kept nagging me, eventually I gave in and agreed.

That evening she didn't want to leave when I was ready to go, I eventually got her boyfriend to drive me back. By now it was pretty late I didn't want to wake the harridan in the bedroom, so I lay down on the old settee on the landing. By the time I woke up, it was too late to go to the office, not that I cared, I was feeling so tired, I went to the bedroom and immediately fell asleep again.

Next day at the office, no one said anything. I did the work as usual and dragged myself home to bed. All I wanted to do was sleep. But the more I slept, the wearier I felt. I was constantly falling asleep at the office and I began to stay away from work more often. I had neither the energy nor the desire to stay awake. I refused to speak to the people in the boarding house. I couldn't care what anyone said anymore. All I could register was this all encompassing weariness.

I lost track of days and people, I think something must have happened to my memory because that period is still very vague and misty. I don't know what happened, I don't know who arranged it, I don't know how or why it was allowed, I suppose Social Welfare was the instigator and motivator of the whole thing. One day there I was on a train under escort on my way to some girl's reform school. The escort was a hardened old bitch. She treated me like scum. I huddled in a corner, missing my baby, hurting miserably and vainly fending off the immense tiredness. Just being in the same space as that woman was torment. She sat with her gimlet eyes unblinking fixed on me, a cigarette dangling from the corner of her mouth. She was slovenly and I felt unclean just being near her. I wondered briefly whether they were taking me to jail and then decided I didn't care where they took me. Nothing mattered any more.

A faint glimmer of hope suggested that maybe wherever they were taking me to, there would be someone who would understand what I was going through, find the reasons for my behaviour, help me! The hope flickered and nearly died when we arrived at the place, the first thing I saw was the bars at the windows.

I could see faces peering from behind the panes and when I walked in, a number of people, staff and "inmates" were hanging around in the corridor and entrance to see me. I wondered what the big deal was. Why were they all so inquisitive? I had closed up so tight by now that nothing bothered me anymore. It registered as a fact and that was it.

I was used to boarding houses and hostels, it seemed to me that that was all I had ever known, so yet another one was not going to have any effect on me. I was completely switched off. Silent, probably just on the verge of sullenness. They let it be know that I was considered little more than a juvenile delinquent.

While there were no prison warders or police, there was pretty strict surveillance. With time I found out that many girls were hardened and stubborn. They were called "*intractable*" and generally ended up running away. I would never understand that, it seemed so pointless, because they were always caught and brought back to some equally senseless punishment.

I kept to myself. I lived in my own private world. I did my own thing and if I was not prepared to do something, I didn't do it, regardless of consequences. I was quite prepared to pay the price.

When I arrived there, they took me to a sick bay type of place. I submitted unresisting to the medical. They discovered acute anaemia and low blood pressure. Not that it changed their verdict of my past behaviour of course. I must say though that they were not unkind or particularly unfair.

The principal was a nice lady, always well dressed, always careful about her person. In many ways it was like going back into the past and having to re-do something I had thought was over and done with.

I still wasn't quite sure exactly why I had been sent there, I had done nothing wrong. I had never taken any liquor or drugs, never even for a fleeting second considered them. I wasn't a thief or a murderer... Some of those girls were there for some hair-raising reasons. I couldn't figure what I was doing there. Did Social Welfare have a grudge because I had fallen asleep at the last job? Because I stayed out late at night to escape from the harridan in my room? Scared I would have another baby? Scared I would sleep around?

The routine was much like it had been at the orphanage or the home. It was dreary, repetitive and to me, mostly meaningless. We studied, had recreation, took part in athletics, had debates, played tennis, had dances on Saturdays and were free to walk around in the grounds. I was a dead loss at the physical exercises because I became so instantly tired, but I enjoyed the studies.

At last, here was something to get my mind into, some of the subjects were really interesting and presented a challenge. It wasn't difficult to start disciplining myself to study again and I derived a genuine pleasure from it. My mind started functioning again and I passed most of the subjects with high grades.

Despite the severity of some of the crimes committed, most of the girls were like myself, little more than kids. Emotionally, I think all of us were handicapped, some very naive, very immature, some so hung up with rejection, hatred and hurt that they were almost incapable of functioning. I learnt a great deal about life and society and the way the latter treats its misfits.

The staff were really quite tolerable. There was no malicious spite or purposeful attempts to hurt and scorn. The housekeeper especially was a jewel. When we got into scrapes, she was always there doing her best to get us out of them. She related to us in ways similar to those of the sisters at the home, but even with her I kept my distance. I was not going to inveigled opening up again, it always brought too much hurt and devastation with it.

I tried to keep occupied as much as possible so that I didn't dwell on thoughts of my little Martoinette. The pain of missing her was unbearable. When it welled up I thought it would drive me mad, so I had to keep busy to stop it from pushing to the fore. Without saying as much in so many words, the principal and staff made it clear that this home was our last chance. Fail this and we would be drop-outs, criminals or scum on the street. Fear began to claw at me again. Where could I go now? How could I get a start in life now? What could I do to get on my feet?

I would lie in bed in the darkness of the dormitory, listening to the breathing, moaning and sighs of the girls and reach out desperately for answers, for hope. As always, I would turn to my Special Friend. I already knew by then that when things really looked bleak and impossible, He would somehow break through and bring an answer. I think the time I entered the home and the first few weeks there were the lowest ebb in my life. I had lost all incentive to live, all purpose. It was so much effort just to get through the days. It just made no sense to keep going. I don't know how much the anaemia had to do with that, but after a fortnight or so of taking the medication, I began to feel better.

I spoke to Jesus from my heart, I complained bitterly of the unfairness I had suffered and the terrible weight He had burdened me with, but I still trusted Him. I knew that He would find a way to help me. I would fall asleep sometimes while I was talking to Him, but wake up with greater peace.

Then the breakthrough came. The Principal had contacted my late mother's sister. How she found her I will never know. She must have gone to great lengths to track her down. She now had two daughters of her own, both more or less my age and she agreed to take me in and help me until I could find a job and get back on my feet again.

When the Principal told me, I didn't know what to say. By now I was a past master of concealing my emotions so I know my face was impassive. But, my whole being was a turmoil. Aunt Barbara! I saw her face as clearly as if it was etched on the wall in front of me. She looked so much like my mother and Aunt Kay. My stomach lurched but no ways was I going to let the Principal see how I felt. I shrugged non-committal and nodded.

"Aunt Barbara? I haven't seen her for many years."

Perplexed, the Principal studied me.

"Well, she has offered to provide you with a home and initial expenses. She and her husband will assist you in finding a job. Social Welfare has vetoed the family and has no objections."

I suppressed a surge of violet anger, Social Welfare... they were like swear words. What business was it of theirs. How dare they interfere? I felt as though they had somehow besmirched the whole business, stained my Aunt Barbara and her family but, I made no response.

"What do you think Amber? You know the final decision is yours."

My heart was pounding so loud and so fast I was breathing short raspy breaths. I was determined not to let her see what I was going through. I kept quiet, I was trying to gain control of my breathing and my emotions.

"I think you must take time to weigh the offer against the various alternatives. You are wise not to make a hasty decision, but at the same time, I would advise you not to reject such an offer out of hand just because it is some time since you have seen your aunt. I know that people change, but I don't believe they change that much and from what I understand, your Aunt was very fond of you as a child."

I nodded. I was beginning to feel faint. I wanted desperately to leave and go and lie down. The Principal was observant and perhaps not as unperceptive as I had thought.

"Amber my dear, believe me, I understand your reserve, but let me speak to you from my heart. You cannot go through life walled up behind a fortress of distrust and bitterness. You have lived through some traumatic experiences, but some of the girls have had a much rougher time than you, and they are learning to cope with life and face the world again. It is not impossible, it will take only your decision and some will power. And I know for a fact that you are most certainly not lacking in will power." She smiled.

"I can understand why you are hesitant to hope and fearful displaying feelings, but part of growing up is learning how to overcome the failures and press on. I can see that you hold a certain affection for your Aunt Barbara, isn't that true?"

Again I nodded, mutely, feeling the defences slowly crumble.

"Well let me tell you, that if she has agreed to provide a home for you after all the questioning and probing the Social Welfare does, then you have nothing to fear!"

I swallowed and tried to focus on a picture hanging behind her head, because I could feel that tears were wanting to seep into my eyes.

"It is you, Amber, who will be the determining factor between success and failure. You must just get into your head that not everyone is bent on rejecting and destroying you. You must learn to open up to those who reach out in sincerity, especially if you decide to accept your Aunt's offer. Don't lock yourself out, don't cut yourself off. You are living in the world, you cannot isolate yourself from it and survive."

I nodded numbly.

"You are going to have to learn a certain measure of compromise too," she added slowly. "You cannot expect the world and the people in it always to conform to your expectations and your desires. It simply doesn't work like that. You cannot just opt out because you don't like something. You are going to have to learn to give and take. That doesn't mean compromising your beliefs or sacrificing your integrity, but there are certain things you are going to have to learn to accept, for the simple reason that you will never be able to change them. You cannot then just cut them off because they aren't what you want. All of us face those situations and circumstances and we all have to learn what can be changed, what must be rejected and what we can only tolerate and accept as unchangeable. The world does not function according to our personal desires and demands. If you expect it to, you will only be crushed. Do you understand that?"

The truth is not always easy to digest. She had hit the nail so squarely on the head that the blow reverberated in every nerve and cell of my body. Knowing it was true did not make it easier to accept. She smiled gently again and then added in a lower voice.

"Amber, life is not kind, and the world is not compassionate. Don't expect either, and when you do encounter them, the joy and the surprise will be so much more fulfilling. Don't expect them, but don't for that reason reject and refuse them when they are offered to you. Now go and think it all over and when you have decided, come and let me know."

I spoke up then.

"I don't need time, I would love to go to my Aunt."

And then to my utter disgust the tears rolled down my face and I started crying. When the initial storm passed, she got up and came to me.

"May I?" she asked, and when I just looked at her, she put her arms around me and gave me a long, tight hug.

"Life is not over Amber, I believe that this will be a new start for you and I have utmost confidence that you will make it. I've seen the stuff you are made of and it is diamond sharp and just as resistant. All you need is understanding, affection and a chance to make a go of it. This is your chance, I am so glad you have decided to accept it and I believe you will not regret it.

INTERIM TWO

Those weeks from the home for unmarried mothers to the reform school constituted a period of such utter despair, it was difficult to look at them again. There were periods of utter nothingness in my mind, like a vacuum had sucked all the memories into a thick blank. It was like looking through a warped window that showed only twisted, contorted reflections. There was mist and vagueness so that people and events were shrouded in formlessness.

All I remember with constant, painful clarity was the longing for my little baby and the hurt that lay heavy and omnipresent in every waking moment.

I have little recollection of the people in the office, the girls in the home, their faces, what they were like, what they - we - did. Yet there are other events and people that I remember with such vivid intensity. I can still hear their voices, discern the words, remember the expressions and gestures. Perhaps it is a defensive quirk of the mind that blunts or shuts out unpleasant experiences.

I remember little of the time in that reform place but the night before my departure for Aunt Barbara's home is as clear as though it were yesterday. I recall how the hope and happiness were insinuating cautious feelers into my thoughts. I remember the excitement I couldn't suppress and the fear that it would be just another disillusionment, just another rejection.

The Principal was right - it was the start of a new life. She was right about opening up - though to be honest I have never managed that completely. She expressed a confidence in my abilities that infused courage in me. It made me feel again as though I was worth something after all.

It was another train journey, another new phase. And it was bringing me back to the city where I knew my baby was growing up.

I think of the person I was then and it still amuses me that I could have been so naive and so immature even after those horrendous experiences. Children of today of half my age then, are ten times more knowledgeable and wise in the ways of the world. I look back and wonder that I was not ground under and destroyed by events and people, but at every crisis I see the hand of my Special Friend, intervening to pull me out and put me on a straight way. He's never failed me yet, though I've often been tempted to believe He had.

The story seems to be taking a long time to unfold. I never for a moment thought that so much would come flooding back. The pain and crying still overwhelm me as I remember, but the weight seems to be lessening. I do owe my life to you, you know. It was only the thought of you somewhere that kept me going when I had reached the end. It was thinking that maybe, some day, I would be able to see you again, or perhaps one day you might need me, that made me pick up the fragments and start again. I kept living because I believed you were there somewhere. I hung on because of you.

I think I knew that I would find you again; I have lived for that day. Sometimes when I sit at home and look through your photographs it seems almost impossible that we have met again. I feel unreal, as though I were dreaming and yet intensely alive.

I'm rambling again, I want so much for you to understand why I did what I did, why I took the decisions that were taken, why I am the person I have become. From the little I know of you, I see how remarkably you are like me, and perhaps in reading this, you will receive answers to your own questions and understanding about your own feelings and reactions.

Well, it's very late. I must do something about sleeping, otherwise I will be walking around like a zombie again. It's just that it feels so good to be able to write to you and know that you are there, really there, that you are alive and well, that we have found each other and that it's not all just a vain fantasy.

Much love -- Mum.

CHAPTER TWENTY FIVE

I wasn't sure what to expect when Aunt Barbara picked me up. There was a tightness and trembling in my stomach, but I was trying hard not to clam up and get defensive. She was just like I remembered her: older with wrinkles and grey streaks in her hair. There was genuine concern in her eyes as she gave me a long, penetrating look of examination.

On the way to her home she explained that her eldest daughter was married, living away from home. But, that the younger one Lisa was working and still living at home. Aunt Barbara sighed deeply, and I sensed the pain and worry.

"Lisa is not well. She is under treatment and often has to stay away from work, so, we thought it more advisable for her to live with us where we can take care of her."

Lisa was tiny, with the most incredibly milk-white complexion and thick fair hair. At a closer look you could see that her skin was almost transparent. The warm, tender smile that caressed her lips constantly could not hide the pain and hurt in her eyes. Nevertheless, the whole family received me with open arms and welcomed me like one of their own.

It was really strange being in a single home with so few people around. I had become so accustomed to the communal situation of dormitories or numerous bedrooms, of huge dining rooms, of large kitchens, people coming and going all the time, bells, shifts and telephones. The first thing that struck me was the space and the silence. I revelled in the privacy. Aunt Barbara was always around, but she was unobtrusive. She didn't interfere, and her presence was comforting. It was like she was saying, "I'm here if you need me, but I won't intrude." I was so grateful for her tact.

It helped me to re-establish a kind of inner equilibrium. She let me understand that I could stay for as long as I wanted or needed to without coming straight out and saying so. I knew though, that I would have to get out and on my own feet again.

I started looking for another job in the city itself, because I felt it is now or never. I wanted to be independent. I wanted to prove that I could make it, that I was not the dead loss that so many, and especially Social Welfare, seemed to think I was. I applied for a job that looked challenging. In fact after I mailed the application I wondered whether I hadn't over-reached myself a bit. Then I shrugged, either I was going to go all out for something or I was going to go and sit in a job and vegetate, and I already knew what that would do to me.

The prospective employers phoned me some days later to fix a time for an interview. I was nervous travelling there and felt intimidated and very unsure of myself, but I also knew that no one would have guessed it. I had my bold, confident face on and the charm tap was open full force!

When I was ushered into the boss's office I was as taut as a coiled spring inside, but forced myself to look relaxed and at ease. He had my application in front of him and studied me from the time I walked through the door. He had very piercing eyes, but at the same time, they had a friendly sparkle to them. I liked the atmosphere in the place, there was an air of enthusiasm and openness and the people who passed by me all had a friendly smile.

"Well, Miss..." and he glanced down at my application again to make sure of the surname.

"Miss Waverley. I must admit I am actually just seeing you on the off-chance, because your qualifications are not really adequate for the job."

My heart sank and I could feel sparks of anger shooting through the disappointment. Then why did he ask me to come? I thought, instead of saying what I wanted to, I smiled.

"Don't underestimate me sir, the paper qualifications don't always tell the whole story. I have had a very chequered career up to now, and I am prepared to guarantee that I will be able to handle and master anything you give me. All I need is some co-operation."

He looked pleasingly surprised at my reaction.

"Why did you apply? You must have realised that you don't really meet the job specifications."

He wanted a fight? I thought grimly, well he wasn't going to see me back down. By now I had decided that I was going to get this job. I wanted it.

"The job looked like a challenge. I am not the kind of person who is prepared to sit down and never learn anything new. I assumed from your advertisement that you needed someone with initiative and spunk.

Someone who was prepared to learn and do something constructive and make a contribution."

I glared at him in defiance. He burst out laughing.

"Dynamite comes in small packages, hey?" and there was a glint of admiration in his eyes.

"So you want to learn?"

I nodded with determination.

"Well my dear, the job's yours. When can you start?"

I was stunned, thrilled and almost didn't believe him, but I grinned happily and stood up.

"As soon as you want, sir! I'm ready now."

He laughingly held his hands up.

"Hold your horses young lady, there will still be a few details to settle and I'm quite sure you have things to organise at your end as well. But let's go and get the formalities over and then you can start at the beginning of the month. OK?"

Aunt Barbara was as delighted as I was. I contacted people who had known me some time ago and they agreed to provide temporary lodgings for me in the city until I could find more permanent accommodation. I could feel the excitement and enthusiasm grow in me, it was like I had a new purpose in life now. I woke up in the mornings feeling that there was more meaning to each day, a reason for getting up and for living.

My friends were very helpful. They suggested that my best bet for accommodation would be with a family as opposed to a residential hotel or bachelor flat. I had been with them a few weeks when the opportunity arose and I went round to see the family.

The Kirbys were a close-knit family, the parents with two children, both younger then myself. When I walked through the door, I knew this was the place for me. The girls, Amanda and Jean were both in their teens and exuberance sparked off them like electricity. Amanda was quieter and a little more introverted than Jean who was very forward, but not in an ugly or brash way. It was Jean who introduced them to me.

"Hello, I'm Jean, Amanda is the quieter one. She's older than me and I think she just draws back a bit so that people think she's more mature, but it's really because she would rather let me handle things."

Amanda looked indignant and pulled her sister's hair.

"Jean you talk a lot of rubbish. You'll put Miss Waverley off."

It was funny to be called "Miss" by a girl who was only a few years younger than me.

"My name is Amber, please don't call me Miss, you make me feel like an old woman."

They were entranced, especially the outspoken Jean.

"Amber! What a lovely name. It's so unusual! How come they called you Amber?"

"Well," I explained seriously, "my father was involved in mining and all the children had the names of minerals, so my brothers and sisters are all called Amethyst, Opal, Jewel, Crystal, Ruby and Jade. By the time I was born, they had run out of names, so rather than call me Bauxite or Uranium or something else, they rather called me Amber."

Mr Kirby was trying to swallow his laughter but Jean was watching me with huge eyes while Amanda studied me somewhat doubtfully.

"Really!" she breathed in wonder, and then started when Mr Kirby roared with laughter.

"Jean I think you'd believe someone who told you that they came from the moon, and that it was really made of cream cheese," he teased.

She flushed and looked confused, then eyed me.

"You mean you made it up?" her tone was almost accusing.

"Sorry, there's not a word of truth in it." I confessed. "But I couldn't resist it, you looked as though you wanted to hear something exotic!"

Mrs Kirby nudged her husband.

"Well, it seems Amber has seen what Jean is about. Come along. I'll show you the room and explain the household set-up, then if the price is agreeable, you can decide whether you would like to take up lodging here."

She needn't have shown me anything more. I felt at peace about the place and there was a bubbling of excitement in me to think that I could really live there with these people. The girls tagged along, Jean was insatiably curious, while Amanda kept trying to restrain her somewhat tactless queries.

The Kirby's took me in as though I were a long lost elder daughter come home. Amanda confessed later how much she appreciated having an older sister.

"It gets very tiresome always being the eldest, you know." She explained gravely. "It's a big responsibility."

It was the break I needed, I was covered with love and care. The Kirby's took an interest in my work and were enthusiastic about the progress I was making there.

At work I couldn't have been happier. The boss must have said a few words to the staff, because they were so helpful. If I was ever stuck about something there was no resentment in giving me a hand or taking time to explain things to me. I learnt quickly and had soon made myself indispensable. The staff members liked me and from the beginning we were on first name terms. The boss and I developed a very good relationship, I could feel that he was very satisfied with the work I accomplished and was starting to entrust me with greater responsibilities. One day as he leaned over my shoulder to watch what I was doing he even voiced his pleasure, much to my delight.

"Well Amber, it seems I didn't make a mistake when I employed you, you have managed far beyond my expectations, good work, keep it up."

I glowed all the way home, and when I broke the good news, Mr Kirby insisted on taking us all out for a hamburger to celebrate the occasion.

I was so happy, but underneath the joy lurked that warning fear, the ugly voice that cautioned.

"Careful Amber, it won't last. Don't start enjoying it. If you open up you will lose it all."

It was true, despite the happiness, I felt as though I were playing with a soap bubble reflecting the most exquisite colours, but, that would burst without warning. And I would be empty handed again. All the time there was the longing for my baby and the wondering about where she was, what she was doing, how she was being treated, how big she was now.

I use to walk to work, with the excuse that it was exercise and that I enjoyed the morning air. But the truth was that it gave me the opportunity to examine all the prams I encountered along the way. I peered into each pram, examined the face of every baby in woman's arms, walked over to the park on the way home from work to observe all the babies there. I knew that I would recognise Martoinette instantly. It was like a reflex action in me, if there were babies around, I was automatically drawn to them like a magnet. I could almost sense their presence. Every time I bent to look in a pram, or peered into a baby's face my heart would stop and my breath would seize up... would it be this time?

But, it never was. I tried mental telepathy. I had come across an article that claimed that if you concentrated with sufficient intensity on something, you would be able to make mental contact. Quite frankly I think that if there was any truth in that I would probably have frizzled Martoinette into a cinder because of the intensity of my concentration. But it didn't work. I concentrated till I almost blew fuses but was never able to establish any contact of any kind whatsoever.

I wanted to contact Social Welfare to find out who had adopted my daughter, but I knew it was useless. They had made that painfully clear. They seemed to think they were God Almighty. They could dispose of your life as they saw fit. They were the untouchables, whose verdict could never be challenged.

Apart from that constant cloud, it was life starting afresh.

I let the shutters slide down over the past and I bolted them firmly down. Raising them now has caused intense pain. Events and hurts I thought that were gone and forgotten have hurtled screaming and thrashing into being again, lacerating and tearing with the ugly claws of the past. Trying to push the lid down on it all has been a struggle almost beyond my efforts. Perhaps this time, when the hurt has scored its jagged furrows into my soul again it will be the last time, and it will be exorcised. Maybe the shadows and nightmares will make peace with me and dissipate, this time for good.

The Kirbys introduced me to a new phase of existence, one that I had never experienced, it was simple family life, the right of every child, a right I had been denied! I became a carefree teenager! I went with Amanda and Jean, to church and barn dances and threw myself joyfully into the fun and games. We went to the beach where we cavorted and splashed with all the other normal young people. There were times when there would be flashes of resentment and almost animosity. Thoughts would lick through my mind like searing flames.

"It wasn't fair. Why did they all take such wonderful living so much for granted? Why could they always have had it and me never? What if I had been privileged to enjoy this "normal" way of living from the start? What if...

Then I would catch myself and shut the thoughts down with a crash. Thinking that way would only lead me into the old labyrinths

of misery and bitterness and I didn't want to end back in there. I
knew there was no way out, I could only plunge deeper into that
blackness once I was in it.

The thick spiky walls of aggression and antagonism began to
crumble. The brazenness and defiance hardly ever tried to insinuate
themselves to the fore. They had no more reason to exist. I was
accepted. I was in a family. I was part of a family that had absorbed
me into their lives and considered me a natural part of their own daily
being.

It was then, when I knew that I had won, that I was on my feet
ready to grow, ready to reach out, that I realised that the time had
come for the next step. My life was wonderful and fulfilling, but
there was a faint dissatisfaction wisping up to let me know that there
was more, there were other things to learn and new challenges to
meet.

I think in a way the past was weighing on me too much, just about
wherever I went there were sights and sounds to remind me of some
bitter experience. I began to want to get away from this city. There
was such a constant drain in me over my baby too that it was slowly
beginning to cripple me. I realised that I needed to get right away and
make a totally clean start in a town where no one knew me, where I
had no recollections of people or events from the past, where
everything was unknown.

Mrs Kirby noticed my preoccupation and early one evening while
she was preparing dinner, she beckoned me to join her in the kitchen.

"Amber, you've been very preoccupied lately, is there something
bothering you? Is there anything we can help with?"

I was about to deny it gaily and put it down to a spell of tiredness,
but then I realised I was being unnecessarily reticent. I knew by now
that the Kirby's really cared for me.

They were devout Catholics too, so they probably prayed quite a
bit for me as well.

She noticed the hesitation but before I could say anything else, she
continued.

"There's no need to be afraid, Amber. If there's any way we can
support or advise you, we will. I think you're starting to feel it's time
to spread your wings a bit, or am I wrong?"

I was amazed at her intuition, but also very grateful that she had
been the one to broach the subject. One of the things that had been

holding me back was the thought that they might be hurt or offended if I said I wanted to leave. I didn't want them to feel that I was ungrateful or unappreciative of the time I had spent with them.

So I was able to put my ideas tentatively to her. I must admit though that I was still very hesitant and wary about it. I had not grown so open that I could easily trust people, even this family who had been so good to me. She listened attentively without interrupting.

"Yes, I think you are on the right road, but at the same time, I would advise caution. Don't rush into something unless you are very sure that it is the correct decision. You know sometimes things look promising at first sight, but as you look deeper into them, they show up all kinds of flaws. Why don't you discuss it with your boss? From what I understand he has a good head on his shoulders and is quite fond of you. You could probably get some good advice from him too. I think you should mention it to Jack as well and let the three of us discuss it more in depth as the idea grows in you."

It was extremely comforting to get this kind of encouragement. I did in fact approach my boss and he was tremendously co-operative.

"Well we will be immensely sorry to see you leave. You've brought a lot of sunshine and laughter into the old place, but I can also see that you are ready for something you can get your teeth into more. So let's all keep an eye on the adverts and see what comes up."

I was the one to see the ad. They were looking for a governess for a seven year old boy, up country. The salary offered was good and there were countless other advantages. It would be very far away from the scenes of all my heartaches and pains. I had no friends, family or acquaintances there. It would be a clean break, a complete new start. But the real reason crouched deep down in my heart. It took me years even to acknowledge that it was there.

I wanted to be a mother, my child had been taken from me. Perhaps I could be a mother to this boy. I was celebrating two birthdays during the year now, mine and Martoinette's. I have done so every year since her birth. I have never shared the celebration with anyone, because it was too precious, too intimate to tell anyone else about. Although I knew what a wrenching it would cause, I realised that I must leave even Martoinette behind me.

Looking for her was growing into an increasing obsession. Over weekends all I wanted to do was go to all the paddling pools, visit the parks, search the streets, look into every pram, trying to find her, trying to discover where they had taken her. I knew that it would affect me so badly that I would become an emotional and psychological wreck, because the thought was constantly there, perhaps she will be around the next corner, in the next pram, held in the next woman's arms. Then I was faced with the horrifying question.

"If I do find her or see her, what am I going to do?"

There was no answer to that.

The reply from up county was positive. I had opened the letter with trembling fingers, at first couldn't read the words because they jiggled and swam before me. Mrs Kirby couldn't stand the tension, she took the letter and read it aloud. Then we both whooped and grabbed each other and twirled round the lounge shouting and laughing with excitement.

My boss was pleased for me. He sat me down in front of his desk and clasping his hands in front of him, leaned forward with a serious expression on his face.

"Amber, we have here all grown very attached to you. I personally am most content with the way you have progressed and the contribution you have made. Contribution that is, not only in the work sense, it has been a real pleasure to have you here and I like to think that we have also been responsible in helping you to get started. I have always been impressed with your capacity for learning and for the way you refuse to let a problem overcome you. I think there are several people in the office that have learnt much from your attitude and your performance.

"But now listen very closely to me. I am immensely pleased with this new opportunity that has risen, I don't want you to doubt that for a moment, but I am not going to let you give notice."

I was appalled. What was he saying? He saw my expression and laughed out loud.

"No, no, don't misunderstand me. I meant I am going to give you leave. You know Pittsburgh is a long way to go and you don't have friends or family there, so what are you going to do if you find you don't like the job or the people? I would hate to think of you getting stuck in a place like Pittsburgh with nowhere to go and very little money to take you there. So this is my suggestion. You go, see the place out, I know for a fact that you have a sixth sense where people are concerned. Feel them out, see what they are about. Then, if you don't like it and you can see the job is not for you, then you come back here. I'll keep your job open for you. How's that?"

I was overwhelmed. Never would I have expected something like that. I couldn't find words, but I think he saw from my face how I was feeling. He nodded with satisfaction.

"Good. Then let's leave it like that. If after a month or so you decide you want to stay up there, then you give me a call and I will record your leaving at the end of that particular month."

So that was how it was. It seemed the whole thing was settled, almost without my having to do anything about it. Something told me, this is it! I was grown up now, in years anyway. It was a step I felt I had to take, but I was still very apprehensive about it. What if it was a wrong step? Then everything would come tumbling down again like a house of cards. I grew cold at the thought. And then? What would I do then? In agitation I brushed the thoughts away. I had to make it work. That is where my bosses reassurance of being able to come back strengthened my resolve.

Mr and Mrs Kirby also told me that their family was open and waiting if I decided to return. So it was almost as if my Special Friend had provided a safety net for me, so that I would have less fear about taking the step I believe He wanted me to.

Outwardly I had become a little lady, I dressed well, had a confident, self-assured air, was friendly and polite. But inside I was still carrying so much hate, buried hurt dams of unspilled tears and a broken heart. But no one at work or at home knew the truth about my life. They knew only that I had no family or home.

While many of them had picked up on the hurt, there had been no prying questions. I remember one person telling me with gentleness that there is room in the sun for everyone.

"God made us mobile, you know..." they had smiled, "and if somebody stands in our son so that we are in the shadow, we must just move on, carefully, so as not to stumble, ever onwards towards the sun." I remember those words because they made sense to me. I have wasted a lot of time trying to make people move out of my sun by being aggressive, rebellious, sarcastic and lashing out at them in various ways. All it had done was break me down. This other piece of advice was obviously a far better solution.

Mr Ashley from Pittsburgh had sent money for an air ticket but I decided to go by train. In the first place I was not too sure about flying and in the second, it would give me more time to think and prepare myself for what lay ahead. The farewells were sorrowful and yet mixed with joy. The people I was leaving behind were genuinely pleased with the break and I knew they were praying for me and hoping for the best. Their words were sincere, but when the train pulled out of the station, I could somehow feel that it was the end of a phase,

Another train journey. Another stage in my life.

CHAPTER TWENTY SIX

When the train pulled into the station, my new boss was waiting for me. I recognised him instantly from the description he had given and the moment he set eyes on me he headed straight for me. I sensed that he was sizing me up and hoped desperately that the first impression would be favourable. His welcome was warm and sincere.

"Amber, Welcome! How was your trip? You must be tired."

I was starting to say that the trip had been fine and no I wasn't tired, but he just carried on talking.

"We'll be going straight home. Keith is very eager to meet you and a bit put out that he couldn't come to the station, but I didn't think it would he a good idea. I felt you and I had to meet each other first and maybe chat a bit so that I could put you in the picture. That way you will know exactly what you are walking into."

He raised a quizzical eyebrow.

"Then if it gives you a fright you can book your return ticket straight away."

A hole of fear opened up in my stomach. What was I getting myself into? This Cedric fellow seemed to be implying that the situation was a lot more complicated and convoluted than I have assumed. I must have looked concerned, because he grinned cheerily and patted my shoulder.

"Don't worry, my dear, I'm just joking! I'm sure you will settle in very quickly with us and be very happy. The references I have received from your ex-boss and from the Kirby's almost burnt my fingers they were so glowing, so I have no doubt that you are just the person for the job."

He was striding down the platform very purposefully and I was almost trotting to keep up, his legs were considerably longer than mine. It was still quite early in the morning, commuters were only just starting to appear on the streets on their way to work and there was a clean freshness in the air which gave me a good impression of the city. It was a lot more open and spacious than I had been expecting.

In the car, he gave me more detail about the job. It stands to reason that I was nervous about the deal because strictly speaking I had no experience as a governess, although I had always had a knack with children and certainly had enough experience in keeping house, what with all the tasks we had to do in my grandfather's house, the orphanage, the home and the reform school. I was excited too and fortunately the eager anticipation was outweighing the nerves. I suppose to summarise, I was to be a substitute mother/housekeeper. As it turned out, I had to learn how to run Mr Ashley's business too, and quickly, because he was subject to periodic bouts of an illness that laid him up in bed for days and sometimes weeks. Previously I suppose his wife had helped out, before they parted and went their separate ways.

Fortunately, the things I had learnt in my previous job stood me in good stead. I was able to grasp the principles of the new tasks quickly and soon had most things at my fingertips.

Little by little. Mr Ashley, Cedric as he soon asked me to call him, began entrusting more of the routine work to me. He was a very well-known and respected businessman locally, and over the months I was introduced to many of his associates. It was a totally new environment, filled with new challenges.

When we arrived at the house I was a bit awed, because it was a lot bigger than anything I had been accustomed to. There was a massive garden too, which thrilled my heart. Little Keith was waiting impatiently on the driveway, he ran ahead of the car as it pulled into the property and stood expectantly on the stairs. He stared inquisitively at me as I got out of the car and then turned almost accusingly to his father.

"But Dad, she's not much bigger than I am!" Cedric cuffed his ears lightly.

"But she's a lot older young man, so you watch your manners and behave. Goodness me, is that the way to treat your governess and our guest?"

Abashed and looking ashamed, he shuffled forward and offered me his hand.

"I'm pleased to meet you Miss Waverley, my name is Keith."

He had an unkempt tangle of brownish hair, his knees were dirty and his shirt hanging out of his trousers, and I was instantly touched! I gave him my hand with a serious expression.

"Hello Keith, I'm pleased to meet you and you can call me Amber, if you are good."

It was the start of a friendship that has lasted to this day. I took Keith under my wing and tried to fill the gap in his life that his own mother had left. In many ways he became dependent on me, but there were areas in his life that he always kept secret and closed. Sometimes I could sense the hurt and confusion, but I never felt that I could broach the cautious defences he had set up around himself. I told myself that if he wanted to talk about those problems or worries with me, then he would take the first step. I didn't want to barge in where I wasn't wanted, or where he would perhaps feel obliged to say something, and then resent it afterwards. So I just watched and listened. I perceived and understood a lot of the things happening in his life, but said nothing. I knew that there was enough sincerity and mutual trust between us for him to come and discuss them with me if and when he wanted. Sometimes he would, but sometimes he kept those things close to his chest and said nothing.

Cedric had come through a very trying period. As I learnt first the broad outlines and then the harrowing details, I was filled with admiration for him. He had kept going despite ugly opposition and terrible personal suffering. He was on his feet again when I met him, although the hurt and torment he had been through had left their mark. In that way there was much in common between us and I believe that I was able to help him because I knew what it was like and could offer understanding and compassion that he was able to receive.

In turn Cedric poured much into my life. He helped me to be myself, to find myself, to come to terms with who I am. He showed me what it meant to stand up for myself when my back was against the wall and others were trying to pull me down. While I had always fought my own battles as a child, and had instinctively hit back at those who attacked me, Cedric gave me a better understanding of what it was all about. There was no longer indiscriminate lashing out on my part. I learnt not to shut myself off from everybody and distrust all and sundry. I learnt to fight back constructively, if I could phrase it like that and selectively.

I was needed in that home, and I was trusted. Those two factors probably did more than anything in my life to restore the ruined and desert areas in my character, my attitudes and philosophy of life. Many supporting wounds in my soul and emotions were healed by the trusting affection that Keith poured on me and the growing respect and confidence placed in me by Cedric.

The world opened up to me, a completely different world from the one that had tried to crush, condemn and destroy me. They took me on holidays with them and I saw places I had only dreamed of before. But even there, I found that the ache for Martoinette was a constant pressure. Again I peered into prams and searched faces. As the years passed, I celebrated her birthday every March, closing the door on my own personal sorrow and letting the tears flow freely. Then one day, as I sat with a little bunch of flowers that I had picked for her, my face wet and swollen from crying, Cedric walked in. He was surprised and concerned.

"Amber! What is the matter? What's wrong? What's happened?"

I started and my heart beat painfully and loudly in my chest.

"Nothing, no, it's nothing. It's just something I remembered. Really it's nothing."

But Cedric was not a person you could fob off with excuses, especially not lame ones like I trotted out. He sat down with me, put his arm around my shoulder and insisted on knowing what was up.

It was so difficult to start telling him, but as the words jerked out, disjointing and saturated with pain, I could feel a release. Something snapped, and I began to open up my heart to him.

That evening he walked in the garden with me, relishing the after-rain freshness. I felt light, new and full of hope. Cedric had listened, quietly and understandingly. There had been not a word of censure or condemnation. Instead, he had suggested that for my own peace of mind, we should perhaps try to find out where Martoinette was. I hadn't been ready for that, but I had stored the offer at the back of my mind, because I knew that the time would come when I would need his help.

Keith became a son to me, and yet could never totally fill the huge emptiness left in me when I lost my own baby. We did most things together. Cedric bought me a bicycle so that we could ride off together on picnics, explorations and just joy-rides. Once I was bumped by a car and fell off. The wheel buckled, so I had to walk back, Keith had rushed home in panic, screaming at the top of his voice.

"Amber's dead, Amber's dead!"

All he had seen was my crash into the roadside shrubbery. He had become almost hysterical and it took us a while to calm him down!

When it came to school, I helped him with the difficult things and stood by him, like I had so desperately wished someone would have done for me when I was his age. He came home once with red knuckles when I found out they had hit him with a ruler, I stormed over there in a fury. No one was going to hit Keith while I was around. I had had enough beatings and hidings as a child, to know how destructive such punishment was, how counter-productive, and I made sure that it would not be repeated.

The principal did not like me much, neither did many of the teachers. On one occasion, he was given lines to do, another senseless punishment that infuriated me. For goodness sake, what good could that possibly do? It meant he spent hours writing out meaningless repetitive phrases, hours he should have employed doing homework. Once again I rode into battle... I began to feel something like a Valkyrie on these sorties to the school, but I derived a certain inner satisfaction from forcing justice out of an innately unjust system. It was as though I was getting my own back after all the years of injustice I myself had suffered.

The teacher who had given him the lines was not amused, but neither was I. Keith being left-handed could not hold three pens at a time like me, so I was left to do the punishment. I pushed my point.

"If you want to punish him for something, then give him extra homework, or make him do something constructive. Can't you see that giving him lines is useless? It means he doesn't have time to do his homework, which means he has to be punished again. It builds up resentment and rebellion, it means his work suffers and it is your fault if in the process he becomes a non-achiever who doesn't want to work in class!"

Keith's results had in fact been atrocious. But over the months and years, his attitude changed radically. Today he holds a LLB degree - I'm not quite sure who shed the most tears getting there, him or me. He had been very rebellious and unhappy at school, and understanding the trauma he had gone through at home and the way he was treated at school, I didn't find it at all surprising.

I think in a way the three of us were involved by mutual healing and restoration without realising it. We were all hurt, disoriented and suffering from the cruelties and injustices inherent in living. As the years passed though, the wounds healed. We regained a new equilibrium, could face life with renewed confidence and hope.

Today I am proud of Keith and what he has achieved. In a sense he belongs to me. It was like finding something very precious, knowing that it doesn't really belong to me, but cherishing it forever, because no one else claimed it, but I had perceived its real value. In turn, Keith has been a pillar of strength to me.

For the first time, instead of just being me, myself and I, living on my own and for myself, I became part of a "we". There had never been a "we" in my life before and it was the most wonderful thing to me. I had a beautiful little porcelain ornament that held pride of place in my room and one day I accidentally knocked it over. It didn't shatter, but it broke, cleanly and very decisively, into about five or six pieces. I was distraught, I had loved that particular little ornament because of its fragile beauty.

Keith was distressed by my upset and before I knew what he was up to, he had bought a tube of super glue, guaranteed invisible.

With utmost care, I started piecing the ornament together, gently fitting the broken pieces in, till it was impossible to see where the cracks were. Holding the restored porcelain in my hands, I realised that it was an image of my own life. I had been broken and torn so many times, but each time my Special Friend had picked up the pieces and carefully and tenderly joined them together again. I looked whole and perfect, but He was very well aware of where the cracks were. No one else could even have guessed the cracks were there, but... He knew.

Many times during the years, I would be overcome with apprehension. I was too happy for it to last. Something would come along and destroy everything. I would lose all the happiness I was experiencing. My whole life would fall apart again. Certainly there were difficult times, times of intense sorrow and pain and some very problematic periods, but somehow we came through them and life carried on.

I lost track of the times I went looking for Martoinette. I had fallen into the habit again of watching children come from school playgrounds, going to parks on my days off to study the kids there, walking past the paddling pools. I knew it was wishful thinking, the chances of Martoinette being in Pittsburgh were probably non-existent, yet the longing would not let me stop.

I actually walked around in public places hoping to be noticed, imagining how someone would come up to me and say that they knew someone who looked just like me, of how someone would start talking to me as if they knew me and then suddenly realise I was not that person. Because then I would know that they knew Martoinette. I knew that she must resemble me.

Part of the work I did for Cedric was to supervise bookings into the apartment blocks. One new arrival, a fairly young man, stared at me very closely when he booked in. Then I would frequently catch him watching me. I still felt a lot of suspicion and distrust when men were concerned, and asked him outright one day,

"Listen, have you lost something?"

Though he was somewhat taken aback, he recovered quickly and smiled.

"Look, I'm sorry if I seemed rude, but you remind me so much of someone I met recently in Sunningdale. You actually have the same mannerisms.

My ears pricked up immediately, and I wanted to know more about her. He was probably surprised about the sudden turn-around in my attitude, but it didn't worry me in the least. He mentioned that she was adopted and was very outspoken too. By now my heart was thumping so loudly I was sure he must have been able to hear it.

Martoinette! It could only have been Martoinette! He said he had some photographs of her and went to fetch his album. I sat there feeling faint and sick. It was my daughter. He had seen my daughter. And the wild hope surged up in me, I could go there and find her, see her, maybe even talk to her, hold her! When the man came back, I perused the photographs with burning eagerness, but somehow I knew in my heart it wasn't her. He asked me how come I was so interested and I spun him some story about having lost contact with my family some years ago and thought that perhaps she could be related to me. He lent me the photograph, and with it I went to the hairdresser and had my hair done in the same way as hers, but somehow I was still not convinced. That evening I took it to Cedric for his opinion.

He and I discussed it at length and the upshot was that I took the train for the town the man had mentioned. Cedric felt it was extremely important that I go, make the attempt, be certain in my own mind that it wasn't her. I think we both realised that I would never have been at peace afterwards, thinking that perhaps I could have found my daughter and had lost the opportunity.

The journey was a nightmare of fears, anguish and hope. I booked in at the hotel and walked the streets for days, staring at the people and peering into every shop and window. Now I wonder sometimes what they thought of me, though it didn't bother me in the least at the time. All I cared for was finding my daughter. I sat in the small restaurant for hours on end, thinking that if anyone from the surrounding farms came to town, they would most certainly go there for a drink. Then at last I saw her, there was no resemblance at all... It wasn't Martoinette.

With a heavy heart I packed and took the train back home. I felt broken, all the pain of her loss had surged to the surface and was as intense as it had been the day I had to let her go.

That was just the first of many fruitless trips. One of Cedric's friends came back from a visit to Northern Sunningdale and told me with great exuberance about the girl he had met there.

"Your spitting image Amber, in fact, if I hadn't known better, I could have sworn she was your younger sister!"

My breath stopped in my throat, I could feel the blood draining from my face and on the pretext of fetching more tea I hurried out to the kitchen. I was shaking and close to fainting. Martoinette, had he seen my daughter?

As a result Cedric and I travelled to Sunningdale to find this girl. We arrived at the address and my mouth was so dry I could hardly swallow. When I knocked at the door I felt so weak that my knuckles just flopped and there was no sound at all. Cedric knocked and the time it took them to answer felt like years. But when I saw the face of the girl who opened it, I realised it was another dead-end.

On the way back home I was choking back tears. Cedric tried to lift my spirits.

"Well Amber, at least you're getting to see the country!"

But further more it was a silent trip. I drew much strength from both Cedric and Keith, who would especially remind me that the world was still beautiful, that flowers still grew, that the sun still shone and that life was still worth living.

Then it seemed we had hit rock bottom. By now quite a few people knew that I was looking for family with whom I had lost touch, no one of course was aware of the truth, that remained a close-kept secret between Cedric and me. We received a lead, a nineteen year old girl of similar description was seen in Namibia. I think that was probably the most devastating search of all. The heat was unbearable, the dust penetrated everything, the roads were interminable and the hunt seemed to lead from one miserable little dusty conglomeration of houses and shops to another equally miserable dusty one. You could see the heat and I began to believe that I was eating, sleeping and speaking dust. I felt dehydrated physically and emotionally.

I carried photographs of myself at the age of nineteen and wherever I went I showed them. Had they seen a girl who looked like this? Perhaps they might have seen her when she was younger? Each shake of the head cut me like a jagged knife. Each negative response crushed the disappointment deeper into me.

I went from hotel to restaurant, to shop, to store, to house, to hovel and then from one small town to another. It was another fruitless journey. The trip back was devastating. I couldn't eat, sleep or talk. By the time I got back home I was a wreck and it took all Cedric and Keith's patience and love to get me back to some semblance of normality.

The searches were bad for me in many ways. The old frustration and anger would come flooding back, the ugly person hiding inside me would come shoving to the front again. I could feel the hurts bursting out from under the scabs where they had lain and festered and they brought resentment and bitterness back with them. Every time I returned from another vain hunt I would swear blind it was the last time I would go on a mad goose chase, and the determination would remain until from somewhere I caught wind of the fact that someone had seen a girl who looked just like me, sounded just like me and off I would go haring again.

But then events overtook me that forced all possibility of searching for and finding my daughter out of the way. Keith was almost a grown man, he had passed through university, doing particularly well and been employed in a job where he was flourishing. He was fulfilled and happy and his future looked promising. But Cedric was slowly failing. More and more of the responsibilities for the business fell on my shoulders. I worked from dawn to dusk and while I enjoyed it, the concern for Cedric weighed increasingly on my heart.

To add to his other ailments, Cedric developed emphysema. When the doctor first told me, it didn't mean a thing, but over the months I was to learn exactly what it meant and all the horror and suffering it entailed. In the midst of one of the attacks, Cedric grabbed my arm

328

and pulled me close to his mouth, panting and heaving for breath. He gasped out that I was not to worry, he had made provision for me in his will, I would be well cared for.

I wanted to scream with anger and denial. Dear God, that's not what I wanted, that's not what I was afraid of. I wanted Cedric to live! I wanted him to get better and not suffer. I couldn't stand to see him in such agony. He and Keith had become part of my life, They had formed the world I lived in, and now it was crumbling.

All the repressed fears hurtled back into my mind. It was a torment, struggling to stop from being overwhelmed by the oppression and to try to keep Cedric from noticing. I always put on a confident, happy face with him to keep his spirits up, but when I got back to my bedroom then I would let the mask drop and break down.

There were periods of relative health at this time. He had stopped smoking by now and he would tackle work for days and sometimes a few weeks on end. When he came back in the evenings, it was nearly always with a little gift, or an item he had picked up that he thought I would appreciate. That was Cedric's nature from the first time I met him. He was a giver, if it wasn't to me and to friends, then it was to the church or to somebody in need. In fact once or twice I got angry with him, because I could see that he was being ripped off by people who were just abusing his goodness.

There were times when we would have quite long chats about, "if his condition should get any worse". If there was one thing he had drummed into me very firmly, it was the fact that under no circumstances was I to allow him to be placed in a hospital.

"I have provided everything here for my care, the oxygen bottles, the masks, all the medication. I have a lot more trust in your ability to care for me than I do for the unfeeling people in hospitals."

It was his constant refrain and while I quailed at the thought, I knew that come what may, I would lay everything down, my life if necessary, to care for him in his sickness.

I knew I had him to thank for the new beginning in my life, for the success I had made of it, for the things I had learnt and for the person I had become. I owed it all to his care and affection. He and Keith had brought the best out in me and had helped me to believe in life again.

As the months passed, he grew increasingly sicker. The weakness debilitated him and it frustrated him to the point of weeping anger.

He was now on oxygen several hours a day and the doctor was training me in the nursing care Cedric had to receive. Once a week a therapist arrived to give him treatment.

In a way it seemed a hideously drawn-out and unnecessary cruelty. The treatment, the medicine, the doctors and nurses only helped to prolong the agony. There were times he cried out to die and I wished I knew how to help him. But all I could do was to stand there, helpless, impotent and weep with him, begging God to end his suffering.

If there was one thing I had dreaded and feared, it was the thought of illness. How I was forced into a situation where I had to tend that illness day and night, week after week. I began to lose my hold on reality. Nightmares flung me awake. I would sit at Cedric's bedside, terrified that he would die in his sleep. If it were only the sickness it might have been easier to bear, but at times Cedric would go haywire. The doctor explained that sometimes the oxygen, for some reason would not get through to his brain. He acted strangely, it was obvious he didn't know what he was doing and it scared the wits out of me.

He went steadily downhill. For two years, with increasingly shorter periods of relative health, the sickness developed. At one stage Keith and I tried to put him in a private clinic where he could receive expert and professional care twenty-four hours a day. We had hardly returned home when he phoned for us to come and fetch him. He was getting claustrophobic and hysterical, he couldn't stand the place.

By then the doctor was coming twice a day to come and help me. My courage was failing. I could hardly stand to go into his room because the sight of his suffering was too much for me to bear. The minister of his church and the doctor sat me down one evening and stressed on me the urgency of the situation. They were very blunt and made it clear that his only hope was hospital care. It took a lot of convincing but eventually, I had to admit that I couldn't handle it any more. I agreed to let them speak to Cedric. They sat and reasoned with him and it was only a matter of minutes before he acquiesced.

I was so relieved to know that he was in the hands of competent experts who knew what they were doing. I was completely drained. Trying to run the business as well as care for him twenty-four hours a day had depleted almost the last reserves of energy and strength left. Now at least the pressure of caring for him was on other shoulders. It didn't really give me more time, every moment not spent at the business I was at the hospital. I could come and go freely because all the nursing staff got to know me very quickly.

Then late one night I received an urgent telephone call... would I please come to the hospital. Cedric had suffered a heart attack and was calling for me.

I rushed over still in my gown. I flew up the stairs and came to a panic-stricken dead stop in front of his door. Two huge male nurses were guarding it with a very aggressive air. What was going on? I approached them very timidly and asked in a tiny voice whether I could go in.

"I'm Amber Waverley, Cedric has asked to see me."

They were just as shocked to see me as I had been to see them.

"Are you Amber?" and in the midst of the drama of the situation, smiled.

I found out that he had suffered some strange mental attack again due to lack of oxygen. In his delirium he had pulled out his drips, hit out at the nurses that came to help and shouted hysterically that... "Amber would come and fix them so well they wouldn't know what had hit them."

At first they wanted to escort me into the room but I told them it wasn't necessary.

It didn't take me long to soothe him. They told me that in the struggle with the male nurses, when he was ripping out drips and fighting to get away, he had suffered a mild heart attack. I stayed until the doctor had examined him thoroughly and they had put him back on the drip and fixed the oxygen mask. Then the doctor asked me to come to his office.

He explained that Cedric must be shifted to the IC Unit. He was having enormous difficulty in breathing and the doctor felt that it was essential to place him on life support systems. The thought horrified me. I couldn't stand the idea of him being strapped into machines and tubes, but the doctor was very sympathetic and patient. He said that when Cedric was in the IC Unit, his suffering would stop. Eventually Keith signed the necessary papers and Cedric was moved.

I had been close to dropping point again, so I was relieved that he was now to be made more comfortable and wouldn't agonise so much. I felt like a robot. I moved around in a trance, I couldn't sleep. I spent all my time working until I past out rather than slept. Then I would get up, drink some tea and start working again. I was too tired to remember whether I had eaten or not. I think the nurses must have seen what was happening, because they started preparing meals for me at the hospital. I didn't even have time to do my hair properly, so I simply tied it up in a scarf.

I would sit in the IC Unit next to Cedric's bed, hour after hour, watching in torment as he struggled for each breath. I wanted him, when he opened his eyes, to see a familiar face. I couldn't bear the thought of how he would feel if he should regain proper consciousness and find himself alone. From time to time I would reach out to touch his hand and talk to him, just so that even sub-consciously he would know that I was there, that he hadn't been abandoned.

What turned the horror of that place into a hell was the squabbling. Family members of the terminally ill would congregate in the waiting room, and openly argue and fight about the possessions that their "loved ones" might be leaving, about unfair wills and money. I was appalled!! Some would even try to persuade him or her to authorise some change in the will, or sign some other documents drawn up by them. It was like watching vultures stick their gory heads into a dying animal's stomach and come out with entrails still hot and pulsing. It tore me into fragments.

I began practising the art of switching off again. There was a time I was so good at it, it almost became instinctive, but over the years I had lost the knack. I resorted to all kinds of psychological ploys to control my thoughts and emotions. I plastered my eyes thickly with mascara, it helped to stop the tears. I knew that if I cried, I would display long runny black lines down my face and that would make people laugh at me. I have never liked being mocked, so it was a very effective deterrent. The doctor used to stare at me with open admiration.

"You are an amazing woman, Miss Waverley," he would say. "I don't know how you manage, what with the demands of the business, the house and now this constant presence at Cedric's bedside. I think you are incredibly brave."

He didn't know that I was crying rivers in my heart. The old stubbornness was reasserting itself, I was not prepared to let the world know I was hurting again.

Then suddenly one day, I arrived at the hospital to find him sitting on the bed. He couldn't talk, he wrote little messages for me on a pad they had given him. He was demanding his glasses so that he could read. I was so overcome with joy I simply broke down. He wrote with a funny twinkle in his eye, then turned the pad for me to read.

"Give me my teeth back!"

They had removed his teeth when they inserted the pipes down his throat.

I was so thrilled and exhilarated that he was alive, that he was up! The doctor arrived as I was getting ready to rush off to fetch his glasses. He explained that the irritation caused by the pipes made it difficult for Cedric to speak. He was very subdued, but at the time it didn't register. It looked as though he wanted to say something to me, because he half-stretched out his arm, as though to detain me, but I was in too much of a hurry to go and fetch Cedric's glasses and books. He was as passionately a reader as I was.

It felt like such a long time, hurrying from the hospital to the house and back, but it was only just over half an hour. I shot up the stairs with a new found hope sending strength into every movement. At the door to his room I checked, stricken, I felt as though a wall had fallen on me. Cedric was back in bed, the pipes in his throat and the hated machine bleep... bleep.... bleeping to the sound of his heartbeat. It was too much! I broke down completely.

The sound of that heart machine haunted my dreams, it echoed mockingly in each hour of the day, ringing derisively in my ears. I felt arms picking me up, waves of dark clouds engulfed me mercifully. When I opened my eyes I was lying on a couch, the doctor was next to me. He held a glass to my lips and before I could protest, he insisted I swallow the stuff. It burnt and tasted weird, but after a while I felt better.

I knew that Cedric was in his final throes. I didn't want to ask the doctor anything. I couldn't possibly have taken sympathy or false hopes. Anyway, all I could do was to look in his eyes, the truth lay there open and naked. I went back to Cedric's room, I was so scared I almost ran out.

I could smell death... almost see it... I felt its presence and knew it was sitting there... moving in.... waiting. I didn't want to go home. It was big, dark and full of loneliness. The streets were empty but threatening, my footsteps echoed hollow and it felt as though things were lurking behind every bush and shadow. I could feel the sticky fingers of death clutching at me. I wanted to break free and run, run, run....

The image of death pressed on my eyelids, the smell filled my nose, it was clinging to my clothes. Almost hysterical with horror and panic, I rushed home as though hell were on my heels. When I opened the door, the emptiness and blackness hit me in the face like a physical force. I didn't want to go past Cedric's room, I knew I would smell and feel death there too. I tore off my clothes and with trembling, frantic hands, burnt them, thinking in some crazed way that I was killing death, and that if I burnt it all to a cinder, I would save Cedric. Fortunately, a girl friend of mine arrived to see how things were going. She tried to calm me down, helped me to bath and tried to get me to lie down and rest.

Next morning I returned to the hospital, the machine greeted me with its horrible bleep... bleep... bleep and the smell of death enfolded me. I tried to back away from it, but it crept relentlessly after me and slowly, inexorably embraced my limbs.

When I woke out of the blackness, I was in an anteroom and someone was giving me an injection. The next thing I knew, Keith was there, gently shaking me. He had been sent for to take me home. It was Thursday, Cedric's death agony dragged out for another one and a half days.

I screamed and rebelled inside against the hideous, mocking cruelty of the attempts to keep him alive, when they all knew it was useless. It was like some leering force was engraving the mockers into my mind with a contemptuous gesture.

"Here Amber, take this and etch it deep, it's another pain to add to the others."

I could almost feel the evil presence trying to crush me with its vicious hatred.

That is when I remembered the things Cedric used to say to me.

"Amber, when things go wrong, get your back against the wall and fight back."

I didn't have far to go to put my back against the wall, I could feel that I had run as far as I could. So, I began to fight back, with an almost Superhuman determination, I pulled myself together. I couldn't leave Cedric alone with death in that room, so I went back.

I was sitting next to him when the machine suddenly faltered.

Then it made a feeble attempt to emit another beep.... and stopped. A long straight line appeared on the monitor. The minister was there with me and Keith was at my side.

It seemed to me that the line had hardly appeared when the men arrived from the mortuary. They seemed to have appeared out of nowhere. Like they had been lurking somewhere beyond the doorway waiting for him to die.

I wanted to scream at them, rush at them clawing and scratching. I wanted to tear their green gowns and masks off and crush their syringes under my feet, but I couldn't move a muscle. I couldn't speak. Then I became aware that the doctor was holding me down and voices were shouting and echoing around my ears. The lights were spinning and Keith's face flashed in and out of my vision. He was scared and worried and his mouth was opening and closing as though he were speaking but I heard nothing. There was a prick in my arm and shortly afterwards... nothing.

I woke up limp and exhausted, I had no desire to fight, struggle or even move. There were no tears, not even hurt, just a big hollow - an emptiness, like I was a dry husk in a parched shell. I had difficulty to think coherently. All I registered was that Cedric had been released from the torment.

"No more hurt for him, no more pain, no more struggling."

The words circled wearily and repeatedly round in my head, like a merry-go-round. Cedric, who had given me so much, who had been kindness and courage and support - he was free now from agonising and struggling.

I had cried my last tears. The sorrow was too deep and the trauma too great for such superficial expression. I became like a deaf mute, walking around like an automat, doing things that had to be done without even realising what I was doing.

The auditors and attorneys came, and I sorted out the papers as they asked without asking questions. I remembered all the instructions Cedric had given me before he died. He had given me detailed lists of what had to be done, and I faithfully executed each and every one of his wishes. Keith made the funeral arrangements, remembering to advertise that all money in lieu of wreaths should be donated to the orphanage, as Cedric's wish was to be cremated. Keith was frequently with me. The hurt and grief was carved deep lines into his face and made his eyes dark and heavy. He knew how much Cedric had trusted and cared for me and left all the various arrangements to my discretion.

I had once seen how family members had fought over a deceased parent's clothing, pulling the article out of the wardrobe, shouting and swearing at one another. I refused to have any of his family in the house. Keith was in full agreement. I wasn't going to let anyone touch or take anything until I said so. I locked the cupboards and his room. I asked his best friends to act as pall bearers and I made it a closed funeral because I couldn't stomach the stares and whispers of people. I was drowning in an overwhelming weariness. I wanted it all over. I wanted to be alone.

The funeral parlour sent a car to take me to the church. To me it seemed as though the whole town was there. We had gone to church every Sunday and were well known, Cedric had been a popular and respected businessman for years, so they all knew us. My body was trembling so badly I could hardly walk. The minister helped me to sit down. Everything around me seemed to dissipate. All I saw was the coffin, prominently placed in the front of the church, with beautiful flowers on the lid. I heard sniffing and crying and couldn't understand why. I was vaguely aware of the minister's voice. Then snatches of the words from Psalm 23 came to me as somewhere people sang. It all meant nothing, I just wanted to go home!! I was so tired...

Then suddenly it was over. I was standing on the pavement next to the hearse and the minister was speaking urgently, impellingly, through a thick mist I heard Keith agree with him. with what? Slowly, as though moving in a dream, I registered their concern, I had been through enough, they seemed to be saying, I shouldn't go to the cremation. Then his wife was there... ah, I understood... she was saying she had arranged for all the people at the funeral to have tea at the church, I could go home, no one would bother me. I felt nothing. Keith told me later my face was totally blank and he hadn't known whether I had understood anything.

I let myself be led to the car. Someone took me home. There was a sea of flowers in the lounge, in the entrance hall, in the dining room. It looked as though they had taken all the gardens and transplanted them into the house. I couldn't understand why they had done it. I walked around stupidly, touching the petals. So beautiful - so fragile and delicate some of them.

Why had they picked them? Didn't they know that they would only die now? I didn't want any more death around me!!

The house was empty. I hated an empty house. I was so alone, but yet I wanted no one with me. One thought kept dragging its weary feet into furrows through my mind.

"I'm going to have to start all over again."

I drank one cup of tea after another. I forgot about food and eating. It somehow didn't seem important. I wanted to cry, but the tears wouldn't come. I walked from one room to another. The scent of flowers filled the house. It was all so useless. Did people think they could replace his presence with flowers?

"What must I do now?" I asked the flowers.

"Tell me what to do? Make me cry!"

The flowers sat silent and beautiful and their scent permeated the air.

"No," I said to myself.

"I can't cry, then they'll think I'm frightened. I thought of Cedric, I was glad he was no longer suffering, but then I thought that he had been the pillar of strength that had supported me all these years, and how it had been torn away from me. I was terrified of having to face life on my own again.

I didn't want to go on!! I was so tired!! I wanted to stop!

I wished Cedric was alive and then berated myself for wanting him to relive that awful suffering. I spent the night staring at the flowers, walking from room to room, gazing blankly at walls and drinking one cup of tea after another.

The next day I took all his clothes from the cupboards, packed them in boxes and took them to Boy's Town. I explained to the Head Master that I hadn't gone through the pockets, that they must please return any documents which they thought important and that they could give any money to the boys. The room and clothes smelt of death. I couldn't wait to get home again, to bath and wash the smell off me. I burnt the clothes I had worn, I scrubbed until my skin was red and almost grazed.

I had no option but to try to pick up the threads of life again. I had to keep the business going, I had always been a private person, and enjoyed being on my own, but I hated the dark. I desperately wanted someone to be there when the dark crept in on me. So I would work through the night hours, sometimes till early morning. The excuse was always that there was so much to do, but it was only an attempt to escape from myself. The tiredness began to catch up with me eventually.

I slept hardly at all and only ate when I remembered that it had been days since I had eaten. I couldn't resign myself to the fact that Cedric was dead. Somehow I couldn't accept that death. It wasn't right. It wasn't fair. It wasn't his time. He couldn't be gone. He must be coming back.

Keith came to fetch me for a weekend. When I answered the door, he stepped back in shock.

"What are you doing to yourself?" He gasped.

I hadn't spent much time looking in mirrors, so didn't really know what he was on about. We went to a restaurant, but when faced with the food, I simply couldn't eat. Keith ordered some soup for me, but they had to bring a straw for me to drink it. I couldn't lift the special soup cup. Keith was worried out of his mind, scolded me some and gave me all kinds of instructions, but I just laughed him off and teased him for being motherly.

As the days went by I felt more and more tired. I was always so cold. It felt as though the cold was slimming into my nerves and muscles, stretching icy shadows into every joint and cell. My fingers wouldn't work properly any more, I would try to pick things up and they would drop out of my hands. It made me so frustrated I wanted to scream, but I simply didn't have the energy to, so I would just stand there and stare at the thing on the floor. I was having difficulty thinking. My thoughts always seemed to go round in circles and come back to the point where they started. Then I collapsed; I could no longer hold myself up. I don't know who called the doctor, they rushed me to a private nursing home. Doctors came and went, I would have moments of lucidity and wonder what I was doing in the place. I could feel indignation rise.

Who on earth had put me here?

But I didn't have the strength to sustain such strong emotions and would soon pass out again. Then there was a period of much bustle and at last, the long desired sleep that I had sought with such longing. I closed my eyes and to my utter relief, felt the heavy waves of nothingness close over me.

It was four weeks before I opened my eyes again. Keith was holding my hands and his eyes were red and swollen. There were

flowers everywhere. I wondered vaguely if it was my funeral. I
looked for the golden sand and the jeep. Then a voice came from my
left.

"Welcome back Amber. We thought for a while there that you
were going off with the angels."

Was that one of the men from the jeep? No!

I couldn't understand where I was?

Before I had opened my eyes I had been in a huge desert with sand
like pure gold. It was wonderful, I was playing, dancing through it
and watching it scatter and sparkle in the sun. I let it run through my
fingers and watched the wind blow it away. Then where the golden
dunes rolled towards the horizon, a jeep trundled into view with three
men, waving and beckoning for me to come. I was filled with an
ecstatic joy and started running towards them. But then someone
called my name from behind me and I turned and started back. After
a few steps, I changed my mind, and wheeling around, headed for the
jeep again.

"Amber! Amber!" the voice shouted from behind me again.
Confused, I stopped and started back. It happened several times. I
ran to the jeep, then turned at the voice calling my name and started
retracing my steps, then back to the jeep again. Suddenly I realised
how tired I was... I sat down... the jeep seemed further away. Maybe
I should rather go back then!

When I tried to focus, all I could see was Keith's face and the
flowers.

I found out afterwards that I had not responded to medication or
treatment of any kind. Keith said he thought I had simply given up.

I suppose that's what dying is...giving up! Stopping the fight!

I could hear crying outside my room, apparently the doctor had
informed my folks that I wouldn't make it through the day. It was my
friends out there, as my family had rejected me many years ago. The
hospital staff had prayed for me every day and I suppose that people
from the church had too.

As the minutes ticked by, I began to recognise objects in the room.
I wanted to get up and go home but was very firmly pressed back into
bed. It felt somehow good to be there, some people from outside
were allowed in and I could feel their relief and joy when I recognised
them.

The next day the treatment began in earnest. I had to learn to stand and walk again. Eating was the worst torment, I couldn't swallow. The food would travel to a certain spot and then refuse to go further. I felt as though I was dying. I had always been strong-willed and once I had decided to do something, nothing had ever been able to stop me. No sickness or weakness could hold me back for long. I grew steadily stronger. Keith was there every day, I realised then that he was more than a son to me, than many a son is to his real mother. It was he who realised that I needed more than words and moral support.

He brought me work to do!

I was in no condition whatsoever to write, but the doctor gave me valium to steady my hands, it wasn't long before that indomitable will had asserted itself and I was going flat out again, self-confident and stubborn as ever.

In conversation with the doctor and friends over the weeks that followed, I gained a hair-raising insight into how close to death I had come. As a result I savoured every minute of life. The wisdom Cedric had taught me returned to my memory. I found again the desire and determination to fight back. I was afraid to look in a mirror. I knew I was still something between a skeleton and a survivor from a concentration camp. I now had a purpose in life again. I had to keep Cedric's business going. That meant I would have to regain my strength, learn to eat normally.

When I left the nursing home my legs were still a bit wobbly, but my resolve was solid. Physically and mentally stronger, I was able to deal with the perpetual hurt and apprehension. I knew that I had only one option and that was to go out and face the world again, no matter how cruel, vicious and hard it had been.

It was not an easy period, it was uphill all the way. The business was demanding and I tired rapidly, but it kept me occupied, mentally and physically. With restoration though, came the realisation that I had to make a new beginning. The life with Cedric and Keith was over. I became slowly aware that I was just winding things up now and preparing myself for what I knew would have to be another break.

I would have to start again!!!

INTERIM THREE

It might seem as though I am leaving huge spaces and long periods unaccounted for. It's difficult to explain. Cedric and Keith were so close and so much like family to me that in many ways that period of my life is so precious I am afraid to speak of it or touch it, almost as if it could disappear if I opened it up.

Keith and I are still very good and close friends. It was Keith who helped me start living again after Cedric's death. I love him very much and think if someone tried to harm him I would become worse than an enraged tigress. It's thanks to him that I met Gary from the Adoption Centre, the two of them were invaluable help when I found out about you.

I feel very empty now, and very tired. At times it seems as though writing this book has gouged huge roots out of my being and left gaping, bleeding holes. I hadn't realised what it would cost me to get this story out .

I don't believe there is a great deal more I can really tell you. Yes, there is a period of about twenty years to cover, but I don't want to go into detail about it, in a way I don't feel it's important for what is to grow between you and me. In another way I don't think I have the strength to live through it again as I have relived this first part of my life.

Perhaps, if you really want to know about it, I will be able to tell you, little by little, those things that are interesting, meaningful, the people and events that have enriched or saddened me, the lessons I have learnt. But then again I ask myself, what for? Will either of us really benefit?

So I think there remains just a final chapter. So that you will know how I arrived at the point where we found each other. You know, the years might have passed, but I don't feel old. I feel very much as I did twenty, even thirty years ago. It's just that sometimes the memories and the old hurts and bitterness become very heavy and very difficult to bear, then I feel very tired.

Now I must tell you about Henry. "I think of him with a tender fondness" - and the years after the parting of our ways.

CHAPTER TWENTY SEVEN

Henry was a policeman whom I met through his family. They were very fond of me and I used to visit them quite often. Henry was very unsure of himself and only just starting out in life. I found I was lifting him up, encouraging him to reach out, stretch himself, develop the potential in him. We laughed a lot together and a really good understanding began to knit us closer together. I was alone and feeling that loneliness intensely. I hated the dark and the emptiness of the house. My life had dribbled into a dozen little rivulets, none of which seemed to be going anywhere, so Henry was an anchor that helped me to pull myself together again.

We were married because it seemed the most logical thing to do. We both knew that it was not a young, passionate love affair, but rather a solid understanding and mutual respect that bonded us. I helped him to get a start in life and he gave me support and stability while I got my act together. It was a good marriage.

Henry was very much younger than I was, although people could see that I was older, no one ever knew just how much older. From the comments we often heard, they all assumed I was at most five or six years his senior. But, as a matter of fact, I was twenty-six years older than him.

We stayed together for ten years, he was a good man and it was a source of quiet happiness and satisfaction to me to watch him develop over the years. He flourished in his job and received promotion sooner than most of the young guys his age. Henry worked hard and was conscientious, not only in his work, but in everything he attempted. I was very fond of him and appreciated the companionship. Keith remained a close friend, coming to visit often. I always kept track of what he was doing, how his life was progressing and it was a constant joy to share in many of the secret sorrows, hopes and ambitions that he cherished.

By the time Henry was established, a bright prospect in the force with a very promising future, I knew the time had come to go our separate ways. We parted very good friends and still contact one another from time to time to share our latest news.

I established myself in Pittsburgh. I have my own little business that keeps me going, in fact sometimes it has me sitting up till the early hours, although that doesn't happen frequently. I go out to work on a part-time basis too. The job gets me in contact with scores of people and I'm good at it, I've always had this ability to charm people, especially on a short-term basis!

At one stage, before settling in the home I now occupy, I was in a block of flats where I became greeting acquaintances with the caretaker. Though she was not really my kind of person, she obviously enjoyed my company and would sit and talk to me for hours... if I were to allow her.

It must have been six months or so after I moved that she phoned me in a very conspiratorial voice.

"Amber, there's a letter for you, but it's still addressed to Mrs van Dyk!"

She sounded excited as though she were on the trail of some great mystery story.

Van Dyk was Henry's surname. I had long since reverted to my maiden name of Waverley.

"A letter?" I queried surprised.

Mail didn't come to my street address, I had had a box number for years.

"What kind of letter is it?"

"Oh, it's one of those brown jobs with a window, you know, like you get for accounts."

"Accounts?" now I was really puzzled.

I didn't have any accounts apart from the usual phone, water and electricity ones, there most be some mistake.

"Well I'll pop down and fetch it some time this week," I said and some days later on my way past the apartments, I picked the letter up.

I was aghast when I opened the thing, from Social Welfare!! My flesh crawled. What did they want with me now?

"Please contact this office in connection with a personal matter..."

I tore the letter up in fury, damn them and all their offices!

I wanted nothing to do with them and their personal matters. What were they prying into now? I did derive a small satisfaction from the fact that they were still addressing me as Mrs van Dyk and sending the letter to a flat I had long since vacated. So they weren't that all knowing as they liked to think!

Some four or five weeks later, the caretaker phoned me with an excited catch in her voice.

"Amber! There's another of those letters here for you!"

I could almost see her eyes sparkle with curiosity as she turned the envelope over and over, trying to induce it to reveal its secrets. I sighed!

It was almost identical to the first, except this time it came from the Pittsburgh as opposed to the Wateridge Office. I tore it up too.

About another month or so later, another of the things arrived. By now I was getting agitated. I couldn't think what they wanted with me. The only thing I could come up with was the packet of Christmas cards, maybe it was something to do with that organisation? I had received an unsolicited packet of Christmas cards in the mail in about October, November the previous year.

The cards had been painted by handicapped people who held the brush in their mouth or toes. I had sent off a small donation and thought nothing more about it. Perhaps it was something to do with them?

I phoned the number given. The woman on the other end had never been taught the meaning of the word tact.

"Oh Mrs van Dyk! Did you give birth to a baby in 1952, that you gave away?"

I felt as though she had hit me in the stomach. After a stunned silence, listening to the female repeat,

"Hello? Hello? Hello?" in my ear.

I lashed out with a viciousness I hadn't used for a long time. "Brainless, tactless half-wit. Was that the way to speak about such a painful topic? What if I had a weak heart? I might have had a heart attack from the shock."

She was totally unaffected by my outburst.

"Well, do you want to contact her?" the voice was almost rude.

I could hardly breathe, half with anger, half with the shock, I exploded. What did she mean contact her? I have spent my whole life longing for her, looking for her, combing Sunningdale, travelling to the most impossible far-flung places because I had heard someone who could be her had been seen there and now this stupid woman wanted to know if I wanted to meet her?

I was shaking so badly I could hardly hold the phone. She gave me a number of the Social Welfare in Sunningdale and told me to call them.

It took me over five minutes to dial the number. The trembling was so bad I kept on dialling the wrong number. The lady who answered was very soft-spoken and kind. Though she was polite and very tactful, her explanation of the way they operated infuriated me to such an extent, that, had I been able, I think I would have commanded the lightning to burn up every vestige and trace of Social Welfare in the country.

My daughter had been looking for me for a long and lonely time. The lady explained to me that if I was not willing to be contacted, then they would simply tell her that I wanted nothing to do with her. And if they had been unable to trace me, I suppose she would have been left with the suggestion, that her mother had given her away once and was now rejecting her definitely.

I was horrified at the thought. What a monstrous way to go about things. The lady wouldn't give me my daughter's number or address. She took my number and said that she would pass it on to her and that the next step would be up to her.

I phoned Keith, he was overwhelmed and thrilled.

"I'm coming too!" he shouted excitedly.

"No! I put him off. I don't think I'm quite ready to face this."

I know now from personal, painful experience what it means to *"die a thousand deaths"*. Time refused to pass, I sat staring at the phone.

When would the woman give her my number? Today? Tomorrow? Next week? The anguish and loss that had been buried for years bubbled and boiled out of the depths of my being. Thoughts were whiplashing crazily through my head, my daughter! She was looking for me!

Did she know I had spent my whole life longing and looking for her?

She would be forty-one now, I had just recently celebrated her birthday, crying bitter, bitter tears over the flowers I had picked for the occasion.

When did she find out about me? What did she think of me?

I felt sick, waves of black oppression started to lap around my consciousness and I could feel the loss of reality take hold. I drifted in and out of a fainting state, grasping at something concrete to try to anchor myself to life. Then the phone rang. It was so loud I felt it reverberated in my blood and jangle wildly in my head. My hand

didn't want to stretch out, it was a terrible battle of will power to
force myself to pick it up.

There was crackling in my ear, then a male voice said.

"Hello? Hello? Is that Miss Waverley?"

Well, I thought remotely. Social Welfare fixed their facts, I had
told the woman in Sunningdale that I had resumed my maiden name.

"Hello? Miss Waverley?"

"Can you hear me?"

I opened my mouth to speak, it was so dry I had to lick my lips
several times before replying.

"Hello, yes, I'm Miss Waverley, who's speaking?"

"Miss Waverley, you don't know me. I'm Hugh Vincent, I'm
your daughter's husband..." a pause, then, with happy amazement.
"Gosh, you sound just like Lorraine!"

My fingers were clenched so tightly around the receiver the
knuckles showed white. He started talking, he must have realised
what a state I was in, he was very tactful and gentle. He told me he
had thought it best if he acted as the intermediary first, he said
because his wife was in a highly emotional state about the whole
affair. I could sympathise; I knew what he meant.

He called her Lorraine... it took me a long time to get used to that
name; to me she was Martoinette, had been for forty-one years! I
somehow couldn't picture her as Lorraine.

Hugh told me that she had discovered her adoption papers when
she was ten and had pestered her adoptive father continuously to
search for me. Neither he nor Social Welfare had acquiesced, they
had not considered it the right thing to do. On and off over the years,
she had taken up the quest again. Then trouble and pain had hit her
own life. She had a grown son of twenty from her first marriage, and
now a daughter of her own from her second husband.

I drank in the information, but it also became too much. Hugh
was very sensitive and he said he would phone back shortly, so as I
could become used to the idea of being a mother, and grandmother
and having a son-in-law.

It was overwhelming, the strain and stress of the emotion drained
me. I had no strength in my limbs. My mind raced off in a thousand
different directions and I had no control over my thoughts and
memories. I don't know what I would have done without Keith.

He was ecstatic about the whole affair. He brought a friend of his over. Gary was himself an adopted child and worked for the adoption society. He gave me a whole lot of new insight into adoption which I had never even dreamed of. He spoke of some of his own personal experiences and feelings, I think between the two of them they did an enormous amount to help me cope with this portentous happening.

I had found my daughter. She wanted to know me. I was so scared she would resent me for having to let her go. Would she understand that I had done it because of the depth of my love for her? How different had her life been because of the opportunities she had been given that I would never have been able to provide?

What was her character like? Would she resemble me in personality, attitudes, nature?

Then at last I heard her voice, I spoke to my child, the aching hole was being closed up. The severed bonds and links were being reattached. The search was over.

I have been very lost and lonely, often in life. I have travelled a lot, leaving the country and visiting foreign lands and climes. Searching for what I thought I couldn't find here, I often considered not returning but I was always drawn back. I suppose I was still searching for the penny I had dropped in the dust.

Repeatedly I have looked for answers to questions I couldn't even formulate properly. So many dark, unlit corners and murky corridors, so many locked rooms. I have tried to shine torches into that blackness, but the light has only penetrated so far, and then been swallowed, defeated. I thought that perhaps if I returned to the scenes, the veils would be lifted, but I think I was afraid to do so on my own.

When Henry and I were married, I revisited the towns of my childhood. There had been quite drastic changes, I went to my old school. It was still there, still peopled by yelling, shouting kids. As I watched, I thought how little things had really changed, intrinsically. Then with Henry in tow, I went to see my grandfather's houses. The first one - downtown had been demolished.

Another building stood in its place. Obliterating all traces of hurt, anger, hatred and persecution. The streets were still the same, and in my minds eye I saw them populated by the figures of long ago. Then to the second house, uptown, where he had slaughtered my chickens and pigs, it had been broken down. A much better home had been built in its place, but I could still see the steps to the entrance and the porch where he would wait, brooding some punishment for me. The garden was there, I could still see my secret spot and remember the tears I cried there. Poor Henry must have thought I was crazy, I stood there for a long time, staring at the house and the garden, tears pouring down my face. He said nothing, just put his arm around me and waited till I was ready to move on.

I went back to the house near the harbour where I had spent the first years of my life, until my mother died. A modern office block stood in its place, cold, clinical and totally unfeeling. I stared up at the windows, looking for answers, reaching out for meaning, but there was nothing.

Then it was the last pilgrimage, the home for unmarried mothers. They had moved premises. It seemed like just another building from the outside, but I could hear the screams of childbirth, the laughter of the girls at some joke, the high pitched wail of babies... All these places, but... no answers. I don't really know what I was expecting. Perhaps I was waiting for some vision, some apparition that would explain it all, give it meaning, but there was none.

Now I read through these words I have been pouring my life into and at times I even question, why have I done it? What is the point?

Will my daughter really want to know?

Deep in my heart I believe she will. I believe that there are keys in this book that will unlock closed doors in her own life. I couldn't sit down and tell her these things. The memories were so vivid and the emotions so intense I simply couldn't sustain it. I would start saying something and then divert the whole flow of the explanation or conversation, because I couldn't stand the impact of those events, the painful memory of the people. I couldn't find the words to explain why I had done what I had done in life, why I made the decisions I did. I didn't want her to think I was trying to justify or excuse myself. I wanted her to know the truth, unadulterated and glaring as it is, but in all its stark reality. I didn't want to pretend. I didn't want her to think I was someone I wasn't, but I found I couldn't answer her questions.

So I had to write this book. It was the only way I could tell her who I was, who I have become and why. It was the only way I could tell her that life is worth living, despite the cruelties and injustices, despite the pain and the losses. It is to be grasped and savoured, it was how I could tell her that people must never be abused or condemned, that each individual is important and counts, no matter how small and insignificant they are. It was the only way I could show her that a mother's love is one of the most powerful forces on earth. That it will leap death and bridge chasms of destruction if it is nurtured with the hope of its child's life. Even if it is deprived totally of the object of its existence, it will live on, it will thrive, it will fight when there is no hope of victory. It will never stop hoping and believing.

It was the way I could tell her of my Special Friend, because I know He cares for her too and will listen to and help her just as He did for me. It was to tell her that something will always break through the blackest darkness, when there is least hope and no apparent way out. I should know!

It was to tell her to hang on to that shiny penny, and that should she drop it in the dust, to search until she found it.